C|PIM PRODUCTION®
&INVENTORY
MANAGEMENT

Strategic Management
of Resources Reprints

Articles selected by the Strategic Management of Resources Committee of the APICS Curricula and Certification Council

Revised December 2001

Preface

As an organization dedicated to furthering manufacturing and operations excellence, APICS strives to shed light on important issues and provide a forum for developing a better understanding of these issues. This volume is a modest attempt to answer the continual demand for updated definitions as well as additions to the body of knowledge. The assumption is that the reader is knowledgeable about the basics and is looking for additional insights.

The articles in this publication were selected by the Strategic Management of Resources Committee based on relevancy of belonging to one of the three main topic areas, and on content which confirms and perhaps challenges our existing body of knowledge. The reprints give the committee the opportunity to quickly cover topics that spotlight state-of-the-art practices and processes.

The objectives of this compilation are as follows:

1. Provide supplementary material to the primary texts and references listed in the *Exam Content Manual* with relevant articles to help the candidate prepare for the Strategic Management of Resources certification exam. Subjects adequately covered by the primary references are not included in these readings.

2. Furnish material that will provide practical information to the practitioners of production and inventory management, and reflect the latest knowledge on the subject. APICS members and other professionals should use these readings as a way to enhance their knowledge and to stay abreast of current and practical approaches to Strategic Management of Resources .

3. Incrementally expand the body of knowledge associated with Strategic Management of Resources. This allows the inclusion of material that has not yet had sufficient breadth of application or time to be considered part of the current body of knowledge. Therefore, the material in these readings may go beyond the current boundaries of the certification exam.

We encourage candidates to be familiar with this material, and to use it to augment their studies in the area of Strategic Management of Resources. We recognize that there are many fine articles that could have been selected, and welcome recommendations for future inclusions.

It is our sincere wish that this volume inform the inquirer, support the test candidate, fortify the project manager, and sharpen the practitioner's skill.

The Strategic Management of Resources Committee:

Quentin Ford, CFPIM (Chair)
Stephen Chapman, CFPIM
Bill Leedale, CFPIM, CIRM
Paul Pittman, Ph.D., CFPIM
Kimberlee D. Snyder, Ph.D., CPIM
Blair Williams, CFPIM

Contents

Reprinted from the 1990 APICS International Conference Proceedings.

Measuring and Controlling Production Strategically

James T. Brown, CFPIM

Why is it that so many of our factories today find tying operational programs to manufacturing strategy so difficult? It seems rather obvious that the way to implement a strategy successfully lies in properly matching tactics with strategy. We should demonstrate a consistent pattern in operational programs that reinforces the competitive advantage sought by our manufacturing strategy. However, there is often a difference between a factory's intended strategy and its demonstrated strategy. You might say its "body language" doesn't match its "mouth." Since behavior is the most important form of communication, the manner in which a factory measures and controls its production operations is the best indicator of its "real" strategy. I believe that in many cases we, the managers, of these factories either do not realize that we have a problem or we do not know how to deal with it. The answer to this problem lies in learning to measure and control production operations strategically. Learning a new strategic approach to operations management is not easily done. Many of the traditional and widely used measurement and control techniques simply will not adequately support today's strategic objectives. We must develop new approaches for defining performance measures, controlling manufacturing and support operations, and empowering employees to support our manufacturing strategies in the 1990s.

Market Driven Manufacturing Strategies

What does it mean to have a "market driven" manufacturing strategy? I hear the term used quite often but I often wonder if we really understand what it means. I believe it means creating a competitive advantage by being better at manufacturing than our competitors. The key to being market driven ties in correctly defining and delivering the product and service characteristics that the targeted customer group really wants. In other words, being "better" than the competition has to be defined by our customers. What combination of price, product features, quality, and delivery characteristics is it that our manufacturing organization has to provide to create a competitive advantage? We should be able to answer this question by examining the way in which we measure and control our operations. However, in many plants we focus almost exclusively on cost. It is as if we were telling our employees that price is the only strategic issue. We must be careful to clearly articulate through our measurement and control processes all the attributes of excellence that matter to our customers, not just one or two.

To do this we should begin by defining key result areas. That is, define the things that will make a real difference to our customers, the things that must be done, if we

are to achieve our strategic objectives. Without defining these areas of strategic importance, we will not be able to determine the types of measures and controls needed. Most of us would emphasize as areas of critical strategic importance some combination of:

- **Quality**. Most customers today expect high quality. It qualifies a supplier but does not guarantee a win.
- **Cost**. This is an especially sensitive issue in slow or no growth markets where excess capacity exists and profit margins are low.
- **Delivery speed**. Time to deliver new products and lead time on existing models is an important issue in many markets.
- **Delivery reliability**. With JIT delivery becoming a common requirement, this has recently become a much more important issue.
- **Flexibility**. The ability to quickly and easily change product mix, production volumes, and designs is becoming the issue in many industries.

However, each plant's strategy may rank the importance of each of these areas differently. Perhaps one of these areas is of little or no importance to your targeted customers. Perhaps there are additional areas that should be included. My point is, we must clearly understand what is important for the achievement of the manufacturing strategy and make these operational issues for everyone in the organization by emphasizing them in our measurement and control systems.

Measuring Operations

With a clear understanding of the strategic objective in mind, we must next define the systems and procedures to accomplish them. These systems and procedures should provide us with measures of our operational performance by capturing accurate data and providing a framework for determining if we are in fact accomplishing our mission. However, we often fail to recognize the importance of our approach to measuring performance. By answering the following questions, I hope to give you a deeper understanding of the performance measurement process that will guide you in developing more effective measures.

What Expectations Are We Communicating by Our Choice of Measures?

By merely measuring some aspect of performance we are stressing its importance. Therefore, what we measure will change behavior. We can use this principle to our advantage by making critical measures highly visible. Post the results of critical strategic measures conspicuously so that everyone will see them. The result can be a mobilizing energy throughout all employees in the plant.

What Kinds of Things Should We Measure?

I think we need to concern ourselves with measuring those few things that are the most important to accomplishing our strategic objectives. For example, is Production Control making realistic and profitable schedules? Is the shop producing high quality products on time and within cost objectives? Are we getting the needed materials, and only the needed materials? How quickly are our employees assimilating their lessons and improving in areas where improvement is critical? Where are our "bottlenecks" or constraining resources and how effectively are we utilizing them?

In Establishing Measures for Individuals and Departments, Are We Stimulating Overall Company Performance?

The measures we establish should cause a correct response that supports our strategic objectives and should not lead to local optimization.

What Is Wrong with Traditional Performance Measures?

The problem is that many of these measures do not provide the kind of information needed by companies seeking to create a competitive advantage through manufacturing. In fact, many of the traditional cost accounting measures can be of negative value in supporting decisions related to strategic objectives. For example, overhead absorption looks better when output is maximized. It does not consider if you needed what was produced or if quality suffered as a result. The biggest problems with these measures is that they falsely assume that by focusing on individual costs, total costs will be reduced and they often encourage the sacrifice of long-term, strategic improvement in favor of short-term departmental performance.

As silly as this question may sound, it is amazing the number of factories that claim to know their product costs with four decimal place precision. The stated precision of the measure creates an illusion—an illusion first that we have a highly accurate measure. (This is seldom true for product cost.) Or, even worse, it is an illusion that we are measuring the right thing. Somehow we have the erroneous idea that only precise measures are good measures. We often hesitate to measure things like the flexibility of our operations or the effort of an employee. We feel it cannot be done with an acceptable level of precision. If it is important, we should measure it, even if a rough measure is all that is possible. In such cases it may be possible to use multiple measurement techniques to get a better approximation of the value or the dynamics of the characteristic in question. For example, the morale of the work force is an important characteristic to measure but a difficult one to measure precisely. By measuring employee turnover, absenteeism, and the number of employee suggestions, however, we can get a fairly good idea of changes in morale.

How Do We Know If a Given Measurement Value Is Good or Bad?

This is a very difficult thing to do without some reference point for comparison. For this reason it is often preferable to measure trends in performance. By analyzing trends we are able to more readily identify causal relations. In fact, many of the statistical process control techniques can be used to help analyze trends and gain a deeper understanding of a wide variety of manufacturing, logistical, and administrative processes.

Are Some of Our Measures Wasting Time and Money?

Too often the answer is yes. A recent study by the Sloan School at MIT found that 87 percent of the data that pushed up through the echelons of management is not used. We must be careful to collect only that information that will be used. We need to develop simple, visible measures that can be used. And we need to capture our data in the most economical manner possible. This means that data should be collected once and made available to all measures requiring it. This will not only lower data collection costs but will also lead to more accurate and consistent measurements.

Is Our Information Timely Enough to Provide Effective Decision Support?

When we need information to help us in making a decision we want accurate, concise, and current information. Note, I said information, not raw, unorganized, unstructured data. If the information is not timely, it will blur what is really going on and can lead to poor decisions. How can we speed up this process? We can decentralize the decision making process, moving it closer to the action. Giving operating personnel direct and immediate access to information without passing it through levels of management for review, analysis, and dissemination can greatly improve the effectiveness of any performance measurement system. Automating the capture and analysis of information might also allow us to save both time and money.

Whose Responsibility Should It Be to Select and Implement Performance Measures?

Measuring manufacturing performance should be a line management responsibility. However, we must accept the fact that there is no one optimum set of measures. Experimentation with various sets of measures is a good idea, especially in the initial stages of realigning measures with our strategic objectives.

In the area of quality, measuring trends in defect rates, causes of defects, quality of data records, and quality costs would likely lead you in the right direction. These measures should help you identify sources of defects and failures and thereby improve quality. It might be of interest to note that many companies find a much higher percentage of problems are caused by system (as opposed to worker) errors than would have been expected. Measuring statistically the time needed to process an item, an order, or a transaction could be helpful. In the shop it makes sense to measure the attainment of schedules instead of mere efficiency. (An assumed efficiency level is implicit in every schedule.) Measuring equipment availability really makes much more sense than measuring its utilization because availability is more directly under the control of manufacturing. Flexibility can be measured by measuring the time and/or cost to make product, volume, mix, or process changes. I also think the degree of labor cross training and skill transference is a good indicator of a plant's flexibility. A very interesting measure of a plant's overall performance is one called Total Productivity Factor. TPF is described by its creators Hayes, Wheelwright, and Clark in their book, *Dynamic Manufacturing* (The Free Press, 1988). This measure provides an integrative perspective of the overall efficiency with which a variety of physical inputs are transformed into products.

Will It Be Easy to Change Performance Measures?

Unfortunately, no. People do not like to change their behavior. If we change their performance measures, they will feel pressure to do so. We cannot, however, control those things that are not measured. If our strategic objectives and our future economic existence depend on satisfactory performance in an area, then we must put forth the effort to measure it as well as we possibly can. At least quarterly, the general manager and key managers from production, materials, engineering, and support departments should meet to review strategic objectives. This will help keep everyone on a focused and coordinated improvement plan.

Redefining Production Control

Another reason we find difficulty in tying our production control programs to our manufacturing strategy lies in the narrow way we define and approach production control. Webster defines the verb *control* as:
1. To check, test, or verify by evidence or experiments.
2. To exercise restraining or directing influence over.
3. To have power over.

Being very honest, not many of us have enough power over our operations. The full scope of production control should provide us with power in three areas: controlling power over material conversion processes; controlling power over the movement of materials between processes; and controlling power over the information we need to manage effectively.

In *Dynamic Manufacturing*, Hayes, Wheelwright, and Clark have done a good job of explaining the narrow way we typically exercise control over our conversion processes. They define four steps of process control—reactive, preventive, progressive, and dynamic. Reactive control implies being able to identify problems quickly and take corrective steps. But a problem must strike before we begin to take action. Unfortunately, reactive control is the most common approach used in our factories today. The next level is preventive control. Preventive control focuses on environmental and internal variables that are carefully monitored by the direct work force to eliminate the sources of abnormal variation. This approach requires a much greater understanding of cause and effect: The ability to not just "know how" to fix problems but to "know why" they occurred. The next level, progressive control, does not assume that the equipment control mechanisms, materials or designs are given. Instead, they become the focus of progressive control. Sources of normal variation are increasingly identified and understood as progressive control seeks to shrink the range of normal variation in a process. The ultimate is dynamic control, which requires a full understanding of the scientific principles governing the process. Through experimentation and research, new concepts lead the way to controlling process characteristics as the process is being changed. As it becomes strategically important for us to improve the quality, cost, speed, flexibility, and reliability of our processes, we must expand our vision and evolve to higher levels of control.

In controlling material movements, it is important to understand that less is always better. Since mere movement adds no value to our products, our approach should always be to make them shorter, faster, or eliminate them completely. Unfortunately, the state of our technology usually requires some material movements. Our job is to put control mechanisms in place that allow us to move materials quickly, reliably, safely, and at the lowest cost. One approach to controlling material movements that is beginning to be used in a number of our factories is the pull system of manufacturing. Under a push system, material movement between conversion processes is controlled by an external mechanism. Usually this requires the use of sophisticated systems for short-term scheduling that attempts to synchronize material movements with conversion requirements. Under a pull system, a simple internal control mechanism is utilized. Almost always, a pull approach will yield a higher degree of control and operational effectiveness.

Controlling the collection and transfer of information is essential to all control activities. Care should be exercised in designing production control systems and procedures to ensure that critical strategic issues are addressed and that appropriate information control mechanisms are in place. Too often we overlook the importance of ensuring that the information system, above all else, is designed to help us achieve our strategic objectives. To this end, it is very important that those responsible for collecting and transferring information have an appreciation, if not a detailed understanding, of what information is being collected and why that information is needed. If it is not the right information, then we should modify our approach immediately. With knowledge of why we need specific information, we will be more likely to perform our information collection and analysis tasks in a disciplined manner and an effective manner. We should always attempt to make processes as easy to measure and control as possible. This will always be the case for simple, highly visible processes that will require less sophisticated measurement and control systems. To ensure that we remain on target, we should regularly audit the accuracy and timeliness of the information generated from our operations. Once we gain a satisfactory level of reactive control over our information needs, we should attempt to progress to a higher level of preventive, progressive, and, finally, dynamic control.

Empowering People for Control

Production control is best accomplished by the people responsible for the task that is being controlled. The question is: How do we empower these workers to successfully control their own operations? Most of our employees today would find interpreting information and correctly directing their work toward strategic goals very new and challenging tasks. Perhaps this is the most difficult and important task in building winning organizations.

I like to use the term employee empowerment rather than employee involvement because it implies two critically important concepts. First, it accurately implies that a shift in power must take place. Giving workers decision making authority requires a change in management's view of workers. It will require both new expectations for workers and new roles for middle managers and supervisors. It will ultimately mean a less hierarchical organization structure. We need a change in the culture of our factories. This level of necessary cultural change does not seem as apparent when we use the term involvement. What we need is to not only involve workers, but to give them authority to manage those parts of the process that they should know better than anyone else.

Secondly, the term empowerment implies an understanding of business and technical principles. It implies the needed ability to correctly analyze information and make effective decisions. Therefore, empowerment suggests a need to increase the capabilities of our workers. This need for understanding and knowledge is an age-old human problem. The book of Proverbs says, "Through wisdom a house is built, and by understanding it is established; by knowledge the rooms are filled with all precious and pleasant riches" (Proverbs 24: 3, 4 NKJV). We desperately need more effective approaches to training and education. Keeping skills compatible with competitive needs is important, but we also need to give our employees the models from whom they will learn their new roles, and the opportunity to practice using new decision making skills in a non-threatening environment. To feel comfortable in their new roles, many workers will need to build self-esteem. This will take time but can be done by increasing their sense of belonging, their sense of individual uniqueness, and, ultimately, their sense of power.

Pulling It All Together

To achieve the benefits sought by our manufacturing strategy, we need to rethink our approach to measuring and controlling our production operations. The traditional measurement and control systems just will not do the job in today's dynamic and highly competitive business environment. Our plants, however, will not change unless the people that operate them change. We must not overlook or avoid the real issue—people. How do we help them to grow into their new roles? The answer begins with establishing an environment that is receptive to change—an environment that welcomes new ways of measuring and controlling production operations that are clearly focused on strategic objectives.

About the Author

As a Manufacturing Systems Consultant for Unisys, James T. (Tom) Brown, CFPIM, advises and assists Unisys industrial sector customers in designing and implementing more effective information systems. Previously, he has been awarded a Bachelor of Science in Management by Georgia Tech and a Master of Decision Sciences by Georgia State University. Since 1968 he has held management positions in the area of production and inventory management with the Ordnance Corps, U.S. Army, Thomas Paint Manufacturing Company, Neptune Meter Company, Southwire Company, and Unisys Corporation.

Tom is a senior member of the Society of Manufacturing Engineers (SME) and is recognized by the American Production and Inventory Control Society (APICS) as a fellow (CFPIM). Tom currently serves as a member of the APICS Certification and Curricula Council's Committee on Strategy and Technology and is a frequent speaker at professional conferences, chapter meetings and manufacturing seminars. Tom was instrumental in the development of the APICS Applied Manufacturing Education Series (AMES) and led an APICS Study Mission on JIT Manufacturing to Japan. He has written articles for the *Production & Inventory Management Review* and the *Production and Inventory Management Journal*. He also contributed to the writing of the *Production and Inventory Control Handbook*, Second Edition.

Reprinted from the 1994 APICS International Conference Proceedings.

Global Markets—JIT Logistics!

John M. Burnham, CFPIM

Resources managers, to achieve profitable competition in the global marketplace, must integrate their logistics systems. Global Logistics Systems (GLS) address strategic and tactical issues of availability and lowest total cost while meeting customers' operational expectations for timely and accurate delivery of defect-free goods.

The goal of logistical management operations is to bring materials from the lowest-tier suppliers through the various conversion processes and into distribution to reach the customer. This materials flow system can be managed just like JIT in the factory, and involves the same challenges.

A filter company's move to group technology is used to show both JIT and its impact on logistics. Two health care company examples develop the concepts and details of logistics strategies and tactics in a regulated context.

Introduction

As never before, tariff and other barriers are coming down (GATT-94, EC-92, and NAFTA), replaced by global or regional agreements covering the international movement of goods. But especially in the United States, much current practice is still domestically oriented and silo dependent, in part due to the enormous size of market. Worse, many systems, rather than recognizing the uniqueness that distinguishes various customer segments from one another, use inappropriate cost measures and averages.

Purchasing and inbound transportation focus on receiving requirements. Production consumes to meet the manufacturing budget. Distribution "ships them critters" and tries to react effectively to consumer demand shifts. Movement overseas is generally somebody else's problem (and more trouble than it's worth?). Economical but competitive customer service seems an oxymoron.

Tradition and Turf

In a recent study of the entire system bringing product to the customer, several personal and professional acquaintances were asked for data for a typical product: size, weight, value, volume, and for a cost accumulation along its path of movement. Although one very useful response was received from a high-value textiles company, other contacts said that their company just didn't have the resources to apply to such a question at the time. And a friend who is corporate director for materials and purchasing at a large electronics firm

... "thought I was onto something" and wished me luck, but with respect to his company, he ruefully noted that ... "Unfortunately, our Accounting systems *are functional* in nature and we are unable to provide the data requested *by product*. This is true

from both a buying and selling perspective" (italics mine).

This suggests that the current emphasis in Activity Based Costing and Management is equally applicable to logistics—the full-stream costs of products and their delivery.

The Challenge

To be profitably competitive in the global marketplace, resources managers must create "Logistically Distinct Businesses" (LDB) [7] that help to differentiate company products along appropriate service levels and dimensions. What's needed in addition to effective LDB focus is JIT Logistics. JIT manufacturing practices, combined with sourcing and mode choices, production and shipping quantities, and investments in information and inventory, can be extended to achieve a combination of global communications and global product positioning in support of business objectives.

Since this seems so important, why isn't it being done universally? The problem, in a nutshell, is the same as U.S. manufacturing has been wrestling with since becoming aware of the Toyota Production System from Japan. Just in Time, embodying new concepts and demonstrated advantages over typical job shop and mass production techniques prevalent at that time in America, was seen as either inappropriate or too difficult to apply, and thus was ignored by most companies. Similarly, W. Edwards Deming—named a National Treasure of Japan and known there as the father of quality—was only slowly accepted in the U.S. as having a worthwhile message. Now, many companies have embarked on JIT and TQM improvement journeys and internal manufacturing costs have, indeed, improved. But many others have not, rejecting these approaches or worse yet "trying it out" and then finding the road too rough, and abandoning the effort in favor of the comfort of long-established practice.

The data supporting the payoffs is clear. For superior service—an important component of total product attributes— customers are willing to pay 7-9% more. And superior service companies grow 8% faster than low-service companies and, on average, they're twelve times as profitable! [5] As Jeffrey Fisher, national transportation manager for Fuji Photo Film USA said, "We're willing to pay a reasonable price for value added by suppliers." [8]

On the negative side, Edwin L. Arzt, CEO of Procter and Gamble, emphasized the need to look beyond internal P&G processes to see the total value chain. "Consumers will not pay for our sloppiness! As an industry, we've estimated total grocery sales in the U.S. to be about $300 Billion. [But] there's between $75 and $ 100 Billion of inventory, much of it unproductive, caught between the manufacturer, the manufacturers supplier, and the retailer. [That's] up to one third of total sales just trapped in the pipeline." [1] A variety of wasteful distribution practices persist in Japan, as well as in the U.S., but these should not make U.S. multinationals aiming at global markets feel any more comfortable. It is just as important for a company to examine logistics practices as it was (and remains today) important to develop and make high-quality, high-value products using JIT and TQM. In fact, if the superior products can't be easily reached by the consumer, then some available other product will be chosen.

In this paper, three examples are used. Two show still-evolving solutions to the global market—JIT logistics challenge, and the third offers a basis for discussion at your company of what logistics approaches to take. The examples also present different levels of problem: FLEET-GUARD addresses the improved scheduling of a multi-product line—the need for improvement driven by high costs, high inventory, and long lead times; PERRIGO shows a top-down customer service commitment and the necessary changes to traditional supplier-customer relationships. BECKMAN INSTRUMENTS offers the promised challenge to the reader.

Some generalizations are given as well. A framework showing relationships across levels of logistics strategy, tactics, and execution planning may have some value for your company's logistics studies. Some criteria for evaluating the strategic aspects of logistics system design can be tested against current software marketing approaches. And some ideas about where to begin—a sort of Pareto analysis—may help focus initial efforts.

Logistics Strategy

Corporate strategic planning must not only balance external and internal factors and capabilities but provide direction that includes logistics management as a critical variable for competitive advantage.

At a recent Association for Manufacturing Excellence conference, Dennis Colard, then the newly appointed Corporate Director for Logistics at Hewlett Packard, demonstrated this while explaining his mission. [4]

> With manufacturing sites, distribution centers, and sales offices spanning five continents, the movement and management of parts, products, *and related information* becomes critical…. (Globalization) will accelerate in the 1990s and HP's ability to react to that growth will have an immediate impact on *the ability to compete.* HP suppliers will be asked to shorten their lead times, providing HP with parts and products more quickly so that HP can react to customer requirements…. *without incurring additional WIP and finished goods inventory.* (Italics mine).

HP was pursuing a systematic cost plus service competitive analysis. The goal was to get a solid grip on the value-added *chain.* This more useful view of logistics still demands a simple statement of *Who* decides *What* about *Which* aspects of the problem!

Strategic Corporate Level Logistics

Note Colard's approach. We are in global marketplaces, so must be competitive in our logistics as well as in our products. Benchmarking addresses how well our competition (or anyone else) is doing. Target-setting takes the benchmark and programs a positive response to achieve the target.

Standardization: Standards can reduce variables to a manageable number. Unit loads, gross volumes and weights for 20-foot containers, packaging standards, pallet sizes, and so forth, make planning much easier and results more predictable. The same can apply to time standards for communications, responses, and fulfillment by receipt of the desired item at the customer's dock, leading to a performance specification for the logistics communication system.

Service, Quality, Maintenance: Sometimes grouped with "standards," all three factors are necessarily established so that they truly reflect the company's goals in customer relationships. Service can be both timeliness of delivery and availability targets ("fill rate"). Quality can connote consistency, or data accuracy, or responsiveness. Maintenance can mean field service support, parts availability, or consumables replenishment (by a rack jobber, for example).

Business Process Reengineering?: Decisions made at this long-horizon level cannot be settled without considerable consultation with other logistics (and other) professionals whose work will be affected. At the April 1994 Operations Management Symposium in Tempe Arizona—Lee A. Sage, a partner with Ernst and Young, gave an example of BPR addressing the flow of customer orders to cash. Such a study would include all of the following specialists:
- Customer Orders/Order Entry
- Transportation
- Scheduling
- Accounting
- Suppliers
- Manufacturing
- Sellers/Marketing
- Distributors
- Customer (Payment)

Note that a number of these are external to the corporation or relate to external constituencies. Thus the existence of a multi-functional, multi-level team is vitally important to effective logistics strategy development (or to BPR).

Support for Investments in Improvement: Global perspectives and long horizons fit with the points noted above. If improvement targets have been set, then resources to enable target achievement must be provided, or means demonstrated (e.g., waste reduction, savings through in-house management).

Global Options Management: Overall global planning includes consideration of strategic factors and makes choices based on corporate success criteria, suggesting ranges for operating choices. Among the many options that need to be determined globally (systemically—for the whole system) are each of these: facilities, distribution, product design, and purchasing.

The goal is not to take away the needed decentralized operations responsibility, but to reduce the choices to a manageable set. For instance, locations and scale of operations choices are made jointly by teams looking at markets, supplies, costs, technology and so forth. These set a framework within which production and distribution facility charters can be developed, plans made, and construction undertaken. [2]

Product design (an engineering and marketing challenge) can have considerable effect on both suppliers and production facilities, and therefore on various aspects of materials movement. Participation in such developments from the standpoint of logistics guidelines and limitations may help considerably in making the more technical choices. [3]

To be effective in logistics operations the responsible individuals must know what options are available. Operations planning might be constrained by timetables for leases, transportation contracts, warehouse expansions, establishing new production or distribution points, new suppliers added or older ones deleted, and so forth. In any reasonable time horizon, demand for materials movement is fairly predictable, though exactly what must be moved may be a bit vague. So at the strategic level, logistics operations planning, like master planning, dwells less on details and more on outlines of what is likely to be needed, and how to provide it. To execute, the JIT logistics system must be in place, and under operational control—essentially self-regulating.

Logistics Strategy and Tactics for the Corporation

Given choices that define the business strategy of the firm and commit resources to its achievement, corporate logistics goals must address an appropriate set of targets for its Logistically Distinct Businesses (LDB) [7] which may be organized around delivery characteristics of various logistical pipelines through which goods may flow. Logistics strategies and tactical guidelines are shown as Table 1. These fall into the broad areas of planning, performance measurement, systems development, and global coordination. Each element is important to the overall logistics system support of corporate requirements. Implicit in all of these decisions and judgments is the availability of comparative cost information, competitive activities, and involvement of corporate and operational logistics staff in determining the short-term and longer-term targets for accomplishment. Also required: leadership, motivation, involvement, ownership, and recognition in terms of those who bring the system to life and run it.

Tactical Implications

Corporate "clout" and vision are often needed to bring the importance of systemwide cooperation home to traditionally oriented specialists. In a way, these are the same needs that apply to most corporate-to-operational linkages, since only through timely and effective communications can the visioning be made effective, and buy-in be achieved.

Purchasing and supplier relationships must include coordinated use of alternative routings between supplier and ultimate consumer, as well as agreement among suppliers to manage inbound parts and materials to maximize service at minimum cost.

Transportation companies can contribute greatly to smooth and low cost shipment of inbound and outbound materials and produces. Logically, transportation is a service and can be coordinated as a part of the revised purchasing responsibilities.

The entire distribution network must be transparent (as appropriate) to its customers. Issues of timeliness, quality and quantity of data, cost of system development and maintenance, reliability, and accessibility are generally not easily resolved at the operational level. The development and implementation of Distribution Requirements Planning (DRP) and of systems for Electronic Data Interchange (EDI) require integration far beyond distribution. The accurate assessment of needs, and involvement of users in determining how to meet such needs, must be carried out to achieve the goal of corporate effectiveness.

And both fixed (front-end, software acquisition and implementation) and operating (personnel, telecommunications,

- **Prompt, accurate communications**: What do suppliers need to know, and when? Does the information needed differ by manufacturing or distribution location? By customer? By customer location? What does the customer need to know? Do these needs differ?
- **Responsibility for timely communications**: accountability, too! Who, or what group, is the logical network manager, and how should performance be measured?
- **Appropriate distribution channels**: balance all ("full stream") costs vs. the need to delight customers with value they will pay for. What "channels" can be exploited? Are there different ways to reach different markets or customers matching defined service needs better, and minimizing total cost? What are the components of relevant total cost: investment, waste, transportation? What about opportunity costs: lost sales, lost market?
- **On-time deliveries**: What services characterize that LDB? What does the customer expect in order shipping and tracking? What does the distributor/subsidiary need? How about the supplier?
- **Global "JIT Logistics"**: right product, right quantity, right time, lowest total cost to please the customer. With this goal in mind, what needs to happen globally?
- **Knowledge of BGP**: best global practice (benchmarking). Who else in the business (both competitors and other suppliers) is doing well? What may we learn from them? What other businesses "enjoy" the same challenges we do?
- **Commitment to meet/beat BGP**: to achieve a sustainable competitive advantage.
- **Coordination function to maintain control**: What controls need to be in place to assure the supplier that BGP is being followed? Hewlett-Packard enables customers to look into the HP logistics data base to track shipments. Is this important to the equipment customer/user? Distributor? Supplier marketing?
- **Achieve integration** across system, including suppliers and transport providers as well as the manufacturing and distribution nodes.

Table 1. Logistics Strategy and Tactics Guidelines

translation/mailbox charges) costs are relevant to the determination of value-based system characteristics.

All these points will be shown in application to the examples which follow.

Issues of Strategy—JIT Logistics Implementation

The realization that JIT can work has helped many companies to challenge other parts of their logistics chain—particularly suppliers and finished product distribution—and to seek improvement opportunities. JIT progress reports also include changes taking place in Purchasing and in Distribution Management. These cover single or few-supplier sources for parts; longer-term contracts; and extension of timely information flow to and from suppliers and from the distribution network. Such activities make formal the de facto interdependencies that have existed among system participants. It allows the substitution of information and control for inventory. And it leads to systemic inventory management thinking.

It has been suggested that JIT can be considered the integration of four major thrusts: Technology, Quality, People, and Manufacturing Control. Whatever groupings have been chosen, the results have been very significant for the companies that have followed the continuous improvement path. The various technologies
- set up reduction
- "suppliers" and "customers" moved close together
- simple "pull" systems driven by the external customer
- small quantities of containerized materials
- frequent material movement through the system
- shortened lead times
- great emphasis on quality

are augmented by the many changes in people relationships
- security, trust, and involvement
- prompt feedback on problems
- problem-solving teams
- self-directed work groups
- visible signals and controls
- supervisory support and evaluation.

When undertaking JIT inside the plant, the objective is to deliver completed work just when it is needed by the next process step, and to receive work when the work center requires it. This applies just as strongly to the internal customer as to the external one, and has been described as the "customer-supplier relationship." This approach leads to awareness of interdependencies, the importance of prompt feedback, and the need to take action to improve the processes.

Key JIT Concepts

Much of the improvement associated with JIT has been derived not from technique or equipment but from "seeing things differently." Some ideas most often associated with industrial engineering and materials handling may be helpful in seeing things differently in logistics operations. Specifically, a team needs to be established to look outside for equivalent logistics improvement opportunities to those that have been implemented inside the plant. These can include lot-for-lot replenishment, a combination of unit load—kanban ideas across the system [Burnham & Mohancy 1990], and re-examination of the communications system to create a good fit with real needs for all the customers of the system. Identifying and standardizing the fundamental materials flow building blocks can optimize the materials movement system.

Continuing new applications of JIT concepts and techniques are bringing vast improvements in manufacturing productivity, quality, and employee satisfaction to many companies. Bear in mind that only a few short years ago traditional production-order manufacturing was "the only game in town." Just-in-Time Manufacturing has changed such traditional concepts, asking for cooperation, for problem-solving teams, and for continuous improvement. Extended across the operational elements called the materials flow system or the Value Chain, this thrust can offer very significant improvements over isolated area management practices. "JIT Logistics," the application of JIT techniques not only to the factory but to materials flow system management, is a major next step for all but the smallest local manufacturers. Keep in mind that the practices associated with the JIT philosophy are not absolutes but, like

logistics itself, must be traded off with the realities of time, distance, costs, and value.

Under JIT practices, inventory has shown large reductions, as cycle stocks have come down with smaller lot sizes. Smaller setup times have allowed the smaller lot sizes, and the increased frequencies of replenishment have reduced lead times. Due to prompt feedback as a result of smaller lots, productivity has improved with less rework even when defects are found. Quality has greatly improved for all of these reasons, since frequent changeovers have led to greater expertise and to precisely positioned tooling. In such companies, manufacturing costs have also come down by amounts exceeding 30%.

Outside-the-Plant Logistics Considerations

Because of the legal independence of many of the participants in a logistics system, it is important to seek opportunities to negotiate for areas of shared interest and benefit. This is much like the workforce involvement and continuous improvement goal of JIT.

Unique and Generic Items: There is heavy dependence between buyers and sellers of unique items (e.g., parts particular) while there is low dependence between buyers and sellers of generic (standard, common) items. Generic suppliers, to diversify risk, usually want many customers, and commodity buyers want many suppliers both for cost minimization and reliability of supply. Uniqueness calls for explicit recognition of interdependence, suggesting the degree of importance to be placed on information, dependability, quality, and so forth.

Cooperation between Sellers and Buyers: Significant financial and other benefits can accompany the exchange of useful information between participants in a GLS. An example is providing a supplier with the output of the manufacturing customer's MRP. The concepts of joint lot sizing, "pull" systems, and DRP all depend on timely and accurate information from the customer, and effective response from the supplier. EDI and bar coding both were developed to allow such information exchange. Daily POS data can be summarized and transmitted to allow cost-effective replenishment with very little "shelf" inventory at the retail end. In each of the following three examples, this cooperation is paramount.

Parameters and Variables

In the shorter term, many system elements can be taken as fixed (constants, parameters). In the longer term, many "constants" can be caused to vary by mutual agreement in order to improve all or many other parts of the system.

An Operational Approach

Most of the successful optimizations have been achieved on a case-by-case basis, by reducing through common sense the number of possible variables. By attacking the specific structure of a single sub-network, the optimal ("best") choice can be made for all relevant decision selections.

Mathematically, as well as practically, a "pilot" study (e.g., GM) makes a great deal of sense. It can provide not only an idea of the mathematical structure and what "variables" can be simplified; it and also can provide credible benefits estimates and learning opportunities.

Some examples of good logistics planning and execution can be examined and perhaps generalized from. But, like JIT, there is a great deal more philosophy and conceptual thinking needed to reach an understanding of the heart of the problem.

Begin with materials flow management in a JIT plant, identifying all of the factors that have been changed to allow the factory to be JIT! Outside the facility, suppliers and their role in the plant JIT can be addressed. Detailed study will show the conflicts. Resolving these conflicts leads to improvement—but only at each interface addressed.

Current practices in the management of finished goods into warehouses and distribution centers can be developed and, again, conflicts and resolutions presented.

The program can then move to customers—needs, expectations, values, and power—to understand how to convert these factors into useful information for managing the logistics system.

Next, the natural systems already used for management: purchasing and supplier quality, production scheduling and control, and physical distribution networks, can be developed and related to the previous materials flow. Suggestions for improvement here include the power of information as a substitute for inventory, and what tradeoffs are needed. These points apply almost one-for-one in the case study which follows.

Example: GT and JIT Production at Fleetguard Inc.

Originally a cost-reduction project of its Cummins Engine parent, FLEETGUARD has become a global competitor in the high-quality, heavy-duty filter market—support for diesel engines powering off-road and over-the-road equipment. With two U.S. plants, two more in Latin America, and another in France, FLEETGUARD quite literally seeks to "guard the fleet" worldwide. By the high-volume nature of most demand, manufacturing facilities tend to be organized into sub-plants, each focused on specific product lines or applications. Demand is from OEM and after-market customers, with less than 20% entering the Cummins system. WIX, Donaldson, FRAM, and other U.S., Japanese, and European filter specialists compete with FLEETGUARD (and sometimes subcontract to it) to supply the global market.

FLEETGUARD is in other businesses (like blood filtration) and serves many lubrication, fuel, air, water, hydraulic, and even pneumatic system applications. However, this discussion will focus on a specific fab/assembly/paint, inspect, package and ship line in one of the U.S. plants. The line handles widely varying volumes of up to 400 different medium-size spin-on filter end items, at rates of up to 1000 units an hour.

According to customers, end-item costs are perceived as high, and lead times long. Small (and erratic larger) special orders disturb carefully developed schedules. While significant plant-wide finished goods inventory reduction has taken place (from 45 days down to about 10 days supply) there is disproportionate investment in this line's cats and dogs, built ahead to minimize interruption to "A" and "B" items.

Normal scheduling practice runs the heavy hitters frequently, and then sandwiches in the smaller and nuisance orders. Scheduling "in isolation" has been necessary to keep running, but ignores the impacts on both finished goods (and customer satisfaction) and on the supplier system. Shared components with other lines has occasionally resulted in "piracy" and the inability to finish a scheduled run. Internal fabrication suppliers serve more than one sub-plant, and work toward internal cost targets, since shells, center tubes, retainers, and nut plates differ for many end

items. External suppliers work on forecasts with updates from Purchasing, via MRP. Filtration media come from one principal supplier, but densities and slit widths vary. The problem is a familiar one and your own experiences may be very similar.

Action: A team used group technology (GT) analysis to identify groups of end items with similar physical commonalities. Five major groups and two minor ones spanned the entire range of 400 possible end items and allowed just six GT line configurations. The scheduled runs were determined by projecting warehouse finished goods shortages using booked or forecast demand (like time phased order point). For the 150 active end items, group lot sizes were roughly determined and rounded to match full shipping pallets. Simulation of the effect of this GT group schedule showed about 25% less running-and-set-up time to meet current demand— and thus, availability for additional product assignments. The projected revenue improvement was substantial.

JIT Logistics: The GT group lot sizes resulted in more frequent group runs, less cycle stock, and a 66% reduction in lead time. The decision to "trigger" from FGI projections has moved the scheduling focus toward the central distribution center, and in most cases, will allow production to be driven by booked orders. Negotiation with Marketing (and the customer) is seeking smoothed demand approximating customer consumption rather than the typically random large orders placed to obtain volume price breaks and transportation economies. The projection is for much less FGI safety stock—perhaps even zero—as demand smooths out. The potential is for true JIT driven by customer-agreed ship dares.

Moving backward into fabrication, the smaller end-item lot sizes will make responsive internal part production easier, and will be less threatening to other schedules. And analysis shows the filtration paper media to differ only in slit width for any of the six GT groups. Purchasing is now studying how to manage the process with the media supplier and avoid conflict with the MRP system. Point-of-use storage for the smaller GT lots, and for parts particular, is beginning, and the goal is to have "pull" replenishment and a two-bin system. There will be other accounting and materials planning challenges, as small mixed supplier deliveries become the norm. Using the Guidelines above (Table 1), FLEETGUARD is at the beginning of the journey. But the incentives to succeed, both positive and negative, are certainly present, due to intra-company and industry competition, and greater customer expectations.

The real challenge will be to extend the FGI replenishment beyond "shipped as promised" from the centralized distribution center to become "delivered as promised," at any customer's receiving dock worldwide!

Example: PERRIGO Company

PERRIGO Company, a private-brand manufacturer and supplier of over-the-counter health and personal care products, is the largest private brander in North America, growing over ten-fold in revenue volume in the past ten years, while handling considerable product diversity and great vertical integration. Vitamins, analgesics, cold remedies, antacids, mouthwashes, and generic OTC drugs represent but a few of PERRIGO's products. The company is moving toward generic prescription drugs as well.

PERRIGO maintains a centralized multi-plant manufacturing complex and a nearby distribution complex furnishing a wide range of OTC health care powders, pastes, liquids, and capsules to such customers as Wal-Mart, K-Mart,

Eckerds, Super-X, and to pharmacy-oriented chains like Revco and Meijers. Most of PERRIGO's "distribution system" is through customer DCs and back-rooms. The company has acquired Cumberland Swan, a Smyrna, Tennessee private brander in personal care products, and this has allowed the two enterprises to rationalize product lines so that Allegan, Michigan can handle all health care, and Smyrna all personal care, products. Smyrna also deals with many of the same customers as does Allegan, and some coordination benefits are possible.

The key to success in private-branded OTC markets is packaging differentiation to suit customer needs, competitive pricing, responsiveness, and high customer service levels under dynamic market conditions. With centralized manufacturing, pipeline length is critical. Product unit prices are relatively modest, and transportation can take quite a bite out of margins. Enter MIMS! To paraphrase Ron Tucker, CPIM, PERRIGO's Customer Service Manager:

MIMS is an acronym for the phrase Minimum Inventory—Maximum Service—a business management philosophy designed to help PERRIGO customers maximize the profit potential of their store brand by reducing non-value-added costs.

Although a customized system is developed with each customer, the prototype agreement assigns to PERRIGO the responsibility for managing both customer and company inventory using customer warehouse movement and point-of-sale data transmitted by EDI. PERRIGO schedules both production and shipping to maintain agreed service levels.

Customers developing an MIMS partnership can expect to receive several benefits: inventory turnover will more than double, back-order and expediting costs will be eliminated, and fresher stock will greet the customer because of the shorter lead times. The expectations, in mid-1992, were that twenty or more of PERRIGO's largest customers would be on variations of MIMS during the next year.

What this leads to is focused management of suppliers, production (compounding or blending and packaging) and distribution in response to actual sales rates. With these large customers, demand is for sufficient volumes that full truckloads are almost always possible to each customer location. Clearly, both the customers and PERRIGO see as beneficial the use of information, rather than inventory, to maintain high customer service levels. This is, of course, much like the textile industry's Quick Response system, pioneered by Levi's and Milliken. It's considerably more complex, however, since the U.S. Food and Drug Administration (FDA) has very specific rules for OTC product manufacturing and packaging— and especially for labeling. Sealing, date, lot number, and shelf life are important. Label counts must be precise, even though an economical production run may not be 100% "sold out" to specific customers. Safety-sealed units may be relabeled, but this is certainly not value-added activity, and is avoided wherever possible.

There are four clear "levels" to accomplishment of such a MIMS or QR system. First is the strategic determination that the greatest sustainable competitive advantage comes from delighting the customer. Second is the analysis of the expense of electronic communications, short lead time logistic system management, and acceptance of system responsibility *by the manufacturer*. Then comes commitment. Finally, there is development of the logistics operating system that actually executes the plan.

In this operating context, just as with JIT, PERRIGO has teams in Distribution, addressing ways to improve the picking, packing, and movement of the large product volumes handled daily. One procedure has led to truck loading that consumes both cube and deadweight on hauls to the West Coast, so that total unit transportation costs are minimized. And many continuing efforts at location analysis, warehouse traffic flows, and customer-specific storage zones have led to considerably greater internal efficiencies. Marketing CSR Managers track performance (and the occasional foul ball). And teams are forming in manufacturing.

The reader might review the guidelines (Table 1) and see how these were deployed at PERRIGO. The MIMS model covers communications, responsibility and accountability, on-time delivery, channel choices, best logistics practices, and control, while seeking improvement opportunities throughout the system.

Quiz: A move to the European market, served by piggyback and sea-land arrangements, seem a likely future step. How should PERRIGO apply its learning to this new venture?

Example: Beckman Company—Reagents Facility, Carlsbad, California

A global organization, BECKMAN provides sophisticated testing equipment to the health care market. At the labs in Carlsbad, reagents required to support the tests and evaluations are batch blended and compounded, packaged, assembled with a kit to support the equipment and designated tests, and readied for sale. Some 500 different end items (kits, etc.) are produced at three locations: California, Ireland, and Puerto Rico, and shipped in support of North American stocking locations ("West and East Coasts, and Canada) and a new distribution center in Europe. Product for the Pacific Rim nations moves from Carlsbad, most frequently by air through Los Angeles.

From Carlsbad, CA, to the North American stock locations, product normally moves by owned vehicles. Puerto Rican production moves by shipboard container through Somerset NJ, thence to both North American and European locations. Ireland meets most European demand by sea-land trucking and air freight.

BECKMAN's market is divided roughly in halves: domestic and overseas, and some one million kits a year are sold worldwide. Some 60-70 end items have shelf lives under 12 months, and the balance of up to 18 months. Historically, shelf life expiry prior to use leads to disposal of 4-5% of the manufactured product, with a lost revenue value approaching $18,000,000. The direct loss in manufacturing cost is $5,000,000, more than justifying a significant investment in waste reduction efforts.

With a manual tracking system (batching date and lot number define expiry date) the triggers for disposal are less than perfect. Some of the 20+ overseas subsidiaries will notify Carlsbad of scrapping while others will scrap without notification. Warehouse personnel at the three North American and one European stocking locations sometimes will note out-of-date materials in reviewing warehouse storage and dispose of them, crediting inventory. And sometimes not!

Consider the application of the guidelines (Table 1) and the concept of Logistically Distinct Businesses (LDB):

Prompt, accurate communications: What does Beckman need to know, and when? Does it differ by manufacturing or distribution location? By customer, by customer location? What does the customer (distribution center, subsidiary, or major end-user) need to know? Do needs differ?

Responsibility for timely communications: accountability, too! Who, or what group, is the logical network manager, and how should performance be measured?

Management Level	Decision	Inputs	Constraints/Considerations
Upper Strategic Level (2-7years)	Changes in: Product Line, Manufacturing Processes, Modes of Transportation, Distribution Network, Suppliers, Information Links with Suppliers and Transporters, Standardization	Changes in: Supply and Demand of Existing Products and Materials, Supplier Performance Ratings Logistics Plan Results	Corporate Goals, Financing Capability, Competition. Future Economy, Regulation, Technological Forecasts
Lower Strategic Level (1/2-2 years)	Changes in: Location of Facilities, Customers, and Suppliers, Supplier and Carrier Development Capital Purchase Changes in: Transporters, Containerization	Location of Customers, Suppliers, and transport Routes, Transportation Costs, Supplier and Carrier Performance Ratings Schedule Results	Regulation, Competition, Geographical Limitations, Product Characteristics, Carrier Competition, Manufacturing Process Limits
Tactical Level (Next-day to 6 months)	in Manufacturing Process Frequency and Amount of Deliveries, Determining Buffer Inventories, Procurement Planning, Vehicle Routing	Strategic Policy Demand Forecasts, Customer Preferences, Manufacturing and Transit Throughput Times, Inventory Carrying Costs, Sourcing Lead Times Operations Results	Plant Capacity, Availability of Workers, Supply Limitations, Forecast Accuracy, Product Limitations and Characteristics
Operations Level (Next hour to few weeks)	Adjusting Inventories due to Variability in Man. Lead Times, Transportation/Transit Time, and Demand Unpredictability, Monitoring and Controlling Actual Min. Flow or Logistics, Prioritizing Late or Special Lots. Reestablishing Steady Flow After System Shutdown, Assigning Personnel	Tactical Decisions Delivery Schedule, Schedule Changes, Current Inventory Levels, Order/Shipment Status, Shipping Contract, Transit Throughput Times	Availability of Materials, Manpower and Machinery, Inventory Carrying Case, Economic Order Quantities, Product Limitations

Figure 1. Logistics

Develop appropriate distribution channels: to balance all costs vs. need to delight customers—with value they will pay for. What "channels" can Beckman exploit? Truck, rail-piggyback, shipboard container, and air freight modes, are all used for transport. But are there different ways to reach different markets or customers that can match the real needs better, and minimize total cost? What are the components of relevant total cost—investment, waste, transportation? What about opportunity costs, lost sales, lost market?

On-Time deliveries: What services does each LDB require as part of product? What does the customer expect in order shipping and tracking? What does the distributor/subsidiary need? How about Beckman?

Global "JIT Logistics": Right product, right quantity, right time, lowest total cost to please customer. What is the impact of PDA regulation on procurement, production, testing, packaging, and distribution, and how will this affect the goal? What about overseas regulations, impact?

Knowledge of BGP: best global practice (benchmarking). Who else in the business (Abbott, HP, etc.) is doing well? What may Beckman learn from them? What other businesses face the same challenges as Beckman?

Commitment to meet/beat BGP: to achieve a sustainable competitive advantage. The substantial margins in reagent kits suggests that, like Kodak, it may pay to almost give the customer the camera (test equipment) in order to sell the film. Could consistently reliable reagent availability with long shelf life remaining be such an advantage? Could it help to sell test equipment, too?

Coordination function to maintain control: What controls need to be in place to assure Beckman that BGP is being followed? Hewlett-Packard allows customers to look into the logistics data base to track shipments. Is this of value to the Beckman instrument user? Distributor? Beckman marketing?)

Integration across the system, including suppliers and transport providers, as well as the manufacturing and distribution nodes. Alliances have been formed among noncompetitors serving health care markets using a national carrier, and consolidating logistics efforts and shipments to mutual advantage. The result has been the ability to "face off" against Baxter/AHSC and Johnson and Johnson. Does Beckman have any natural partners in meeting its global demand? What is the makeup of an effective team to execute the study and its implementation?

A Framework Model

John A. Welch, under my direction, has created **Figure 1**, reflecting these many relationships. When examining Figure 1, the various planning horizon levels of decisionmaking should be kept in mind. Corporate "visioning" and communication of needs is but one aspect of the system. Top-down projection of requirements and restrictions (column 3) and decisions (column 1) is derived using the relevant inputs as given in column 2. But since all of the operational detail is only available at the dispatch and tactical levels, these will develop and execute plans based on what is possible—and communicate the results upward—leading to adjustments to future logistics plans.

Conclusions

Companies that can "start from scratch" and build the whole enterprise rationally seem to have success in reaching a very good logistics system. Systems analysis—the description and improvement of a process by studying outputs, the transformation processes themselves, and the needed inputs to sustain the needed outputs—can be used to demonstrate both the principles and practices of logistic system design for new projects.

Mode and routing choices are broadly available in most industrialized nations. Ownership and leasing trade-offs exist. Either through ownership or lease, attractive locations can still be obtained for manufacturing, for distribution centers, and for retail outlets. Natural resources can, of course, make some conversion locations more attractive than others, as can demographics and population density affect distribution. But on balance, trade-offs can be quantified, and rational decisionmaking undertaken.

The enormous number of variables and combinations can lead to very large programs with uncertain validity or values. Docs this then mean that an investment in understanding how logistics systems work is a waste? Only if strategic planning is also a waste! As General Dwight D. Eisenhower is said to have quipped, "The plan is nothing, but planning is everything!" For only through the planning process can one logically approach what the trade-offs are likely to be, given the existence of some strategic criteria for their evaluation.

Beyond this lies the even more important domain of logistical strategy. Tactical and strategic factors that have strong influence on corporate performance appear in Table 1, and are portrayed through the Framework of Figure 1. These include establishing a "vision" of what the GLS can become as a competitive weapon, integrative performance measures and standards, and development of effective communications in support of GLS.

References

References will be provided on request.

About the Author

John Burnham has practical, consulting, and instructional experience spanning over thirty years, having helped many companies with training and advisory needs. He served the International APICS organization as National Vice President for four years. Since 1980, he has continuously been one of the small group of experts on the Curricula and Certification Council—which designs and maintains the APICS Certification Examinations—for Inventory Management and JIT Concepts and Techniques and is currently on the Logistics Examination Committee for the new Certification program in Integrated Resources Management (CIRM).

Burnham's primary goal is improving the overall performance of manufacturing organizations, and his focus in this paper is on worldwide logistics optimization. He accompanied the original APICS Study Mission teams which visited Japanese JIT plants, and reported their findings to the Society. He has worked on manufacturing system improvements with Alcoa, Collins & Aikman, and many other smaller companies, and has delivered training seminars for TRW, IBM, and TEXTRON Aerostructures, as well as for APICS. A Professor at Tennessee Technological University in Cookeville, Tennessee, he teaches Operations Management and Business Policy to MBA students.

Reprinted from the 1999 APICS International Conference Proceedings.

Methodology for Translating the Business Strategy into Manufacturing Strategy

Richard Cole and Paul Henderson

The business strategy of a firm is the sum of the individual strategies of its component functions. For an organization to be aligned, all operational strategies, including the manufacturing strategy, must be derived from the business plan. In a successful firm these strategies interlock to provide the maximum competitive advantage of which the firm is capable. No function is left out, and no function dominates. However, in some companies the business strategy is dominated by non-manufacturing functions with the result being "thrown over the wall" to manufacturing. The strategic planning process is hierarchical. First, the corporate level articulates the vision of the firm and its strategic posture; next, the business managers develop business strategies in consonance with the corporate thrusts and challenges; and, finally, the functional managers provide the necessary functional strategic support. It is important to ensure that the business strategies and the resulting manufacturing strategy are properly linked. (See **figure 1**.)

Manufacturing does not always interface well with strategic planning and instead attempts to be all things to all people. As a result, manufacturing often struggles to meet business objectives. For most industrial companies, the manufacturing operation is the largest, the most complex, and the most difficult to manage component of the firm. The formation of a comprehensive manufacturing strategy affects, and is affected by many organizational groups inside and outside the firm. These are mainly business units, other functions, competitors, and the various external markets. It can be observed that in developing the strategy, manufacturing has to interact with all the remaining managerial functions of the firm. Cooperation and consistency of overall objectives is the key to success in these interactions. (See **figure 2**.)

When a manufacturing strategy does exist, decisions follow a neat, logical pattern. When there is no strategy, the pattern is erratic and unpredictable. The essence of manufacturing strategy is to formulate explicitly how manufacturing decisions and actions will be made to support attainment of the business plan. Every manufacturing enterprise has a manufacturing strategy, even if not formally identified or declared. Sometimes this manufacturing strategy is a result of ad hoc developments, and not of predetermined actions. Ideally, the manufacturing strategy derives from and

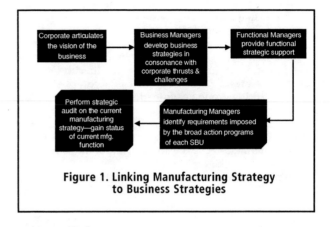

Figure 1. Linking Manufacturing Strategy to Business Strategies

therefore supports the business direction. The objective of this presentation is to provide a practical how-to methodology to translate the business strategy into a manufacturing strategy.

It is useful to think of the business strategy as consisting of three elements: goals, product-market domain, and competitive advantage. The business strategy makes a time-phased determination of the markets, products, services, and processes that the organization chose to compete on. Since in most cases these determinations

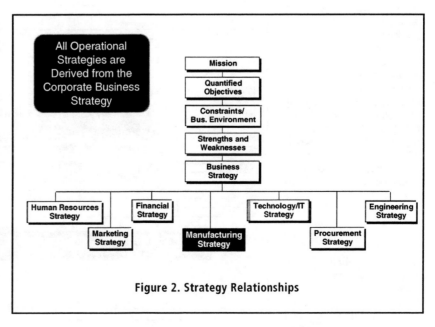

Figure 2. Strategy Relationships

are implicit, the methodology starts from the identification of existing "strategic drivers"—the metrics that represent the desired outcomes of the manufacturing organization. Once the strategic drivers have been identified, our methodology determines the desired position of each "manufacturing enabler"—the capabilities that provide the means to produce. (See **figure 3**.)

As a functional area within the business hierarchy, manufacturing has to develop a strategy that outlines how it will help achieve the business unit strategy. It must also complement the other functional strategies in the business hierarchy. In any manufacturing firm, there are three important questions that need to be addressed:

1. Does the firm's manufacturing strategy support and/or add to the company's overall business strategy?
2. Is the firm's manufacturing organization doing the right things that support this strategy?
3. Is the firm's manufacturing organization doing things right to generate the best returns for the organization?

The first step in the process is to assess, understand, validate and quantify the firm's business direction and supporting strategic plan. Once that is accomplished, the manufacturing group needs to identify their as-is strategy to support the business plan. If a misalignment exists between the manufacturing strategy and the business plan, a revised to-be manufacturing strategy must be designed to migrate manufacturing toward full attainment of the objectives.

Typically, the drivers for a manufacturing strategy are cost, quality, performance, delivery, flexibility, innovativeness, and channels. You must keep in mind that many manufacturing companies compete in several market segments, different product lines, or technology applications. As an example, when looking at the channel drivers, OEM's focus may be on technology. Each of these segments or lines will have its own set of drivers. The attribute of a driver describes the method of measuring or assessing that driver. Therefore, drivers and metrics coincide. An example of the cost attribute is unit cost or total order cost. An example of the quality attribute is 99.9 percent first-pass yield or 6 sigma.

Manufacturing enablers represent the capabilities that provide the means to produce. The choices made for each manufacturing enabler should support the drivers, as determined by the business strategy. Early in the planning process, a strategic audit should be performed on the current, as-is manufacturing strategy. It is very useful at the outset to extract the participating managers' feelings about the status of their manufacturing function. The as-is manufacturing strategy assesses the current position of each of the manufacturing enablers to determine the strengths and weaknesses of each enabler. Using quality function deployment (QFD) techniques, for example, our methodology determines which manufacturing enablers need to be "aligned" to achieve the business objectives and

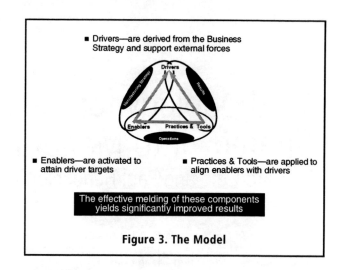

- Drivers—are derived from the Business Strategy and support external forces
- Enablers—are activated to attain driver targets
- Practices & Tools—are applied to align enablers with drivers

The effective melding of these components yields significantly improved results

Figure 3. The Model

which capabilities are required to make these alignments. (See **figure 4**.)

The goal is to design to-be manufacturing enablers that will satisfy the business drivers and market requirements. Traditionally, the focus of manufacturing professionals has been improvement of the manufacturing enablers. Although manufacturing personal are familiar with the importance of cost, quality, performance, delivery, innovativeness, flexibility, and channels, it is not uncommon that they are not familiar with their use for the determination of the manufacturing enablers that constitute a manufacturing strategy. (See **figure 5**.)

A manufacturing strategy must be comprehensive, but at the same time the complex web of decisions required must be broken down into analyzable pieces. These decision categories can be referred to as the enablers. These 10 enablers include facilities, process technologies, product scope and new product introduction, human resources, quality management, capacity, sourcing, production planning and control, manufacturing organization and infrastructure, and environmental compliance. The choices made for each manufacturing enabler should support the drivers, as determined by the business strategy. The to-be manufactur-

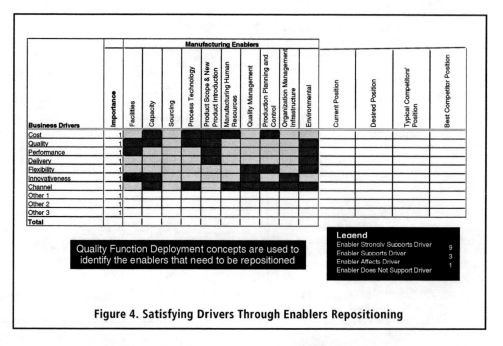

Quality Function Deployment concepts are used to identify the enablers that need to be repositioned

Legend
Enabler Strongly Supports Driver — 9
Enabler Supports Driver — 3
Enabler Affects Driver — 1
Enabler Does Not Support Driver —

Figure 4. Satisfying Drivers Through Enablers Repositioning

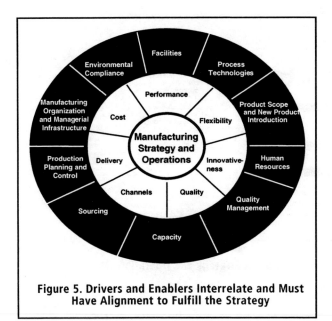

Figure 5. Drivers and Enablers Interrelate and Must Have Alignment to Fulfill the Strategy

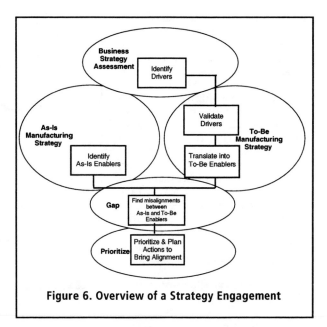

Figure 6. Overview of a Strategy Engagement

ing strategy consists of the aligned or intended position of each of the manufacturing enablers. (See **figure 6**.)

The approach we use for a manufacturing strategy initiative consists of three phases:

- Phase 1—Translate business objectives into drivers of the manufacturing operation.
- Phase 2—Identify the optimum position of the manufacturing enablers to satisfy drivers.
- Phase 3—Identify the gaps between the optimum and the current enabler positions and prioritize manufacturing operations improvement efforts to close the gaps.

The above process differentiates itself from the traditional feedback loop between operations and planning in that it includes manufacturing strategy in the entire feedback cycle, thereby closing the loop. (See **figure 7**.)

The gap between the current or as-is manufacturing enablers and the intended or to-be enablers represents areas that do not satisfy the business plan as defined by the drivers. There is a misalignment that needs to be corrected before the business objectives can be fully achieved. This correction can be made through the application of specific tools to reposition the manufacturing enablers. These tools and disciplines include the following: waste free manufacturing, quality cost reduction, rapid response, equipment effectiveness, activity-based management, materials

management and logistics, and sales and operations planning. Success in closing the gaps and bringing alignment between drivers and enablers comes from the identification and prioritization of improvement actions, fast implementation, and integration of precise metrics to monitor results. The prioritization of the initiatives to reposition the manufacturing enablers is dependent on the cost, resources, time, extent of change, and payback associated with each initiative. (See **figure 8**.)

The practical methodology described above provides you with a unique opportunity to make a difference in your company's future. It is a helpful tool to assist manufacturing professionals in establishing a manufacturing strategy to identify and close the existing gaps between the drivers and enablers, with a focus on achieving the business plan. Companies whose manufacturing organizations are geared to become more responsive through focus on the drivers command a definite competitive advantage. (See **figure 9**.)

In today's very competitive environment, the ability of a manufacturing organization to respond quickly to customer needs is a critical element for success. A company that recognizes its challenges and effectively derives its manufacturing strategy and operations improvement from its business objectives will succeed. (See **figure 10**.)

About the Authors

Richard J. Cole is one of the initial members and current vice president of Meritus Consulting Services in Endicott, New York. Prior to joining Meritus, he had 39 years of experience with IBM, most recently as a division vice president and general manager.

His experience includes managing domestic and European manufacturing, product assurance, and technology development operations. As the VP and general manager of IBM technology complex in Endicott, he was responsible for the productivity and efforts of 10,000 employees. Prior to this position, Mr. Cole directed the activities of 15 plants and 4 product assurance laboratories in Europe. He also directed the company's initial effort to compete for the MBNQA in 1988.

Mr. Cole holds a B.A. in business administration from Marist College. He completed the Management Program

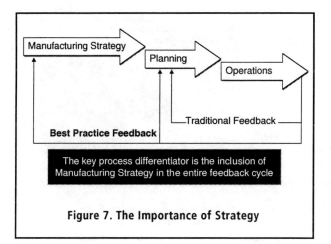

Figure 7. The Importance of Strategy

for Executives at the Graduate School of Business at the University of Pittsburgh.

Paul G. Henderson is a managing director with Meritus Consulting Services. He has broad management experiences in consulting and operations environments in the automotive, defense, chemical, and electronics industries. His primary focus has been on driving positive impact to the P&L via implementation of enterprise-wide business process improvements. His past experiences include senior management responsibilities implementing team-based continuous improvement programs in manufacturing, finance, engineering, purchasing, scheduling, materials management, and quality.

Mr. Henderson held responsibility for all manufacturing and quality activities company-wide for a paper manufacturing and packaging corporation. He was involved in improving performance at Fortune 500 manufacturing organizations by on-time delivery, first-pass yield, and operating profit. He was also involved in project management and operations improvements via implementation of speed-driven management principles and methodologies.

Mr. Henderson has a B.A. from the University of Michigan and an M.S. in industrial management from Central Michigan.

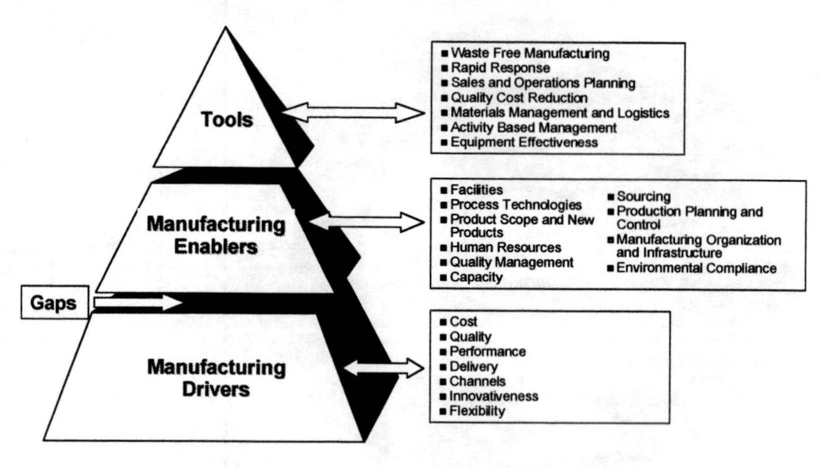

Figure 8. Manufacturing Strategy and Operations Model

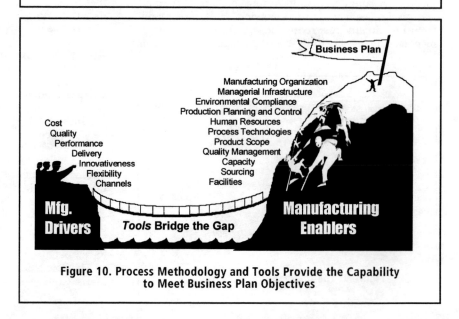

Figure 9. Translating Manufacturing Strategy Goals into Organizational Results

Figure 10. Process Methodology and Tools Provide the Capability to Meet Business Plan Objectives

Reprinted from APICS—the Performance Advantage, *March 1997.*

Getting Lean: New Strategy for Remanufacturers

Matthew H. Cooper IV, CPIM, and Paul L. Wellener IV, CPIM, CIRM

Predictable product mix and predictable customer demand are two of the similarities between remanufacturing and high-volume repetitive manufacturing that are key to the success of lean principles in both environments. Predictable mix and demand in classic lean manufacturing is achieved through heijunka, or level scheduling through the production process. Heijunka smoothes the pull signals being sent upstream through the supply chain to previous operations and suppliers by consistently consuming a steady amount of the resources necessary across time, rather than placing sporadic demands on suppliers and support systems. Heijunka also includes line balancing, which is the sequencing of production to optimize the consumption of operational capacity and minimize setup times between product changeovers. For heijunka to be possible, the level of demand variation in the production process must be less than 20 percent, which implies a stable and predictable customer base. Because this is seldom the case, manufacturers often carry some level of finished goods inventory to buffer customer volatility.

In a remanufacturing environment, the closed-loop cycle of component use is determined by setting either the number of uses or length of time components will be in service, or the degree of wear components can experience before they enter the remanufacturing process. The cycle may be based on engineering estimates, historical information, or maintenance data and analysis. For example, the auxiliary power units for a fleet of aircraft may all be scheduled for depot maintenance and overhaul after a fixed number of flying hours, or the aircraft landing gear may be scheduled for return to depot after a fixed number of take-offs and landings. Heijunka may be established in the remanufacturing process by tracking the flying hours of the entire fleet, scheduling routes or sorties to normalize the demand placed on the fleet whenever possible, and determining remanufacturing capacity and material requirements based on this information.

Several texts address the question of how to calculate the level of finished goods buffer necessary to guarantee a certain service level to customers. These formulas are based on how much a customer's actual demand for a product deviates from the forecast demand for that product. The stark reality many manufacturers and remanufacturers must face is that often customers do not know or cannot predict what their requirements will be, and long- or even medium-range forecasts of demand may be highly unreliable. In many cases, this is a fact that cannot be affected.

What can be affected is the length of the forecast horizon manufacturers use to make these service level calculations. By shortening throughput times and making the production process as responsive as possible to customer demand, we positively affect the amount of finished goods

buffer required to support the same service levels to customers. The quicker we are able to respond to a customer request, the shorter the customer's planning horizon. In most cases, shorter range forecasts are more accurate and less volatile than long-range forecasts. Shortening throughput times will always decrease the finished goods buffer stock required to support a given service level, regardless of the customer's forecast volatility.

The importance of the supplier base increases as throughput times decrease. The raw materials and components necessary for production must be in place when they are required for a production process to be able to react quickly to customer demand. Further, the necessary reduction of work in process (WIP) that enables the decrease in throughput times also means that when the materials necessary for production are not available, the entire production pipeline will dry up immediately.

At the same time the importance of reliable suppliers is highlighted, however, the opportunity to improve their reliability and involve them in the production and planning process also increases. Because the very definition of "lean" carries with it a mandate to identify and eliminate all waste in a process, both remanufacturers and their suppliers will be encouraged to pursue quality partnerships and certification programs that will allow for the elimination of non-value-added processes such as incoming material inspection. Partnerships will also reduce the warehousing and inventory management resources required by the remanufacturer by decreasing the amount of raw materials that must be carried and controlled. Eventually, these partnerships should lead to ship-to-use deliveries and point-of-consumption invoicing practices, increasing the goal alignment between the remanufacturer and its suppliers while further reducing wasted effort.

Other Disciplines Provide Lean Manufacturing Lessons

Successful applications of lean manufacturing in process industries provide lessons on innovation that are helpful when applying these principles in other non-classic, lean environments such as remanufacturing. In one case, an aluminum rolling facility removed 45 million pounds of WIP inventory by challenging existing paradigms on how performance was judged for the rolling process. Before their transition to lean, an irrefutable measurement for process success in the facility was recovery rate: the percent of incoming aluminum ingots that could be processed from the beginning to the end of the rolling process without having to be recovered, remelted and returned to ingot stock. The facility reprioritized its success measures to align the goals of all of its functional areas in the direction of increased customer satisfaction and enterprisewide waste reduction. Deciding to accept a 1 percent loss in recovery rate made it possible to reduce mid-process rolled aluminum stock part numbers from 35 to six. This contributed significantly to the overall WIP reduction (from 21 days to five) in the facility.

Enterprisewide goal alignment is critical to improving operations whenever lean principles are applied. Marketing, design, production, support and finance functions must all participate in concurrent engineering and development efforts to remove complexity and waste from the supply chain and reduce time to market.

Lean remanufacturing lessons in the areas of process rationalization also come from make-to-order, discrete manufacturers. One example is an electronic assembly manufacturer producing approximately 400 finished goods part numbers comprising 3,500 total raw material components and assemblies being managed in nine different product classes. Growth through the acquisition of new businesses and historically poor coordination between functional areas had driven slow-moving and obsolete inventory levels to more than 30 percent of total inventory holdings. WIP on the shop floor for the fastest moving product family represented one week of inventory, and in the worst case, 10 weeks. Ninety-four percent of the time materials spent on the shop floor was for non-value-added activities. Sub-assemblies were managed at every level of the production process, and the actual production requirements for individual customers varied an average of 70 percent from the customers' three-week short-range forecasts.

The improvement process for this manufacturer began by redesigning both the production process and support functions into cells focused on product families. The product families themselves were redefined to logically group production with similar material and equipment requirements. Aligning production into focused cells allowed master scheduling to take place only at the finished goods level, eliminating the requirement to individually schedule subassembly production at different process levels. Simultaneously scheduling the entire cell for the production of a finished good also limited WIP. If material or equipment problems at any stage of manufacturing prevent the complete processing of raw materials into finished goods, those part numbers are rescheduled until the problems are resolved. This enhanced communication was made possible by focusing production into U-shaped cells, decreasing unnecessary transportation distances between processes, and making operators more aware. Also, by eliminating the management of subassemblies, subassembly part numbers could either become phantoms in the bills of material or could be eliminated entirely, simplifying the MRP process. Throughput times decreased from an average of more than 70 hours to less than one, making the organization better able to react to changing customer demands.

Three major lessons exist in this example for lean remanufacturers. First, cellular production provides visual management tools that help prevent scheduling mistakes from being made in the first place. To avoid kitting of materials, which creates another level of inventory management complexity, requires tightly linked processes with visually obvious lineside storage of materials. Proper visual management of needed materials provides a low-effort method of increasing inventory accuracy.

Second, while completely flexible operations that can produce any part number required are the best resources to have, they may not always be available. In cases where they are not, assigning specific resources for certain product families or production requirements does have some advantages.

The criteria used for assigning production to certain cells should include limiting the number or type of setups required to produce all of the part types assigned to the cell. Reducing the number of different ways a machine must be set up or used will decrease the amount of variation introduced into the process. Reduced setups may also decrease the amount of wear on equipment or equipment fixtures. The long-term improvement goal of a lean remanufacturer should be universal flexibility, instant machine setups, and no process variation between part numbers.

The third lesson is that decreased throughput time has no downside. The closer we come to instantly satisfying the customer's requirements, the better off we are in terms of managing our internal costs and being able to react to our external environment.

What Does a Lean Remanufacturer Look Like?

A conceptual design for a lean remanufacturer closely resembles the design for a typical lean manufacturer with a few notable exceptions. For a lean manufacturer, kanban pull signals are transmitted from customers to production either via a withdrawal of stock from the finished goods warehouse in build-to-stock environments, or directly to production control. Internal kanbans are then scheduled for the appropriate production centers or cells and sequenced for heijunka. Meanwhile, customers are submitting a fixed horizon rolling forecast which is input into the master production schedule for capacity planning purposes and to identify potential seasonal or anomalous events that would drive load leveling beyond that required for heijunka. This model also takes into account the reality that despite our best efforts to partner with lean suppliers so that we will be able to order and receive material on a Just-in-Time basis, some suppliers may have production lead times that will prohibit the scheduling of their production and shipping activities solely via kanban. Therefore, MRP is included as a supplement to the supplier's kanban loop.

The relationship a lean remanufacturer has with its customers drives the differences between the lean manufacturing and remanufacturing models. For a lean remanufacturer, customers essentially become de facto suppliers. The "cores" to be remanufactured have already been consumed to some degree by the same markets that will eventually receive those same cores back as finished products ready for consumption again. The levels of materials being returned for remanufacture may be very predictable, or very unpredictable if cores are being returned from a number of different sources. Additionally, the degree or extent to which products have been "consumed" may vary greatly across the same product family based on the user and the operating environment (for example, automotive brake shoe components). For this reason, the condition of incoming units entering the remanufacturing process must be assessed. Timely information on the numbers of units being received and their condition must be available to affect production schedules, as well as material and capacity planning. Trends must be tracked so that the appropriate factoring can be entered into future planning. The incoming assessment process must differentiate between units that are good cores for scheduling and those that are not. Those determined to be unsuitable for remanufacture can either be cannibalized for component parts or scrapped entirely. Finally, the consumption of raw materials, the purchase of new cores, and cannibalization of stock are all driven by pull signals being transmitted by kanbans from the production process. Inventory of all types must be carefully tracked to drive the correct purchases of raw materials from suppliers and to fully utilize the materials being returned from the incoming assessment process.

The differences between manufacturing and remanufacturing dictate a different set of implementation priorities for the lean remanufacturer. Usage data measured along the dimensions of time, quantity and degree of wear must be tracked and put into the MRP II process. And inventory managers must supply the production process with materials being received from two very different sources.

Lean Fundamentals Used in Manufacturing Are Very Effective in Remanufacturing

The internal production process of a lean remanufacturer may be identical to a typical lean manufacturer. As described earlier, all of the benefits of cellular manufacturing can be realized in a remanufacturing environment. In remanufacturing processes that are capital intensive or that involve processes that are not geographically co-located, encompassing the entire production process within one cell may not be practical. In other situations, the remanufacturing process may be completely flexible to a point, and then may require specific equipment or processing to meet certain product or customer requirements.

The theory of constraints tells us that scheduling should be especially sensitive to bottleneck processes that pace production through the rest of the line. We should be equally aware of the loading we place on resources with capabilities peculiar to certain product families. Simply doing a "net sum" of capacity and comparing scheduled demand against that number will lead to missed shipments and the growth of WIP as production backs up behind inflexible processes. Poor scheduling of inflexible resources will create artificial bottlenecks that gross capacity planning will not identify. Inflexible processes can be fully loaded and visually managed by logically grouping product families and assigning them to specific operations. Flexible resources work smoothly to stock the buffers supplying the inflexible operations. The buffers and lineside storage put in place to focus and streamline production will provide visual indicators as to the health and balance of the line. This will make the MRP II process more robust by providing continuous physical evidence of the effectiveness of material and capacity planning systems. The buffers put into place to support noncontiguous operations will provide the same smoothing and visual management benefits as the buffers for inflexible operations. The additional function they serve is to ensure continuous production during the transit time required to move material between processes.

About the Author

Matthew H. Cooper IV, CPIM, and Paul L. Wellener IV, CPIM, CIRM, are, respectively, a manager and partner in the Cleveland office of the Deloitte & Touche Consulting Group. Both specialize in manufacturing and operations.

Reprinted from the Production and Inventory Management Journal, *First Quarter 1989.*

Toward the Measurement of Manufacturing Flexibility

Taylor Cox Jr., Ph.D.

In a recent review of the manufacturing strategies of 11 assembly plants, most of them high performers, I was struck by the inconsistency in treatment of manufacturing flexibility. While a majority of the plant managers interviewed identified flexibility as a critical task for future competitiveness, none of the plants included it among their top three formally tracked objectives for planning and control. This observation was reinforced by the recent research of 270 large manufacturing firms, conducted by The Manufacturing Roundtable of Boston University, in which flexibility was ranked from fourth to eighth (depending on the industry) in importance for future competitiveness, and first in the size of strategic gap (i.e., the difference between current capability and future needs), but did not appear at all in a list of 10 key performance measurements offered by the executives who responded. [2]

My analysis is that there are two primary reasons for this discrepancy. First, in contract to cost, delivery, and quality, which have been the cornerstones of manufacturing planning and control for many years, the idea of flexibility as a top priority has only recently come to the fore. Consequently, it tends to be treated, even on a conceptual level, less often and usually on a somewhat abstract as opposed to concrete basis. Second, and partly because of the first, the technology for measuring flexibility is poorly developed.

From these observations I concluded that there is a strong need to develop, both conceptually and operationally, a measure of manufacturing flexibility. Ideally such a measure would have the following characteristics: (1) straightforward and easy to apply, (2) sufficiently comprehensive to be a meaningful indicator of the plant's behavioral capabilities that it is expected to represent, (3) applicable to plants with different product mixes. Accordingly, this article proposes a method for treating flexibility as a formal objective of manufacturing plants that can be quantified and used in the management control system in the same way that cost, quality, and schedule compliance have been used.

The Meaning of Manufacturing Flexibility

The managers that I've talked to seem to agree that manufacturing flexibility refers to the quickness and ease with which plants can respond to changes in market conditions. This includes both volume and product-mix flexibility, the two primary types of flexibility that have been identified by earlier writers [3, 4]. Volume flexibility refers to the capacity to quickly expand the quantities of a given product mix produced, while mix flexibility addresses the ability to quickly change the types of products produced in the

Vendor Network
    1. Lead time on orders*
 	
Labor
 	
    2. Number of job classifications*
    3. Extent of worker cross-training
    4. Extent of workers "doing" multiple jobs
 	
Facility and Equipment
 	
    5. Setup time*
    6. Production cycle time*
    7. Extent to which equipment is programmable
    8. Extent to which equipment is special purpose*
 	
Production Control Processes
 	
    9. Lot size*
    10. Extent to which a strict "pull" system is used
    11. WIP inventory*
 	
    * *indicates an inverse relationship between*
    this item and flexibility

Table 1. Key Dimensions of Production Systems for Product-Mix Flexibility

plant. The latter includes both changes to existing products and the addition of new ones.

In some ways, these two forms impose similar demands on the production system; however, there are also differences that suggest the desirability of separating them for analysis. In particular, the requirement for system slack imposed by volume flexibility is not shared by product-mix flexibility.

Thus the concept of flexibility is essentially a measure of the efficiency of the process of change. It derives from the efficiency of the production system not in making products, but in changing either the number or types of products made. Like other measures of efficiency, it has to do with both speed and cost of accomplishing a task. Accordingly, the framework for analysis presented here addresses the four major system components for evaluating the speed and cost of a manufacturing task: (1) input-supply network, (2) labor force, (3) facility and equipment, and (4) production control processes. A breakdown of relevant dimensions for measurement suggested by applying this framework to mix and volume flexibility, respectively, appears in **Tables 1 and 2**.

Focusing first on product-mix flexibility, Table 1 shows the relevant dimensions for system evaluation. The negative signs in parentheses indicate those items that have an inverse relationship with system flexibility. Thus, longer

Vendor Network
1. Lead time on orders*
2. Volume range for orders obtainable within lead time

Labor

3. Work-time slack

Facility and Equipment

4. Production cycle time excluding queue time *
5. Production capacity slack

Production Control

6. Scheduling slack

- *indicates an inverse relationship between
  this item and flexibility*

**Table 2. Key Dimensions of Production Systems
for Volume Flexibility**

(a) Product-mix Flexibility

Element	Measure/s*
1. Vendor lead time	% inputs which can be obtained in X days or less
2. Labor: job classes	100 − number of job classifications
3. Labor: cross training	% of work force cross trained to do two or more jobs
4. Labor: transference	% of work force doing more than one production job in a given month
5. Setup time	% of equipment changed over in X minutes or less
6. Cycle time	Make time/total time in system
7. Programmable equipment	% equipment programmable (via number control or software)
8. Multipurpose equipment	% equipment with multiple versus single product design
9. Lot size	% of products for which economic lot size is smaller than X
10. "Pull" production	% of product made under kanban or a similar system
11. WIP inventory	Work-on-station/total work on floor

(b) Volume Flexibility

1. Vendor lead times are put into operation in the same way as before.
2. Volume range for orders may be treated as the percentage by which normal previous order quantities can be increased within the minimum lead time specified in item 1 (e.g., within three days). An alternative to this is the percentage of inputs purchased for which orders may be increased by X amount (e.g., 15%) without affecting the specified minimum lead time.
3. Production cycle time: 100 − number of days needed to make a product.
4. The slack-time items could be treated simply as percentage of slack or percentage of product made for which a specified level (e.g., 15%) of equipment, labor, and scheduling slack exists. The latter is preferable, since it acknowledges that there are practical limits to the provision of system slack.

Measures for all entries except Element 2 should be multiplied by 100.

Table 3. Objective Measures of Plant Flexibility

lead times for supplies, a more specialized work force, longer setup times for equipment, longer production cycle times, use of single-product equipment, bigger lot sizes, and larger work-in-process inventories all tend to reduce plant flexibility. The opposites of these enhance flexibility, as do programmable equipment and the use of "make-to-use-rate" production control processes. The latter is often facilitated by the use of kanbans.

Turning now to volume flexibility, Table 2 specifies relevant dimensions for evaluation. Here we are concerned not only with vendor response time but also with the ability to expand order sizes without extending lead times for delivery. The wider the range of input volumes attainable within a given lead time, the greater the plant's ability to vary volumes quickly.

Although shorter cycle times enhance volume capacity for a given time period, the inclusion of scheduling slack necessitates a different measure of production cycle time when looking at volume versus mix flexibility. Here, it is the actual production time needed excluding queue time that is relevant, since queue time may be increased by scheduling slack and volume adjustments on orders in process. Scheduling slack is needed to provide capacity for expanding quantities on orders in process without significant damage to on-time delivery performance.

The need for resource slack to increase volumes in a short time frame tends to work against the system-streamlining objective of product-mix flexibility. This is a source of significant differences between system specifications for volume versus product flexibility and suggests the importance of identifying which type of flexibility is the higher priority in the design and management of the system. Demand analyses should seek to determine how the uncertainty breaks down between shifts in quantities for existing products and shifts in types of products demanded. Of course, the two are often interrelated to the extent that there is substitutability among the products in question. When substitutability is high, rising demand for a new product will mean lower volumes for certain existing products. In other cases, however, the substitutability is so low that the volume needs will be nearly independent among the products.

A related issue is that the cost implications of system slack are such that maintaining it is far from a "free lunch." Therefore, for both cost/ROI reasons and because the types of flexibility entail different requirements and their priority differs for different environments, it is important to make flexibility decisions that fit other manufacturing strategy elements. Questions such as the comparative importance of flexibility versus other objectives to the corporate strategy, and whether volume or mix flexibility is more critical, must be addressed early on.

Finally, it is noted that inventory slack has been omitted because its net effect on volume flexibility is unclear. Spare inventory is useful when volumes vary upward but present a hindrance to downward volume adjustments. Also, the effect differs by category of inventory. Higher parts, material, and finished goods inventories would appear to facilitate upward adjustments in volume, but the same may not be true for WIP inventories. Moreover, meaningful measurements of inventory slack in this context are not obvious. Thus, while inventory levels are relevant to volume flexibility, their precise relationship seems too ambiguous for inclusion in this preliminary measurement framework.

Quantification of Plant Flexibility

Now that the relevant measurement dimensions have been identified, it remains for them to be put into operation as quantifiable elements of an overall measure of manufacturing flexibility. In order to use flexibility as an objective in a management control system, it is desirable to quantify it. A meaningful and straightforward way to accomplish this is suggested in **Table 3**.

Clarification of Table Specifications

Although most items of Table 3 are straightforward, a few may warrant clarification. Vendor lead times measure how quickly suppliers can react to a change in orders. It should be noted that this item is more critical for shifts in order composition of existing products than for new product introductions because the latter have a longer planning cycle and should permit greater opportunity to change vendors.

In treating workforce flexibility it is important to include measures of the extent to which workers are actually being used on multiple jobs. There are two reasons for this. First, in many plants the proportion of workers cross-trained exceeds the proportion actually utilized on multiple jobs by as much as 50 percentage points, and skills not utilized after training will erode quickly. Second, the utilization of workers across job categories is inhibited in some plants by restrictive work cycles (particularly in unionized plants).

The cycle-time measure computes the ratio of actual time needed to produce the product (make time) to total time that a product is on the shop floor. Another way of thinking about this measure is the percentage of total time that a product is in the system, which is process-time versus queue-time. JIT consultants have found that this ratio is often as low as 5% in large-batch operations [5]. Average cycle times for products may be used and a composite measure computed by weighting the individual products in accordance with their predominance in the plant's product mix.

The percentage of "pull" production refers to the proportion of total production for which quantities made at each work station match exactly the requirements of downstream work stations for that day. Often this is achieved by requiring that a card or order carton (kanban) be sent from the downstream station before any additional product is made upstream.

The percentage of equipment (items 5, 7, and 8 in (a) of Table) can be specified in several ways. Perhaps the most precise basis is the proportion of total product processed on equipment of the type indicated. One way of approaching this is to break down the product mix into proportions that pass through each machine type and assign a score of 100 to types possessing the characteristic and 0 to those that do not (or an appropriate score in between if the machine partly fits the criterion). Then compute a composite score based on the sum of the percentage of product affected times the assigned score for the machine type for each item.

For example, assume there are three primary machine types (A, B, and C), and that parts made in the plant pass through these machine types at the rate of 30%, 100% and 80%, respectively. The proportional process rates are computed as 0.14 for machine-type A (30/210), 0.48 for type B (100/210), and 0.38 for type C. If types A and C are programmable but type B is not, the measure for item 7 of Table 3 would be: $(0.14 \times 1) + (0.48 \times 0) + (0.38 \times 1) = 0.52$. This measure should be a reasonably accurate one; however, it is complicated to compute in plants with many products and flow sequences. A less precise, but computationally simpler, measure is the percentage of total machines in the plant that meet the specified characteristic.

The suggested measure of work-in-process inventory is the ratio of products actually being processed on a work station to the total products in the system. As this ratio approaches 1.0, the amount of buffer inventory is declining, and cycle times should improve. I am aware of several plants that are already using this measure.

Computation of Overall Flexibility

The suggested measures of Table 3 are defined so that all have a positive relationship with flexibility. Assuming equal weight on all items, the overall flexibility index is simply the average of the items. The scale is 0 to 100, and in many cases plants of different product groups may be compared. If desired, priority among the items may be provided by weighting them in accordance with their expected importance to overall flexibility, and then computing a weighted average score. Empirical work is needed to determine more precisely the leverage of the various components of the model in impacting system responsiveness. An example is the work done by Krajewski, King, Ritzman, and Wong [1] in which it was shown that setup-time reduction was the single most important factor in reducing inventories and improving customer service. Although this research did not address leverage for plant flexibility per se, it is illustrative of the type of research needed. Until such research data is available, management judgment may be substituted in defining component weights. With regard to flexibility, it is expected that cycle times, setup times, and the extent of programmable equipment are the high-impact items of (a) in Table 3.

If preferred, some elements of (a) in Table 3 may be consolidated to form a more parsimonious index. For example, the labor items may be combined (by an average of the three items) into a single measure of labor flexibility, the four equipment measures into one measure of equipment flexibility, and so on.

Finally, the rules for combining elements for the overall measure of volume flexibility could be the same as for mix flexibility. Items thought to be especially industry specific can be handled by either restricting comparisons to plants making similar products, or, if preferred, by deleting these items.

Standards of Measurement

The X symbols in Table 3 point up the need for specification of standards or benchmarks for some of the items. There is some help on this in published information on "world-class plants." For example, it has been reported [3] that the best Japanese and U.S. plants have achieved economic lot sizes of one. Nevertheless, the standards of excellence for some items are not clear, and it may be necessary to make adjustments for industry differences. Two points should be made in this regard. First, if hard data for the industry of interest is not readily available to establish benchmarks, it is still possible to proceed by establishing levels based on current performance and then measuring progress based on improvement over time. Second, it is important in the long run to seek external comparative data, and this can be pursued by reference to published research, by contact with industry and trade associations, through the formation of consortia with competitors, and through memberships in professional associations such as APICS.

1. How well does this plant adapt to unexpected changes of order volume for existing products?
2. How quickly does this plant respond to changes in product mix demanded by customers?
3. How cooperative is the management of this plant in working with you on responding to unexpected volume and/or product changes?
4. To what extent are product changeovers smooth and problem-free versus difficult and problem-laden?
5. To what extent is quality *unaffected* by unexpected changes in product mix? (same question for volume shifts)
6. To what extent is cost unaffected by unexpected shifts of demand?
7. To what extent is delivery performance unaffected by unexpected shifts in demand?

Table 4. Sample Questions for Perceptual Measures of Plant Flexibility (to be answered on a scale of 1 to 10)

Perceptual Measures of Flexibility

In addition to the more objective, concrete measures of flexibility discussed above, it is suggested that "perceptions of responsiveness" be included to create a more comprehensive picture. Here the interest is in the extent to which critical constituencies of the plant perceive the manufacturing system to be adaptable and responsive to shifting market conditions. It is my view that this approach should only be used as a supplement to the method of measurement already described, but it adds important information about the climate in the company for capitalizing on the flexibility that does exist.

The key here is to identify the appropriate respondents and to provide anonymity for individual respondents so that adverse effects on interpersonal relations, which may result from negative ratings, can be controlled. There are three groups that should clearly be included in this phase of the measurement process: engineering, marketing, and other downstream clients (i.e., consumers or other plants for whom your plant serves as a supplier). The inclusion of engineering is important because of prototype work as well as response to change orders on existing products. The rationale for the others should be obvious.

If this supplemental measurement is used, it is suggested that the ratings be converted to a 100-point scale to promote consistency with the primary measure. The two measures can then easily be combined using the same rules of averaging and weighted averaging already discussed. A sample of the types of questions that might be included appears in **Table 4.**

Conclusion

In this article I have suggested that many manufacturing managers now believe that plant flexibility to respond to changes in market conditions is among the top priority objectives of manufacturing and perhaps the most critical to achieving or maintaining a competitive advantage. In spite of its importance, however, flexibility is rarely measured explicitly and is often excluded from the operational control systems of manufacturers. I believe that manufacturing flexibility can and should be measured quantitatively. Further, if management has determined that system flexibility is critical in order for manufacturing to meet its responsibilities to corporate strategy, objectives on flexibility should be set, action plans developed, monitoring systems put in place, and so on, just as they have been for the key goals of quality, cost, and delivery.

Toward this end, I have offered an approach for the measurement of plant flexibility that I believe meets the criteria of simplicity, comprehensiveness, and comparability across plants. Through the systematic measurement of flexibility and its inclusion in the standard planning and control processes of plants, the pursuit of flexibility should be enhanced. The business climate of recent years, which features high rates of environmental change and greater intensity of competition, increasingly demands that this be done.

Acknowledgment

Work on this article was funded by the National Science Foundation Grant No. 3330878.

References

1. Krajewski, L.J., King, B.E., Ritzman, L.P., and Wong, D.S., "Kanban, MRP, and Shaping the Manufacturing Environment," *Management Science*, Vol. 33 (1987), pp. 39-52.
2. Miller, J.G., and Roth, A.V., "Manufacturing Strategies," unpublished research report of the Boston University School of Management Manufacturing Roundtable (1987).
3 Schonberger, R.J., *World Class Manufacturing*, The Free Press, NY (1986).
4. Skinner, W., "The Focused Factory," *Harvard Business Review*, Vol. 52 (1974), pp. 113 - 121.
5. Walleigh, R.C., "What's Your Excuse for Not Using JIT?" *Harvard Business Review*, March - April 1986, pp. 38 - 54.

About the Author

Taylor Cox Jr., Ph.D., is assistant professor of business administration at the University of Michigan at Ann Arbor. He teaches both courses and executive workshops on manufacturing strategy and organization theory and behavior. In addition to academic work, he has nine years of managerial experience. Current research interests include a study of manufacturing focus and application of principles for effective management of infrastructure elements of manufacturing strategy as popularized by the Japanese.

Reprinted from APICS—The Performance Advantage, *April 1995.*

Inventory—Asset or Liability?
Richard E. Crandall, CPIM, CIRM

Accounting calls inventory an asset. However, some production and operations management (POM) authorities call inventory a liability, or at least not an asset (Sharma 1993). Is one right and the other wrong, or are they talking about different things? This article describes these apparent differences and explains how the positions between accounting and POM should be reconciled if a company is to manage its inventory effectively. It addresses the specific questions of:

- Why is inventory called an asset by accounting and never a liability?
- When is inventory considered an asset by POM? a liability?
- What is excess inventory? What are the causes of excess inventory?
- How can excess inventory be disposed of? prevented?
- What changes in management practices will be needed?

Managers who understand both the accounting and operations viewpoint of inventory will do a better job of inventory management for their company.

Background

Accounting views an asset as something a company owns, and a liability as something a company owes; therefore, inventory will always be considered as an asset by accounting. For POM purposes, an asset is something that has greater value than its cost, and is able to generate income for the company.

If inventory were always an asset, in both the accounting and POM sense, there would not be a difference in viewpoints. This ideal situation exists when finished goods inventory is readily salable and moves quickly through the distribution steps from the manufacturer to the customer. Agreement also exists when the work-in-process inventory is moving steadily through the manufacturing process without undue delays, such as in a Just-in-time environment. Finally, both parties believe that a raw materials inventory that is compatible with the needs of manufacturing is also an asset. In essence, inventory is an asset when it includes the right quantities of the right goods at the right place at the right time.

Conversely, for POM, a liability is something that has greater potential cost than value, or its presence prevents sales of other products, thereby causing it to generate a loss of income for the company. When and how can inventory become a liability in the POM sense? A simple answer is when a company has excess inventory at any point along the value chain from raw materials to customer shipment. Rosenfield (1993) defines excess inventory as existing when "the potential value of excess stock, less the expected storage costs, does not match the salvage value." If

excess inventory is viewed as a liability, there is a need to determine which inventory is excess and what can be done about it. Often a company doesn't recognize that they have excess inventory because the management reporting system (usually a part of the accounting system), does not adequately identify where and how much excess inventory exists.

Causes of Excess Inventory

How does a company end up with excess inventory? What, or who, produces it? The following examples are representative, but not exhaustive, of the causes of excess inventory.

- Marketing—Marketing may want to have inventory available for a fast response to the customer, or simply, to have product available for immediate sale. To do this, they must forecast demand for a variety of items and, no matter how diligent they are and methodologically sound their forecast method, the resultant forecasts are never perfect. Consequently, some finished goods inventory does not move as expected and eventually becomes unnecessary, or excess. Another possibility is that new products replace existing products, making obsolete the inventory of the replaced products. With the increasing emphasis on customer service and shorter lead times, it will be difficult for marketing to avoid generating excess inventories. Marketing decisions generally affect finished goods inventories.
- Production—Production may want to avoid unfavorable labor variances or to improve their labor efficiencies and machine utilizations. This can be done by producing at a level capacity load that also avoids fluctuations in the work force; however, it also produces excess inventories at times. Excess inventories also result when the manufacturing process produces good, but out-of-spec, products that can be sold only if a customer is found who can use them. The temptation is to keep and value these products even with no known customer. Finally, some processes require starting a quantity of parts higher than the order quantity to allow for process defects and assure having enough good units to ship. This often results in an excess of units that may not be shippable but are good units. Again, the inclination is to hold these units in expectation that a repeat order will make them shippable; often, however, they end up as slow-moving, or excess, inventory. Production decisions can affect both work-in-process and finished goods inventory.
- Purchasing—Purchasing may want to buy a larger quantity to get a price discount; this can easily result in excess inventory at the raw materials or purchased parts

stage. While this approach may look good in the short term, with favorable purchase price variances, it can generate excess inventories that will be costly in the long term.

- Production planning—Production planning may want to utilize available capacity in the shop. To do so, they schedule the production of standard products that are in constant demand. Eventually, some of these standard products become nonstandard, and excess inventory results. Another possible scenario is that a customer requests a manufacturer to produce and hold a certain amount of inventory, at any stage in the process, for that customer's exclusive use. While this situation implies that the manufacturer will not end up holding this special inventory, sometimes they do. Decisions by production planning can affect inventory at any stage of completion: raw materials, work-in-process, or finished goods.

The conditions described above, and others, can lead to excess inventories. Often, the different functions within an organization are in conflict about how much inventory to have. Top management may have to choose a compromise position with respect to inventory levels and product mix. Obviously, nobody wants excess inventory or sets out to create it. But what are the reasons behind its creation?

Why is Excess Inventory Created?

Sometimes, the performance measures used in a company cause the buildup of inventory to be attractive. For example, most companies use income, or costs, as a measure of performance, especially for production managers, purchasing agents and marketing managers. These groups tend to focus more attention on the income statement than on the balance sheet. If the level of inventory does not change, there is no effect on income. An increase in the level of inventory often increases income because it reduces the unfavorable labor and overhead variances that occur when there is erratic or less-than-ideal capacity levels of production. Conversely, a reduction in the level of inventory often causes a reduction in income by introducing variable work loads and unused capacity, causing unfavorable labor and overhead variances. Fry (1992) provides an excellent explanation of this effect.

While the increase in inventories generates income, it has the opposite effect on cash flows by decreasing available cash. A reduction in inventories has the reverse effect—positive cash flow. This presents a conflict in that managers in most companies use income more as a measure of performance than cash flow. However, the ultimate measure of a company's value is its cash flow—a position that accounting understands but does not always communicate to the rest of the organization.

Another cause of excess inventories is the mistaken idea that having inventory on hand is always desirable. Most persons view assets as something good, and liabilities as something bad. A better way is to view inventory as stored costs that will eventually be charged to the income statement. Inventory buildup, then, is a way of postponing the reporting of costs until those costs are, in theory, matched against the sales to which they belong. The Accounting Review Board Ruling 43 says that: "In accounting for the goods in the inventory at any point in time, the major objective is the matching of appropriate costs against reverses in order that there may be a proper determination of the realized income."

The present methods used to value inventory are limited in helping us to deal with excess inventories.

How Is Inventory Valued?

Two questions need to be addressed in deciding how to value inventory: (1) Is the individual unit of inventory correctly valued, or has excess cost been assigned to each unit? and (2) Does the inventory contain excess units that should have less than full value? The latter question involves evaluating the probability that the unit will be sold and when it will be sold.

These questions require a way to assign an initial value to the unit, and some way to revalue the units as the units remain in inventory unsold.

Initial Valuation

Accounting provides two ways of valuing inventory: cost or market value, whichever is lower. The lower value purports to provide a conservative value for the company and its reported income. While conservatism is the objective, it may not be the result. As pointed out below, full absorption costing is the least conservative way of valuing inventory of the methods described, yet it is the only one generally accepted by accounting practice.

Market value—Market value is not a practical way to value inventory, in most cases. It not only requires a way to determine the market value of inventory but also a way of adjusting the value of inventory as the market value fluctuates. Trying to develop a dynamic (adjusted through time) estimate of this factor is beyond the capability of most accounting departments. As a result, most companies do not attempt to use market value of inventory as an ongoing valuation method.

Cost value—One of the key decisions in valuing inventory is to decide which costs should be stored. These costs include direct materials, direct labor, and fixed and variable overhead expenses. Historically, accounting practice required that all of the above elements be assigned to the product and stored in inventory until the product is sold. In recent years, several alternative viewpoints have been proposed: activity-based costing (ABC), direct costing and theory of constraints (TOC).

- **Activity-based costing (ABC).** This supports the traditional approach of assigning all overhead costs to the product and storing them in inventory; however, it questions the methods of allocating the overhead expenses to the products. This approach allocates the overhead expenses differently, and goes beyond just cost allocation to emphasize a closer analysis of overhead to eliminate the non-value-added portion as unnecessary.
- **Direct costing.** Many management accountants like this costing method for use in planning, analysis and control; however, financial accountants have never accepted it as a method for valuing inventory. It advocates the assignment of fixed overhead expense to the period in which they were incurred, and not to be stored in inventory as a product cost. This means that inventory has a lower cost value, and therefore, less impact on the income statement. It also more clearly identifies overhead elements, offering greater opportunities to reduce them.
- **Theory of constraints (TOC).** As with direct costing, this approach advocates that all overhead should be a

period expense. They go further to say that even direct labor is more fixed than variable in today's manufacturing environments and should be a period expense. This means that only direct material purchase cost would be stored as costs in inventory, resulting in even lower inventory values than for direct costs. TOC also promotes the idea that only sold product that is sold (throughput) should be recognized as inventory (8).

FUNCTION	REASONS TO INCREASE	REASONS TO DECREASE
Marketing Finished goods	• Increase sales through immediate delivery • Reduce lead time to customers	• Change mix to have salable items available • Make cash available for other programs
Production Work-in-process	• Fill in low load periods to level production • Increase labor efficiency and machine utilization	• Reduce congestion on shop floor • Reduce lead times to provide faster service
Purchasing Raw materials	• Obtain quantity (volume) discounts • Reduce number of purchase orders required	• Shift emphasis from cost to quality and delivery • Reduce number of vendors to be dealt with
Production planning	• Reduce the number of late shipments to customers • Ship more from stock to meet shorter due dates • Reduce number of production orders	• Keep production capacity open for customer orders • Shorten due dates by wait times in the process • Increase flexibility to respond to customers
Accounting	• Reduce overhead volume variances • Increase working capital	• Reduce physical inventory task • Reduce cash requirements

Table 1. Incentives to Increase/Decrease Inventory

Note: Although valuing inventory at the cost of materials may initially appear to be a very conservative valuation, it may not be. As manufacturers move more toward being final assemblers and increase their purchases of subassemblies or fabricated parts, the direct materials portion increases to a point where it represents 60-70 percent of the cost of sales (2). However, accounting practices can be misleading. Material costs to a final assembler are material, labor and overhead to a subassembler; material costs to a subassembler are material, labor and overhead to a fabricator; and material costs to a fabricator are material, labor and overhead to a materials processor. Figure 1 shows how the cumulative effect of this sequence could be to reduce the direct material content to a very low portion if one considers only the materials cost of the materials processor. The most conservative way to value inventory is at the scrap value of the raw materials used.

Each of the above positions is different from the traditional method of full absorption costing that assigns the maximum amount of cost to the product. The traditional approach stores the greatest amount of costs to be "matched" against subsequent revenue; the more recently proposed approaches store less for future release against revenue and, as a result, cause less distortion of the income statement during inventory buildup and reduction. Even more important, the three approaches listed above actively promote the analysis of overhead costs and the elimination of costs that are unnecessary. The full absorption method disguises overhead and discourages careful analysis; it is a financial accounting tool, not a management accounting tool.

The current thinking of many managers, including some accountants, is to store less costs in inventory and reduce the impact of inventory changes on the income statement.

Revaluation of Inventory

Most companies use full absorption costing to value inventory. This does not present a problem if inventories are low and goods are moving smoothly through the manufacturing and distribution process. In this situation, the overhead costs are not storied in inventory very long and do not seriously affect the income statement.

However, when inventories build up and become excess to the needs of the business (when the probability that they will be sold at a price higher than their accumulated cost is low), they become liabilities and the inventory valuation should reflect this through some reevaluation process. [term used in text] Inventories that do not sell promptly fall into this category. However, most companies do not discriminate among inventories when assigning an initial value; they assume that all product will be sold, no matter why it was created.

Auditors attempt to assess such factors as age, potential obsolescence, damage and other degradation of inventory in assigning an overall reduction in the inventory value. However, they usually do this only during the annual audit and seldom do it in a way that would be of benefit to inventory managers in identifying the causes of excess inventory that could lead to preventing or reducing the buildup of excess inventory.

There is a need to develop a way to adjust, usually reduce, inventory values as time passes and the probability of sale diminishes. While this is logical, there are practical problems that must be faced, and most companies do not have a formal way of adjusting inventory values.

A more desirable solution is to prevent the accumulation of excess inventories, i.e., prevent the problem, not find a better way to report it. How can this be done? A company must first identify which inventory is excess; then it must sell or otherwise dispose of the excess inventory; and, finally, it must establish practices that prevent the recurrence of excess inventory. Rosenfield (1993) offers a way in which excess inventory can be identified, and White (1989) describes several ways in which a company can dispose of excess inventory.

Changes Required

To reduce existing excess inventory and prevent its recurrence, a company requires changes in attitudes, objections, performance measures, operating methods and accounting practices. It also requires the integration of various functions within the organization.

Changes in Attitudes About Inventory

Managers need to change their thinking about the desirability of having inventory versus the desirability of not having inventory. **Table 1** contains a comparison of the reasons for having inventory (the traditional perspective) and the reasons for not having inventory (the contemporary perspective).

These changes in attitude come from the realization that today's competitive environment requires attention on customer service, product flexibility and product quality, as well as product cost. White (1989) describes how customer service can be improved by removing the slow-moving inventory ("sludge") from the inventory base. Beddingfield (1992) also points out the competitive advantages of improved inventory management.

Changes in Objectives

Transition from the traditional way of thinking to the contemporary requires a combination of rethinking strategic objectives and changes in the performance measurement system. Both topics are important and several authors have discussed these issues, especially Dixon et al. (1970) and Vollman et al. (1993). Part of this change process involves establishing global objectives that can be translated into local objectives for each organizational function, such as marketing, production, materials management and accounting. As previously mentioned, the choice of inventory level and product mix may present conflicts among functions and requires a holistic approach to reach a common objective.

Changes in Performance Measures

It is necessary for the local (functional) performance measures to be closely related to the general financial performance measures, such as income and return on investment. As previously mentioned, building inventory is a way to show improved performance in income, which is used directly, or in some related form, as a measure of performance for functional areas such as marketing, production and purchasing. If other performance measures were used, such as customer service levels, the practice of building inventories, especially the less-salable, would probably decrease.

Changes in Operating Practices

Marketing, production and purchasing have to effect the needed changes to eliminate existing excess inventories and minimize the buildup of future excess inventories. To do this, they need help from the accounting function in identifying and measuring the status and causes of the excess inventories.

- Marketing—The burden of disposing of excess inventory usually falls to sales and marketing. This is not a welcome task and often has a lower priority than new product or key account programs; however, it must be done. Marketing should be among the most enthusiastic supporters of programs to prevent excess inventory. They can help by working more closely with customers to obtain better forecasts of customer demand; communicate with engineering and production about introductions of new products and phaseouts of discontinued products; participate in the reduction of production and delivery lead times to reduce the need for finished goods inventories; and become a closely integrated link in the company's planning and control system.

- Production—Several current movements in production and inventory management include a focus on reducing the level of inventories. Just-in-Time (JIT) includes a major emphasis on reducing the causes of inventory to reduce the absolute level of inventory. Materials requirements planning (MRP), when properly applied, will reduce excess and slow-moving inventory. Total quality management (TQM) attempts, among other things, to reduce the level of defects. Lower defects result in less uncertainty and fewer overruns on production orders. These

programs help to reduce the cycle time from customer to delivery and to improve on-time deliveries.

Changes in Accounting Practices

Accounting can help to identify, reduce and prevent excess inventory; however, they must change some of their practices, particularly about inventory valuation—changes necessary to make accounting information more useful to production/operations managers. These changes include how to value inventory, how to revalue inventory over tie, how to reduce buildup of excess inventory through proper financial performance measures, and how income and cash flow must both be considered in planning inventory.

Initial valuation—The initial valuation of inventory should be a discriminating process to separate the planned and readily resalable product in inventory from the unplanned product with uncertain resalability. This process also should be dynamic, in that the status of certain products will evolve as they move through the product life cycle. To show the extremes of this method, a regularly sold, standard product could be valued with full absorption costs, as done currently; at the other extreme, inventory of nonstandard product generated as the result of a production overrun, could be valued at the scrap value of the material.

A factor to be considered in the initial valuation is the probability that the unit will be sold. In the standard unit described above, the assumption is that the probability of sale is near 100 percent and the unit can be assigned full cost value. In the overrun unit, the probability of sale as a completed unit is near zero, and the unit value is only the revenue generated when sold as scrap. The values for these extreme groups of products are logical; however, how about units of inventory that fall between the end groups? How does a company value them?

When the probability of sale is less than 100 percent, one approach is to value the units at some cost less than full absorption cost, such as the direct cost or the purchased material cost. This is a way of reducing the average cost of the units in inventory and allowing some costs to flow through as period expenses during the production period. However, it is an expedient method of devaluing, and does not address the logic of the situation, namely, what is the probability of sale?

Another approach is to value the units at full absorption cost and then group them in a category of "25 percent probability of sale," "50 percent probability of sale," etc. This forces an evaluation of the potential salability of the product, but it requires extensive additional attention and record keeping; however, it reflects the reality of the situation. In addition, it offers a way to assign responsibility to the source of the excess inventory, thereby suggesting a way to prevent reoccurrences.

Revaluation of inventory—The total inventory should be classified by major product lines, and by method of initial valuation. It should be reviewed regularly (higher usage, or "A" items more frequently) to decide the need for revaluation. As with the initial valuation, certain guidelines could be developed. Some parameters to be considered include the age of the inventory, its physical condition and shelf life, the degree of obsolescence, and the number of sales days on hand. These adjustments could be handled in an "Allowance for Inventory Revaluation," in much the same way as an "Allowance for Uncollectible Accounts Receivable."

While this method requires judgment, this judgment can be systematically applied, and the process will identify major areas of concern or potential liability to the company. Adjustments in inventory value are not unheard of. Retail stores do it through the markdown procedure. This reduces the income when product is sold, and cost is matched with the sale. Wholesale companies, because of very narrow gross profit margins, sometimes revalue inventories higher when notified of price increases by suppliers. This has the effect of increasing income at the time of purchase, not at the time of sale, presumably because the inventory has increased in value. These adjustments make sense and are convenient; something similar should be done for manufacturing inventories, though it is less convenient and more difficult to determine the true value.

Clearly, the processes described above for valuation and revaluation of units of inventory would be time-consuming and an added expense; as a result, the emphasis should be on prevention of excess inventory, not accounting for it, or disposing of it. As with many problems, the best answer is avoidance, not correction.

Integration of Organization Functions

Identification, disposal and prevention of excess inventories requires a coordinated effort by all functions of a business, particularly marketing, operations and accounting. This coordinated effort starts with the strategic planning process and carries through to the day-to-day operations.

If all parties concerned were more aware of the effect of inventory changes on both income and cash flow, better decisions could be made about the best levels of inventory and the most desirable product mix. This requires better communications among the operating groups and accounting during the business planning processes and recognition of the responsibilities of the marketing and production groups in the cash management program.

Inventory is not an asset to a company if it is excess inventory. The sooner production/operations management and accounting recognize this and adjust their performance measures and operating practices, the sooner companies will be motivated to identify and reduce, or better still, to prevent excess inventory.

References

1. Beddingfield, Thomas W., "Reducing Inventory Enhances Competitiveness," *APICS—The Performance Advantage*, September, 1992, pp. 28-31.
2. Dixon, J. Robb, Alfred J. Nanni and Thomas E. Vollman, *The New Performance Challenge, Measuring Operations for World-Class Competition*, Dow Jones-Irwin, Homewood, Illinois, 1990.
3. Farmer, James R., "Re-engineering, Achieving Productivity Success," *APICS—The Performance Advantage*, March, 1993, pp. 38-42.
4. Fry, Timothy D., "Manufacturing Performance and Cost Accounting," *Production and Inventory Management Control Journal*, Vol. 33, No. 3, pp. 30-35.
5. Gaither, Norman, *Production and Operations Management* (Fourth Edition), The Dryden Press, Chicago, 1990.
6. Jenkins, Carolyn, "Accurate Forecasting Reduces Inventory," *APICS—The Performance Advantage*, September, 1992, pp. 37-39.
7. Lee, Hau L. and Corey Billington, "Managing Supply Chain Inventory: Pitfalls and Opportunities," *Sloan Management Review*, Spring, 1992, pp. 65-73.
8. Rosenfield, Donald B., "Disposal or Excess Inventory," *Operations Research*, Vol. 37, No. 3, May-June, 1993, pp. 404-409.
9. Schaeffer, Randall, "A New View of Inventory Management," *APICS—The Performance Advantage*, January, 1993, pp. 21-24.
10. Sharma, Ken, "Adding 'Intelligence' to MRP Systems," *APICS—The Performance Advantage*, March, 1993, pp. 53-58.
11. Umble, M. Michael and M. L. Srikanth, *Synchronous Manufacturing*, SouthWestern Publishing Co., Cincinnati, 1990, p. 28.
12. Vollman, Thomas E., William L. Berry and D. Clay Whybark, *Integrated Production and Inventory Management*, Business One Irwin, Homewood, Illinois, 1993.
13. White, R. Douglas, "Streamline Inventory to Better Serve Customers," *The Journal of Business Strategy*, March/April, 1989, pp. 43-45.

Reprinted from the 1994 APICS International Conference Proceedings.

Practical Quality Function Deployment

Kenneth Crow, CPIM

Quality Function Deployment (QFD) is a structured approach to defining customer needs or requirements and translating them into specific plans to produce products to meet those requirements. The "voice of the customer" is the term to describe these stated and unstated customer needs or requirements. The voice of the customer is captured in a variety of ways: direct discussion, surveys, focus groups, customer specifications, observation, warranty data, field reports, etc. This understanding of the customer requirements is then summarized in a product planning matrix or "house of quality." These matrices are used to translate higher level "whats" or requirements into lower level "how's" or means to satisfy the requirements.

While the QFD matrices are a good communication tool at each step in the process, the matrices are the means and not the end. The real value is in the process of communicating and decision-making with QFD. QFD is oriented toward involving a team of people representing the various functional departments that have involvement in product development: Marketing, Design Engineering, Quality Assurance, Manufacturing/Manufacturing Engineering, Test Engineering, Finance, Product Support, etc.

The active involvement of these departments can lead to balanced consideration of the requirements or "what's" at each stage of the development process and provide a mechanism to communicate hidden knowledge. The structure of this methodology helps development personnel understand essential requirements, internal capabilities, and constraints. QFD helps development personnel maintain a correct focus on true requirements and minimizes misinterpreting customer needs. As a result, QFD is an effective communications and a quality planning tool.

The Voice of the Customer

Basic customer needs should be identified. Frequently, customers will try to express their needs in terms of "how" the need can be satisfied and not in terms of "what" the need is. This limits consideration of development alternatives. Development and marketing personnel should ask "why" until they truly understand what the root need is. Breakdown general requirements into more specific requirements by probing what is needed.

Once customer needs are gathered, they then have to be organized. The mass of interview notes, requirements documents, market research, and customer data needs to be distilled into a handful of statements that express key customer needs. Affinity diagramming is a useful tool to assist with this effort. Brief statements which capture key customer requirements are transcribed onto cards. A data dictionary which describes these statements of need is prepared to avoid any misinterpretation. These cards are organized into logical groupings or related needs. This will make it easier to identify any redundancy and serves as a basis for organizing the customer needs for the first QFD matrix.

In addition to "stated" or "spoken" customer needs, "unstated" or "unspoken" needs or opportunities should be identified. Needs that are assumed by customers and, therefore not verbalized, can be identified through preparation of a function tree. These needs normally are not included in the QFD matrix, unless it is important to maintain focus on one or more of these needs. Excitement opportunities (new capabilities or unspoken needs that will cause customer excitement) are identified through the voice of the engineer, marketing, or customer support representative. These can also be identified by observing customers use or maintain products and recognizing opportunities for improvement.

Product Planning

Once customer needs are identified, preparation of the product planning matrix or "house of quality" can begin. The sequence of preparing the product planning matrix is as follows:

1. Customer needs or requirements are stated on the left side of the matrix as shown in **Figure 1**. These are organized by category based on the affinity diagrams. Ensure the customer needs or requirements reflect the desired market segment(s). Address the unspoken needs (assumed and excitement capabilities). If the number of needs or requirements exceeds twenty to thirty items,

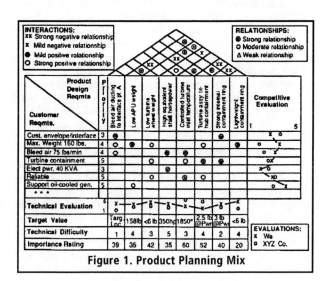

Figure 1. Product Planning Mix

decompose the matrix into smaller modules or subsystems to reduce the number of requirements in a matrix. For each need or requirement, state the customer priorities using a 1 to 5 rating. Use ranking techniques and paired comparisons to develop priorities.

2. Evaluate prior generation products against competitive products. Use surveys, customer meetings or focus groups/clinics to obtain feedback. Include competitor's customers to get a balanced perspective. Identify price points and market segments for products under evaluation, Identify warranty, service, reliability, and customer complaint problems to identify areas of improvement. Based on this, develop a product strategy.

   Consider the current strengths and weaknesses relative to the competition? How do these strengths and weaknesses compare to the customer priorities? Where does the gap need to be closed and how can this be done—copying the competition or using a new approach or technology? Identify opportunities for breakthroughs to exceed competitors' capabilities, areas for improvement to equal competitors' capabilities, and areas where no improvement will be made. This strategy is important to focus development efforts where they will have the greatest payoff.

3. Establish product requirements or technical characteristics to respond to customer requirements and organize into related categories. Characteristics should be meaningful, measurable, and global. Characteristics should be stated in a way to avoid implying a particular technical solution so as not to constrain designers.

4. Develop relationships between customer requirements and product requirements or technical characteristics. Use symbols for strong, medium and weak relationships. Be sparing with the strong relationship symbol. Have all customer needs or requirements been addressed? Are there product requirements or technical characteristics stated that don't relate to customer needs?

5. Develop a technical evaluation of prior generation products and competitive products. Get access to competitive products to perform product or technical benchmarking. Perform this evaluation based on the defined product requirements or technical characteristics. Obtain other relevant data such as warranty or service repair occurrences and costs and consider this data in the technical evaluation.

6. Develop preliminary target values for product requirements or technical characteristics.

7. Determine potential positive and negative interactions between product requirements or technical characteristics using symbols for strong or medium, positive or negative relationships. Too many positive interactions suggest potential redundancy in "the critical few" product requirements or technical characteristics. Focus on negative interactions—consider product concepts or technology to overcome these potential trade-offs or consider the trade-offs in establishing target values.

8. Calculate importance ratings. Assign a weighting factor to relationship symbols (9-3-1, 4-2-1, or 5-3-1). Multiply the customer importance rating by the weighting factor in each box of the matrix and add the resulting products in each column.

9. Develop a difficulty rating (1 to 5 point scale, five being very difficult and risky) for each product requirement or technical characteristic. Consider technology maturity, personnel technical qualifications, business risk, manufacturing capability, supplier/subcontractor capability, cost, and schedule. Avoid too many difficult/

high risk items as this will likely delay development and exceed budgets. Assess whether the difficult items can be accomplished within the project budget and schedule.

10. Analyze the matrix and finalize the product development strategy and product plans. Determine required actions and areas of focus. Finalize target values. Are target values properly set to reflect appropriate trade-offs? Do target values need to be adjusted considering the difficulty rating? Are they realistic with respect to the price points, available technology, and the difficulty rating? Are they reasonable with respect to the importance ratings?

Determine items for further QFD deployment. To maintain focus on "the critical few," less significant items may be ignored with the subsequent QFD matrices. Maintain the product planning matrix as customer requirements or conditions change.

One of the guidelines for successful QFD matrices is to keep the amount of information in each matrix at a manageable level. With a more complex product, if one hundred potential needs or requirements were identified, and these were translated into an equal or even greater number of product requirements or technical characteristics, there would be more than 10,000 potential relationships to plan and manage. This becomes an impossible number to comprehend and manage. It is suggested that an individual matrix not address more than twenty or thirty items on each dimension of the matrix. Therefore, a larger, more complex product should have its customers needs decomposed into hierarchical levels.

To summarize the initial process, a product plan is developed based on initial market research or requirements definition. If necessary, feasibility studies or research and development are undertaken to determine the feasibility of the product concept. Product requirements or technical characteristics are defined through the matrix, a business justification is prepared and approved, and product design then commences.

Product Design

Once product planning is complete, a more complete specification may be prepared. The product requirements or technical characteristics and the product specification serve as the basis for developing product concepts. Product benchmarking, brainstorming, and research and development are sources for new product concepts. Once concepts are developed, they are analyzed and evaluated. Cost studies and trade studies are performed. The Pugh concept selection matrix can be used to help with this evaluation process.

The Pugh concept selection matrix shown in **Figure 2** lists the product requirements or technical characteristics down the left side of the matrix. These serve as evaluation criteria. Product concepts are listed across the top. One product concept, typically the current product concept or traditional concept is used as the datum and identified in the first column. For each criteria, the various product concepts are judged with respect to the datum. If the product concept is about the same as the datum, a zero (0) is placed in the column. If the concept is clearly superior a plus (+) is placed in the column. If it is clearly inferior, a minus (-) is placed in the column. The total number of pluses, minuses, and zeros are added up. The preferred concept will have the most pluses and fewest minuses. This concept selection technique is also a design synthesis technique. For each minus with the preferred concept's column, other

Criteria	Datum	Concept A	Concept B	Concept C
Low APU Weight		+	+	0
Low turbine wheel weight		0	+	0
Controlled turbine inlet temperature		0	+	0
Acceptable turbine assembly life		0	-	+
Turbine assy tri-hub containment		+	-	-
High equivalent shaft horsepower		-	-	0
Total +'s		2	3	1
Total -'s		1	3	1
Total 0's		3	0	4

Figure 2. Pugh Concept Selection

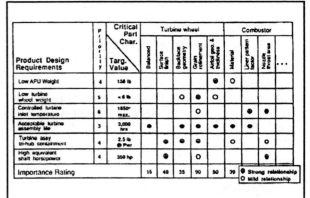

Figure 3. Deployment Matrix

concept approaches with pluses or zeros for that evaluation criteria are reviewed to see if a new approach can be synthesized by borrowing part of another concept approach to improve on the preferred approach.

Based on this and other evaluation steps, a product concept is selected. The product concept is represented with block diagrams or a design layout. Critical subsystems, modules or parts are identified from the layout. Criticality is determined in terms of effect on performance, reliability, and quality. Techniques such as fault tree analysis or failure modes and effects analysis (FMEA) can be used to determine criticality from a reliability or quality perspective.

The product requirements or technical characteristics defined in the product planning matrix become the "whats" that are listed down the left side of this matrix along with priorities (based on the product planning matrix importance ratings) and target values. The subsystem, assembly or part deployment matrix is prepared in a manner very similar to the product planning matrix. These product requirements or technical characteristics are translated into critical subsystem, assembly or part characteristics. This translation considers criticality of the subsystem, assembly or parts as well as their characteristics from a performance perspective to complement consideration of criticality from a quality and reliability perspective. Relationships are established between product requirements or technical characteristics and the critical subsystem, assembly or part characteristics. Importance ratings are calculated and target values for each critical subsystem, assembly or part characteristic are established.

Process Design

QFD continues this translation and planning into the process design phase. Pugh concept selection can be used to evaluate different manufacturing process approaches and select the preferred approach.

Again, the "hows" from the higher level matrix (in this case the critical subsystem, assembly or part characteristics) become the "whats" which are used to plan the process for fabricating and assembling the product. Important processes and tooling requirements can be identified to focus efforts to control, improve and upgrade processes and equipment. At this stage, communication between Engineering and Manufacturing is emphasized and trade-offs can be made as appropriate to achieve mutual goals based on the customer needs.

In addition to planning manufacturing processes, more detailed planning related to process control, quality control, set-up, equipment maintenance and testing can be supported by additional matrices. **Figure 3** provides an example of a process/quality control matrix. The process steps developed in the process planning matrix are used as the basis for planning and defining specific process and quality control steps in this matrix.

The result of this planning and decision-making is that Manufacturing focuses on the critical processes, dimensions and characteristics that will have a significant effect on producing a product that meets customers needs. There is a clear trail from customer needs to the design and manufacturing decisions to satisfy those customer needs. Disagreements over what is important at each stage of the development process should be minimized, and there will be greater focus on "the critical few" items that affect the success of the product.

QFD Process

QFD begins with product planning; continues with product design and process design; and finishes with process control, quality control, testing, equipment maintenance, and training. As a result, this process requires multiple functional disciplines to adequately address this range of activities. QFD is synergistic with multifunction product development teams. It can provide a structured process for these teams to begin communicating, making decisions and planning the product. It is a useful methodology, along with product development teams, to support a concurrent engineering or integrated product development approach.

0QFD requires discipline. It is not necessarily easy to get started with. The following is a list of recommendations to facilitate initially using QFD.

- Obtain management commitment to use QFD.
- Establish clear objectives and scope of QFD use. Avoid first using it on a large, complex project if possible. Will it be used for the overall product or applied to a subsystem, module, assembly or critical part? Will the complete QFD methodology be used or will only the product planning matrix be completed?
- Establish multifunctional team. Get an adequate time commitment from team members.
- Obtain QFD training with practical hands-on exercises to learn the methodology and use a facilitator to guide the initial efforts.
- Schedule regular meetings to maintain focus and avoid the crush of the development schedule overshadowing effective planning and decision-making.
- Avoid gathering perfect data. Many times significant customer insights and data exist within the organization, but they are in the form of hidden knowledge. On

the other hand, it may be necessary to spend additional time gathering the voice of the customer before beginning QFD.

QFD is an extremely useful methodology to facilitate communication, planning, and decision-making within a product development team. It is not a paperwork exercise or additional documentation that must be completed in order to proceed to the next development milestone. It not only brings the new product closer to the intended target, but reduces development cycle time and cost in the process.

QFD Workshop

Training and hands-on use of QFD are essential to begin applying it. This session will include several of our workshop exercises to help demonstrate this methodology. An outline of the standard two-day workshop (on which the workshop part of this session is based) is as follows:

1. Introduction
   - Product Planning and Voice of the Customer
   - Kano Model and Types of Customer Requirements (Spoken and Unspoken)
   - Methods and Considerations for Capturing the Voice of the Customer
   - QFD Approach and Methodology—House of Quality
   - Basic QFD—The Four Phases
2. Product Planning (House Of Quality)
   - Development of the Product Planning Matrix Based on Voice of the Customer
   - Guidelines, Lessons Learned & Alternate Approaches
   - *Exercise 1: Organizing Customer Requirements, Evaluating the Competition and Developing a Product Strategy (Team Development of a New Pocket Calculator Product)*
   - *Exercise 2: Developing Technical Characteristics for the New Product & Establishing Relationships with Customer Requirements*
   - *Exercise 3: Performing a Technical Evaluation (Product Benchmarking with Competitive Calculators)*
   - *Exercise 4: Considering Interactions, Risks, Importance Ratings, & Other Factors for Development*
   - *Exercise 5: Analyzing the Product Planning Matrix and Establishing Target Values*
   - QFD with Complex Systems/Products: Two Approaches
3. Subsystem/Part Deployment
   - The Product Development Process and Preparation of the Deployment Matrix
   - *Exercise 6: Deploy Design Requirements & Identify Other Basic Functions*
   - Determining Critical Assembly/Part Characteristics—Performance & Reliability
   - The Role of Design of Experiments (DOE), Fault Tree Analysis (FTA) and Failure Modes and Effects Analysis (FMEA) in QFD
   - Taguchi Method Case Study (optional)
   - Concept Development & Product Benchmarking
   - *Exercise 7: Develop & Select Product Concept - Pugh Concept Selection*
   - *Exercise 8: Determine Critical Part Characteristics, Relationships, Importance Ratings & Target Values*
4. Process Planning
   - Deploy Selected Part Characteristics
   - Evaluate and Select Process Approach
   - Determine Process Relationships & Critical Process Parameters
   - Evaluating Where to Improve Process Capabilities and Invest in New Equipment
   - *Workshop Exercise (optional)*
5. Production Planning
   - Deploy Critical Processes
   - Establish Quality Control, Test, Process Control and Maintenance Parameters
   - Develop Work Instructions and Training
6. QFD Framework and Process
   - Enhanced QFD Framework—an Approach for Complex Products
   - QFD and Systems Engineering
   - Applying QFD to Services, Software Development and Business Processes
   - Planning and Managing the QFD Project
   - Team Membership and Operation
   - Management Support, Training and Avoiding Pitfalls
   - QFD Software Tools

Critical Part Characteristics / Critical Process Steps	Turbine wheel: Balanced	Turbine wheel: Surface finish	Turbine wheel: Backface geometry	Turbine wheel: Grain refinement	Turbine wheel: Airfoil geo. & thickness	Rating	Part Control Parameters
Priority	2	4	4	9	6		
Mold preparation	○	●			●	51	- Surface finish - Airfoil geometry
Hot isostatic pressure casting	○	●		●	●	96	- Surface finish - Inclusions, cracks, porosity - Blade tip fill
Mass center balancing	●					10	- Machine centers
Turbine tip OD & shroud line contour machining		○				12	- Outer diameter - Profile geometry - Surface finish
Low stress grind - backface	○	●	●			46	- Backface geometry - Surface finish

Other Data:
- Equipment
- Location
- Tooling

Figure 4. Process Planning Matrix

Critical Process Steps	Process Control Parameters	Control Points	Control Method	Sample Size & Freq.	Check Method
Hot isostatic presurre casting	Mat'l temp. Mold temp. Remelt %	Mat'l prop. Heat treat FPI	Cert.	100%	N/A
Mass center balancing	Balance mach. calibration Speed	Detailed balance	Cert.	100%	N/A
Turbine tip OD & shroud line contour machining	Set-up Speeds & feeds Tool wear	Dim. insp. Surface finish	X bar & R chart	4 pieces/ lot	Elect. gage Check fixture Visual
Low stress grind - backface	Speeds & feeds Diamond dressed wheel	Dim. insp. Surface finish	N/A	100%	CMM Visual
Florescent penetrant insp. & proof spin	Speed	Cracks Inclusions O.D.	N/A	100%	Visual Spin test

Figure 5. Process Control/Quality Control Matrix

Workshop Exercises

You will be divided into groups of five people to work as a team. You will use QFD, specifically the product planning matrix or "house of quality," to plan a new product (a pocket calculator) to complement and improve on your company's current product. This product will extend your company's product line. Extensive market research, customer meetings and focus group sessions were used to develop the customer requirements listed on the matrix.

A QFD matrix and instructions for the workshop exercises will be handed out to participants during the workshop. Samples of the existing product and competitors products will also be provided to add realism to the workshop exercises.

About the Author

Kenneth A. Crow is President of DRM Associates, a consulting firm for the manufacturing and high technology industries. His firm focuses on improving product development through the implementation of integrated product development, process reengineering, time-to-market, and total quality management practices. He is a recognized expert in the field of integrated product development with over twenty-one years of experience directing major operational improvement programs, implementing systems, and providing product development consulting and education.

He has worked internationally with many Fortune 500 companies. He has written articles and papers, contributed to books, presented at conferences, and conducted workshops in Australia, North America, Europe and the Middle East on product development, manufacturing, quality function deployment, and teams. In addition to his 17 years in APICS, he is a founding member and on the Board of Directors of the Society of Concurrent Engineering.

Reprinted from the 1996 APICS International Conference Proceedings.

Effective Performance Measurements
Larry G. Curry, CPIM

When your company is sluggish and products or information isn't moving like it should, do you know how to figure out why? This presentation will show you how measuring performance can identify the problems, and "root cause analysis" can help identify the solutions. In addition, it will show you how to use performance measurements to constantly monitor the health of your company to prevent it from becoming sluggish in the first place.

People who are interested in keeping their bodies in tip-top shape monitor their health indicators (heart rate, blood pressure, cholesterol levels, etc.) on a regular basis. You need to do the same thing to keep your company in tip-top shape. Performance measurements are the "health indicators" of your company. If you don't monitor the right ones on a regular basis, you may not find out that there is a problem until it is too late. Even if it is not too late to save the company, fixing the problem(s) will probably not be simple and will be very expensive.

Companies that use performance measurements to identify problems early have the opportunity to fix them quickly before they get out of control. In conjunction with performance measurements, you must do "root cause analysis" to ensure that you are really solving the problem and not just putting a bandage over a symptom. Only by eliminating the cause of the problem does it go away forever.

Why Measure?

The sole purpose for taking measurements is to help identify the areas of the company that need attention. Only when management has demonstrated that uncovering and reporting problems is good, will they get the full support of the entire work force. Only when you have the support of the entire work force can you get maximum benefits from the measurement process. Even when measurement policies and procedures are put in place, it is often difficult to get accurate and timely data, because everyone knows that when management starts measuring things, they are looking for someone to blame for all of the company's problems. Changing this mind-set is one of the hardest tasks a company will ever undertake.

Where Do You Start?

There is no wrong level in an organization to start taking performance measurements. Measurements will be required from the top (performance against the business plan) to the bottom (performance against operation due dates on the shop floor dispatch list.)

What Do You Measure?

Each company will require a different set of measurements based upon the product flows and processes used. However, there are also some measurements that are required for everyone. It is also important to note that sometimes it is necessary to use the information from several measurements to find the root cause of a problem. Using a single measurement could lead you in the wrong direction. You must ask "why" enough times to ensure that you are deep enough into the process that there are no longer any excuses.

Suppose your company is having difficulty shipping product on-time. Why? Answer—manufacturing never finishes final assembly on schedule. Why? Answer—there are too many parts shortages. Why? Answer—on-time delivery from outside suppliers is only 78%.

This is where the process normally stops. We have seemingly chased the problem to an area outside of our control. Our measurement of supplier delivery has indicated a problem. The logical solution is to put pressure on our suppliers to do a better job of delivering on-time. But is that the right solution? Maybe we need to ask our suppliers "why?" If they respond that they have had problems with machines or attendance, or that business has been very good and they have taken on more orders that they can fill, we have probably found the cause of our problem. However, the chances of this being true with all, or even a majority of our suppliers at the same time are very slim. More likely, we will hear things like "If you would give me the order on time, I would be happy to deliver on time." Now we need another performance measurement. We need to measure the percentage of orders released to our suppliers inside lead time. If that measurement is 53%, we need to ask "why?" The rest of the story goes like this. The buyer releases the order late, because the demand showed up in MRP late, because it was added to the bill of material late, because engineering finished the design late, because sales got the specification from the customer late. Our measurement of changes to customer orders inside the firm time fence in the master production schedule will tell us if this is a common occurrence or something that rarely happens. Finding and fixing the root causes of problems requires that timely and accurate data be available.

Typical Measurements

Performance to Budget

In its simplest form this is a measurement of actual profit versus planned profit. However, in order to know why the two don't match, you will also need to know if you spent more than planned or sold less than planned.

The sales and operations planning process sets forth a sales plan and an operations plan for the company. Both of these plans are done by product family. Measuring performance against these two plans will often help us understand why we are off budget.

Performance to Sales Plan

This measurement compares what we actually sold to what we had planned to sell. If there is a difference, we need to be able to answer "why." We also need to be able to determine if the planned sales that did not materialize were lost or simply delayed, since that will impact our future sales plan. Not being able to answer those questions makes it impossible for the people in production to know what to plan to build.

$$\text{Performance to sales plan} = \frac{\text{Actual sales}}{\text{Planned sales}}$$

Performance to Production Plan

This measurement tests what we actually built against what we said we would build. If we missed plan we must be able to answer the questions of why, how long the condition(s) that caused us to miss schedule will continue to exist, and how soon we will be back on schedule.

$$\text{Performance to production plan} = \frac{\text{Actual build}}{\text{Planned build}}$$

Inventory Record Accuracy

This measurement tells us what percentage of the time we have the right quantity of the right parts in the right location. Location must be a part of this measurement. It does no good to know that you have parts if you can't find them. The industry accepted minimum for inventory record accuracy is 95%.

$$\text{Inventory record accuracy} = \frac{\text{Number of correct records}}{\text{Number of audited records}}$$

Bill of Material Accuracy

This is a measurement of single level bills of materials. The measurement includes the elements of parent component relationship, quantity per, and unit of measure. If any of these elements is incorrect, the entire bill of material for that parent is considered incorrect.

The industry accepted minimum for bill of material accuracy is 98%.

$$\text{Bill of material accuracy} = \frac{\text{Number of correct bills}}{\text{Number of bills audited}}$$

Routing Accuracy

This measurement is for companies that must track performance against individual operations in order to maintain control of the work in the factory. It is used to ensure that all operations are listed and are in the right sequence. Industry accepted minimum is 95%.

$$\text{Routing accuracy} = \frac{\text{Number of correct routings}}{\text{Number of routings audited}}$$

On-Time Release of Shop Orders and Purchase Orders

There is often times a tendency to blame our problems on manufacturing or our suppliers because orders are delivered late. As mentioned earlier, this measurement will help us determine where the true problems lie.

$$\text{On-time order release} = \frac{\text{\# of orders released with full lead time}}{\text{Total number of orders released}}$$

Percentage of Orders Changed After Release

This is a measurement of schedule stability. It also helps to ensure that people are not playing a numbers game. If management uses measurements incorrectly it is easy to get into the habit of managing the numbers instead of managing the business. An example of this would be placing an order with full lead time and then rescheduling it the next day to the real need date. This would make the above measurement look good and would hide the fact that problems exist.

Shop Orders Completed on Schedule— Purchase Orders Received on Schedule

On-time order receipt is another major measurement. If we continually miss this one, we will probably be putting customer shipments at risk. If we miss this one and still deliver to the customer on-time, we are probably working overtime, which adds cost and reduces profit, or our manufacturing or assembly lead times are too long resulting in excess work in process inventory and has a negative impact on cash flow. This is another example of why we sometimes need several measurements to determine the root causes of problems. The industry accepted minimum for on-time order receipt is 95%. A tolerance of +5, -0 (5 days early, 0 days late) is often applied to this measurement.

Percentage of Customer Orders Shipped on the First Promised Date

This is a measurement of how well we meet our commitment to our customers.

$$\text{Percentage of on-time shipments} = \frac{\text{\# of orders shipped on schedule}}{\text{\# of orders scheduled to ship}}$$

Percentage of Customer Orders Shipped on the Customer Requested Date

At first glance this looks like the same measurement as the one above. However, this is a measurement of how well we meet our customer's needs. It is important to understand the difference. If we always hit our 5-week lead time, but the market is demanding a 3-week lead time, our performance to our commitments is good, but our performance to our customer's needs is bad. When this situation exists there is a tremendous opportunity for the competition to steal our customers.

Customer Satisfaction

There are two methods for measuring customer satisfaction. You can measure their attitude or their actions. Measuring their actions will give you a better understanding of how satisfied they really are. Measurements of the two areas are accomplished by ATTITUDE:

    Telephone follow-up
    Focus groups
    Reply cards, etc.

And ACTIONS:

    Customer retention
    Annual revenue per customer
    Customer referrals
    Customers request that you participate in the design of their new products

Summary

In most cases capturing the data for these measurements can be done by the computer. This makes the measurement process easy. Unfortunately, many companies still fail to recognize the importance of the process. Once they reach the accepted minimums, they stop the measurement process. As time passes new people come onto the job, or the people in the job start to get careless and the processes start to deteriorate. Without the correct measurements in place and on going, severe problems can exist before anyone realizes that something is wrong. Don't let your company suffer poor health because you failed to look for and heed the warning signals. Install measurements systems today and monitor them forever.

About the Author

Larry G. Curry, as a consultant and educator, has spent the last 10 years helping manufacturing management teams, in both Commercial, Aerospace, and Defense companies, in gaining control of their businesses and using MRP II and Continuous Improvement techniques.

Larry spent 19 years in manufacturing. He was actively involved in the implementation of Class A MRP II at Hyster Company in Portland, Oregon. During his last six years there, he held management positions in capacity planning, several areas of material planning as well as responsibilities for engineering change control and new product introduction.

Larry later served on the Core Team, responsible for implementing MRP II at Intel Corporation in Hillsboro, Oregon. During that implementation, he also held positions of Production Planning Manager and Capacity Planning Manager.

Larry is an active member of APICS and is a certified Fellow of the society. He has developed and taught several certification courses for APICS and has spoken for APICS audiences from Portland, Oregon, to Portland, Maine.

Larry joined the Oliver Wight Companies in 1984.

The New Industrial Engineering: Information Technology and Business Process Redesign

Thomas H. Davenport and James E. Short

Those aspiring to improve the way work is done must begin to apply the capabilities of information technology to redesign business processes. Business process design and information technology are natural partners, yet industrial engineers have never fully exploited their relationship. The authors argue, in fact, that it has barely been exploited at all. But the organizations that have used IT to redesign boundary-crossing, customer-driven processes have benefited enormously. This article explains why.

At the turn of the century, Frederick Taylor revolutionized the workplace with his ideas on work organization, task decomposition, and job measurement. Taylor's basic aim was to increase organizational productivity by applying to human labor the same engineering principles that had proven so successful in solving the technical problems in the work environment. The same approaches that had transformed mechanical activity could also be used to structure jobs performed by people. Taylor came to symbolize the practical realizations in industry that we now call industrial engineering (IE), or the scientific school of management. [1] In fact, though work design remains a contemporary IE concern, no subsequent concept or tool has rivaled the power of Taylor's mechanizing vision.

As we enter the 1990s, however, two newer tools are transforming organizations to the degree that Taylorism once did. These are information technology—the capabilities offered by computers, software applications, and telecommunications—and business process design—the analysis and design of work flows and processes within and between organizations. Working together, these tools have the potential to create a new type of industrial engineering, changing the way the discipline is practiced and the skills necessary to practice it.

This article explores the relationship between information technology (IT) and business process redesign (BPR). We report on research conducted at MIT, Harvard, and several consulting organizations on nineteen companies, including detailed studies of five firms engaged in substantial process redesign. After defining business processes, we extract from the experience of the companies studied a generic five-step approach to redesigning processes with IT. We then define the major types of processes, along with the primary role of IT in each type of process. Finally, we consider management issues that arise when IT is used to redesign business processes.

IT in Business Process Redesign

The importance of both information technology and business process redesign is well known to industrial engineers, albeit as largely separate tools for use in specific, limited environments.[2] IT is used in industrial engineering as an analysis and modeling tool, and IEs have often taken the lead in applying information technology to manufacturing environments. Well-known uses of IT in manufacturing include process modeling, production scheduling and control, materials management information systems, and logistics. In most cases where IT has been used to redesign work, the redesign has most likely been in the manufacturing function, and industrial engineers are the most likely individuals to have carried it out.

IEs have begun to analyze work activities in non-manufacturing environments, but their penetration into offices has been far less than in factories. IT has certainly penetrated the office and services environments—in 1987 *Business Week* reported that almost 40 percent of all U.S. capital spending went to information systems, some $97 billion a year—but IT has been used in most cases to hasten office work rather than to transform it.[3] With few exceptions, IT's role in the redesign of nonmanufacturing work has been disappointing; few firms have achieved major productivity gains.[4] Aggregate productivity figures in the United States have shown no increase since 1973. [5]

Given the growing dominance of service industries and office work in the Western economies, this type of work is as much in need of analysis and redesign as the manufacturing environments to which IT has already been applied. Many firms have found that this analysis requires taking a broader view of both IT and business activity, and of the relationship between them. Information technology should be viewed as more than an automating or mechanizing force; it can fundamentally reshape the way business is done. Business activities should be viewed as more than a collection of individual or even functional tasks; they should be broken down into processes that can be designed for maximum effectiveness, in both manufacturing and service environments.

Our research suggests that IT can be more than a useful tool in business process redesign. In leading edge practice, information technology and BPR have a recursive relationship, as **Figure 1** illustrates. Each is the key to thinking about the other. Thinking about information technology should be in terms of how it supports new or redesigned business processes, rather than business functions or other organizational entities. And business processes and process improvements should be considered in terms of the capabilities information technology can provide. We refer to this broadened, recursive view of IT and BPR as the new industrial engineering.

Taylor could focus on workplace rationalization and individual task efficiency because he confronted a largely stable business environment; today's corporations do not have the luxury of such stability.[6] Individual tasks and jobs change faster than they can be redesigned. Today, responsibility for

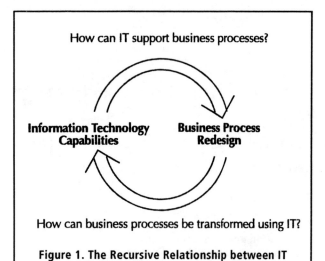

Figure 1. The Recursive Relationship between IT Capabilities and Business Process Redesign

an outcome is more often spread over a group, rather than assigned to an individual as in the past. Companies increasingly find it necessary to develop more flexible, team-oriented, coordinative, and communication-based work capability. In short, rather than maximizing the performance of particular individuals or business functions, companies must maximize interdependent activities within and across the entire organization. Such business processes are a new approach to coordination across the firm; information technology's promise—and perhaps its ultimate impact—is to be the most powerful tool in the twentieth century for reducing the costs of this coordination.[7]

What Are Business Processes?

We define business processes as a set of logically related tasks performed to achieve a defined business outcome. This definition is similar to Pall's: "The logical organization of people, materials, energy, equipment, and procedures into work activities designed to produce a specified end result (work product)." [8]

A set of processes forms a business system—the way in which a business unit, or a collection of units, carries out its business. Processes have two important characteristics:

- They have customers; that is, processes have defined business outcomes, and there are recipients of the outcomes. Customers may be either internal or external to the firm.
- They cross organizational boundaries; that is, they normally occur across or between organizational subunits. Processes are generally independent of formal organizational structure.

Common examples of processes meeting these criteria include:

- developing a new product;
- ordering goods from a supplier;
- creating a marketing plan;
- processing and paying an insurance claim; and
- writing a proposal for a government contract.

Ordering goods from a supplier, for example, typically involves multiple organizations and functions. The end user, purchasing, receiving, accounts payable, etc., and the supplier organization are all participants. The user could be viewed as the process's customer. The process outcome could be either the creation of the order, or, perhaps more usefully, the actual receipt of the goods by the user.

Our examples so far are of large-scale processes that affect whole organizations or groups. There are more detailed processes that meet the definitional criteria above. These might include installing a windshield in an automobile factory, or completing a monthly departmental expense report. IT-driven process redesign can be applied to these processes, but the implications of redesigning them may be important only in the aggregate. In many of the firms studied, analyzing processes in great detail was highly appropriate for some purposes, for example, the detailed design of an information system or data model to support a specific work process. However, the firms that were truly beginning to redesign their business functions took a broader view of processes.

A Brief History of Process Thinking

Process thinking has become widespread in recent years, due largely to the quality movement. Industrial engineers and others who wish to improve the quality of operations are urged to look at an entire process, rather than a particular task or business function. At IBM, for example, "process management will be the principal IBM quality focus in the coming years." [9] But process discussions in the quality movement's literature rarely mentions information technology. Rather, the focus is usually on improving process control systems in a manufacturing context; when IT is discussed, it is in the context of factory floor automation. Recent IE literature also borders on process thinking when advocating cross-functional analysis, [10] although, as we will discuss, cross-functional processes are only one possible type of process.

Other than quality-oriented manufacturing process redesign, most processes in major corporations have not been subject to rigorous analysis and redesign. Indeed, many of our current processes result from a series of ad hoc decisions made by functional units, with little attention to effectiveness across the entire process. Many processes have never even been measured. In one manufacturing company studied, for example, no one had ever analyzed the elapsed time from a customer's order to delivery. Each department (sales, credit checking, shipping, and so on) felt that it had optimized its own performance, but in fact the overall process was quite lengthy and unwieldy.

Even fewer business processes have been analyzed with the capabilities of IT in mind. Most business processes were developed before modern computers and communications even existed. When technology has been applied, it is usually to automate or speed up isolated components of an existing process. This creates communication problems within processes and impediments to process redesign and enhancement. For example, in a second manufacturing firm studied, the procurement process involved a vendor database, a material management planning system, and accounts payable and receivable systems, all running on different hardware platforms with different data structures. Again, each organizational subunit within the process had optimized its own IT application, but no single subunit had looked at (or was responsible for) the entire process. We believe the problems this firm experienced are very common.

Redesigning Business Processes with IT: Five Steps

Assuming that a company has decided its processes are inefficient or ineffective, and therefore in need of redesign, how should it proceed? This is a straightforward activity,

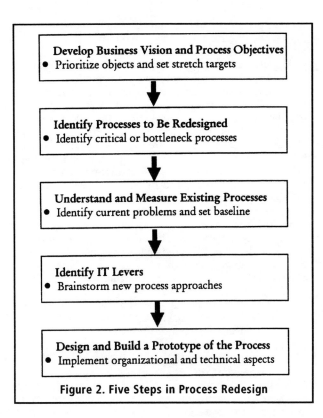

| Develop Business Vision and Process Objectives |
| • Prioritize objects and set stretch targets |

↓

| Identify Processes to Be Redesigned |
| • Identify critical or bottleneck processes |

↓

| Understand and Measure Existing Processes |
| • Identify current problems and set baseline |

↓

| Identify IT Levers |
| • Brainstorm new process approaches |

↓

| Design and Build a Prototype of the Process |
| • Implement organizational and technical aspects |

Figure 2. Five Steps in Process Redesign

but five major steps are involved: develop the business vision and process objectives, identify the processes to be redesigned, understand and measure the existing process, identify IT levers, and design and build a prototype of the new process (see **Figure 2**). We observed most or all of these steps being performed in companies that were succeeding with BPR. Each step is described in greater detail below.

Develop Business Vision and Process Objectives

In the past, process redesign was typically intended simply to "rationalize" the process, in other words, to eliminate obvious bottlenecks and inefficiencies. It did not involve any particular business vision or context. This was the approach of the "work simplification" aspect of industrial engineering, an important legacy of Taylorism. An example of the rationalization approach appears in a 1961 "Reference Note on Work Simplification" from the Harvard Business School:

> A good manager asks himself why things are done as they are, extending his inquiry to every aspect of the job and the surroundings in which it is performed, from the flow of paper work to the daily functioning of his subordinates.... He is expected to supply the stimulus and show that job improvement or simplification of work is not only important but also is based on common-sense questioning aimed at uncovering the easiest, most economical way of performing a job.[ll]

Our research suggests strongly that rationalization is not an end in itself, and is thus insufficient as a process redesign objective. Furthermore, rationalization of highly decomposed tasks may lead to a less efficient overall process. Instead of task rationalization, redesign of entire processes should be undertaken with a specific business vision and related objectives in mind.

In most successful redesign examples we studied, the company's senior management had developed a broad strategic vision into which the process redesign activity fit.[12] At Xerox, for example, this vision involved taking the perspective of the customer and developing systems rather than stand-along products; both required cross-functional integration. At Westinghouse, the vision consisted largely of improving product quality. Ford's involved adopting the best practices of Japanese automobile manufacturers, including those of Mazda, of which it is a partial owner.

Each of these visions implied specific objectives for process redesign. The most likely objectives are the following:

- **Cost Reduction**. This objective was implicit in the "rationalization" approach. Cost is an important redesign objective in combination with others, but insufficient in itself. Excessive attention to cost reduction results in tradeoffs that are usually unacceptable to process stakeholders. While optimizing on other objectives seems to bring costs into line, optimizing on cost rarely brings about other objectives.

- **Time Reduction**. Time reduction has been only a secondary objective of traditional industrial engineering. Increasing numbers of companies, however, are beginning to compete on the basis of time.[13] Processes, as we have defined them, are the ideal unit for a focused time reduction analysis. One common approach to cut time from product design is to make the steps begin simultaneously, rather than sequentially, using IT to coordinate design directions among the various functional participants. This approach has been taken in the design of computers, telephone equipment, automobiles, and copiers (by Digital Equipment, AT&T Bell Labs, Ford, and Xerox, respectively).

- **Output Quality**. All processes have outputs, be they physical—such as in manufacturing a tangible product—or informational—such as in adding data to a customer file. Output quality is frequently the focus of process improvement in manufacturing environments; it is just as important in service industries. The specific measure of output quality may be uniformity, variability, or freedom from defects; this should be defined by the customer of the process.

- **Quality of Worklife (QWL), Learning, and Empowerment**. IT can lead either to greater empowerment of individuals, or to greater control over their output. Zuboff points out that IT-intensive processes are often simply automated, and that the "informating" or learning potential of IT in processes is often ignored.[14] Moreover, Schein notes that organizations often do not provide a supportive context for individuals to introduce or innovate with IT.[15] Of course, it is rarely possible to optimize all objectives simultaneously, and in most firms, the strongest pressures are to produce tangible benefits. Yet managers who ignore this dimension risk failure of redesigned processes for organizational and motivational factors.

Some firms have been able to achieve multiple objectives in redesigning processes with IT. American Express, for example, set out to improve the cost, time, and quality of its credit authorization process by embedding the knowledge of its best authorizers in an "Authorizer's Assistant" expert system. This successful redesign led to a $7 million annual reduction in costs due to credit losses, a 25 percent reduction in the average time for each authorization, and a 30 percent reduction in improper credit denials.

Finally, all firms found it was important to set specific objectives, even to the point of quantification. Though it is difficult to know how much improvement is possible in advance of a redesign, "reach should exceed grasp." Setting goals that will stretch the organization will also provide inspiration and stimulate creative thinking. For example, a company might decide to reduce the time to bring new products to market by 80 percent. In the accounts payable process at Ford, the "stretch" goal was to eliminate invoices— to pay suppliers upon receipt of their products or services. This goal has been achieved with help from an information system to confirm expected deliveries at the loading dock. As a result, Ford has eliminated three-quarters of the jobs in accounts payable.

Identify Processes to Be Redesigned

Most organizations could benefit from IT-enabled redesign of critical (if not all) business processes. However, the amount of effort involved creates practical limitations. Even when total redesign was the ultimate objective, the companies we studied selected a few key processes for initial efforts. Moreover, when there was insufficient commitment to total redesign, a few successful examples of IT-enhanced processes became a powerful selling tool.

The means by which processes to be redesigned are identified and prioritized is a key issue. This is often difficult because most managers do not think about their business operations in terms of processes. There are two major approaches. The exhaustive approach attempts to identify all processes within an organization and then prioritize them in order of redesign urgency. The high-impact approach attempts to identify only the most important processes or those most in conflict with the business vision and process objectives.

The exhaustive approach is often associated with "information engineering" (developed by James Martin in the early 1980s), in which an organization's use of data dictates the processes to be redesigned.[16] For example, one information engineering method, employed at several divisions of Xerox, involves identifying business activities and the data they require using a data-activity matrix. The clusters of data activity interactions in the cells of the matrix are the organization's major business processes. Once processes are identified, Xerox managers prioritize them in the order in which new IT applications support should be provided. Although process identification in some Xerox divisions has taken as little as three months, many companies find this approach very time consuming.

The alternative is to focus quickly on high-impact processes. Most organizations have some sense of which business areas or processes are most crucial to their success, and those most "broken" or inconsistent with the business vision. If not, these can normally be identified using senior management workshops, or through extensive interviewing.[17] At IBM, the salesforce was surveyed to determine the relative importance of various customer support processes; the generation of special bids emerged as the highest priority and was the first process to be redesigned.

Companies that employed the high-impact approach generally considered it sufficient. Companies taking the exhaustive approach, on the other hand, have not had the resources to address all the identified processes; why identify them if they cannot be addressed? As a rough rule of thumb, most companies we studied were unable to redesign and support more than ten to fifteen major processes per year (i.e., one to three per major business unit); there was simply not enough management attention to do more. And some organizations have abandoned the exhaustive approach.[18]

Whichever approach is used, companies have found it useful to classify each redesigned process in terms of beginning and end points, interfaces, and organization units (functions or departments) involved, particularly including the customer unit. Thinking in these terms usually broadens the perceived scope of the process. For example, a sales manager may be aware that there are inefficiencies in customer order entry. A skilled process consultant might decide that the whole process—negotiating, receiving, and fulfilling orders—needs to be redesigned. Whether the problem is broken down into three processes or viewed as one is not important; expanding the scope of the process analysis is the key issue.

High-impact processes should also have owners.[19] In virtually all the process redesigns we studied, an important step was getting owners to buy in to both the idea and the scope of process redesign at an early stage. In several companies, managers felt that the process owner's job should be either above the level of the functions and units involved, or, if on the same level, that the owner should be willing—and able—to change the status quo. The difficulty, however, is that some processes only come together at the CEO level. In this situation, the CEO should designate a senior manager as owner and invest him or her with full authority. Processes that are fully contained within a single function or department can normally be owned by the manager of that area.

Understand and Measure Existing Processes

There are two primary reasons for understanding and measuring processes before redesigning them. First, problems must be understood so that they are not repeated. Second, accurate measurement can serve as a baseline for future improvements. If the objective is to cut time and cost, the time and cost consumed by the untouched process must be measured accurately. Westinghouse Productivity and Quality Center consultants found that simply graphing the incremental cost and time consumed by process tasks can often suggest initial areas for redesign. These graphs look like "step functions" showing the incremental contribution of each major task.

This step can easily be overemphasized, however. In several firms, the "stretch" goal was less to eliminate problems or bottlenecks than to create radical improvements. Designers should be informed by past process problems and errors, but they should work with a clean slate. Similarly, the process should not be measured for measurement's sake. Only the specific objectives of the redesign should be measured. As with the high-impact process identification approach, an 80-20 philosophy is usually appropriate.

Identify IT Levers

Until recently, even the most sophisticated industrial engineering approaches did not consider IT capabilities until after a process had been designed. The conventional wisdom in IT usage has always been to first determine the business requirements of a function, process, or other business entity, and then to develop a system. The problem is that an awareness of IT capabilities can—and should—influence process design. Knowing that product development teams can exchange computer-aided designs over large distances, for example, might affect the structure of a product development process. The role of IT in a process should be considered in the early stages of its redesign.[20]

Several firms accomplished this using brainstorming sessions, with the process redesign objectives and existing process measures in hand. It was also useful to have a list of IT's generic capabilities in improving business processes. In the broadest sense, all of IT's capabilities involve improving coordination and information access across organizational units, thereby allowing for more effective management of task interdependence. More specifically, however, it is useful to think about IT capabilities and their organizational impacts in eight different ways (see **Table 1**).

Capability	Organization Impact or Benefit
Transactional	IT can transform unstructured processes into routinized transactions.
Geographical	IT can transfer information with rapidity and ease across large distances, making processes independent of geography.
Automational	IT can replace or reduce human labor in a process.
Analytical	IT can bring complex analytical tools to bear on a process.
International	IT can bring vast amounts of detailed information into a process.
Sequential	It can enable changes in the sequence of tasks in a process, often allowing multiple tasks to be worked on simultaneously.
Knowledge	IT allows the capture and dissemination Management of knowledge and expertise to improve the process.
Tracking	IT allows the detailed tracking of task status, inputs, and outputs.
Disinformation	IT can be used to connect two parties within a process that would otherwise communicate through an intermediary (internal or external).

Table 1. IT Capabilities and their Organizational Impacts

There are undoubtedly other important IT capabilities that can reshape processes. Organizations may want to develop their own lists of capabilities that are specific to the types of processes they employ. The point is twofold. IT is so powerful a tool that it deserves its own step in process redesign, and IT can actually create new process design options, rather than simply support them.

Design and Build a Prototype of the Process

For most firms, the final step is to design the process. This is usually done by the same team that performed the previous steps, getting input from constituencies and using brainstorming workshops. A key point is that the actual design is not the end of the process. Rather, it should be viewed as a prototype, with successive iterations expected and managed. Key factors and tactics to consider in process design and prototype creation include using IT as a design tool, understanding generic design criteria, and creating organizational prototypes.

- **IT as a Design Tool**. Designing a business process is largely a matter of diligence and creativity. Emerging IT technologies, however, are beginning to facilitate the "process" of process design. Some computer-aided systems engineering (CASE) products are designed primarily to draw process models. The ability to draw models rapidly and make changes suggested by process owners speeds redesign and facilitates owner buy-in. Some CASE products can actually generate computer code for the information systems application that will support a modeled business process.

  Several Xerox divisions, for example, are moving directly from process modeling to automated generation of computer code for high-priority processes. They report improved productivity and high user satisfaction with the resulting systems. A further benefit is that when the business process changes, the IS organization can rapidly modify the affected system. Use of code generation products generally presumes that process designers will use the exhaustive approach to process identification.

- **Generic Design Criteria**. Companies used various criteria for evaluating alternative designs. Most important, of course, is the likelihood that a design will satisfy the chosen design objectives. Others mentioned in interviews included the simplicity of the design, the lack of buffers or intermediaries, the degree of control by a single individual or department (or an effective, decentralized coordinative mechanism), the balance of process resources, and the generalization of process tasks (so that they can be performed by more than one person).

- **Organizational Prototypes**. Mutual Benefit Life's (MBL) redesign of its individual life insurance underwriting process illustrates a final, important point about process design. At MBL, underwriting a life insurance policy involved 40 steps with over 100 people in 12 functional areas and 80 separate jobs. To streamline this lengthy and complex process, MBL undertook a pilot project with the goal of improving productivity by 40 percent. To integrate the process, MBL created a new role, the case manager. This role was designed to perform and coordinate all underwriting tasks centrally, utilizing a workstation-based computer system capable of pulling data from all over the company. After a brief start-up period, the firm learned that two additional roles were necessary on some underwriting cases: specialists such as lawyers or medical directors in knowledge-intensive fields, and clerical assistance. With the new role and redesigned process, senior managers at MBL are confident of reaching the 40 percent goal in a few months. This example illustrates the value of creating organizational prototypes in IT-driven process redesign.

Creating prototypes of IT applications has already gained widespread acceptance. Advocates argue that building a prototype of an IT change usually achieves results faster than conventional "life cycle" development, and, more important, that the result is much more likely to satisfy the customer. Building prototypes of business process changes and organizational redesign initiatives can yield similar benefits.[21] The implications of this extension are that process designs, after agreement by owners and stakeholders, would be implemented on a pilot basis (perhaps in parallel with existing processes), examined regularly for problems and objective achievement, and modified as necessary. As the process approached final acceptance, it would be phased into full implementation.

Defining Process Types

The five steps described above are sufficiently general to apply to most organizations and processes. Yet the specifics of redesign vary considerably according to the type of

Process Dimensions and Type	Typical Example	Typical IT Role
Entities		
Interorganizational	Order from a supplier	Lower transaction costs, eliminate intermediaries
Interfunctional	Develop a new product	Work across geography; greater simultaneity
Interpersonal	Approve a bank loan	Role and task integration
Objects		
Physical	Manufacture a product	Increased outcome flexibility process control
Informational	Create a proposal	Routinizing complex decisions
Activities		
Operational	Fill a customer order	Reduce time and costs; increase output quality
Managerial	Develop a budget	Improve analysis; increase participation

Figure 3. Types of Processes

process under examination. Different types require different levels of management attention and ownership, need different forms of IT support, and have different business consequences. In this section, we present three different dimensions within which processes vary.

Understanding and classifying the different types of processes is important because an organization can appear to be a seamless web of interconnected processes. With various process types in mind, a manager can begin to isolate particular processes for analysis and redesign, including activities that, without process thinking, might otherwise be overlooked.

Three major dimensions can be used to define processes (see **Figure 3**). These are the organizational entities or subunits involved in the process, the type of objects manipulated, and the type of activities taking place. We describe each dimension and resulting process type below.

Defining Process Entities

Processes take place between types of organizational entities. Each type has different implications for IT benefits.

Interorganizational processes are those taking place between two or more business organizations. Increasingly, companies are concerned with coordinating activities that extend into the next (or previous) company along the value-added chain.[22] Several U.S. retail, apparel, and textile companies, for example, have linked their business processes to speed up reordering or apparel. When Dillard's (department store) inventory of a particular pants style falls below a specified level, Haggar (apparel manufacturer) is notified electronically. If Haggar does not have the cloth to manufacture the pants, Burlington Industries (textile manufacturer) is notified electronically. As this example of electronic data interchange (EDI) illustrates, information technology is the major vehicle by which this interorganizational linkage is executed.

For most companies, simple market relationships are the most common source of interorganizational processes. All the tasks involved in a selling-buying transaction form a critical process for sellers, and an increasingly important one for buyers seeking higher quality, cost efficiency, and responsiveness. Yet much of the focus has been on a simple transaction level, rather than on an interorganizational business process level. Again, how EDI is used illustrates this point.

Buyers and sellers have used EDI largely to speed up routine purchasing transactions, such as invoices or bills of materials. Few companies have attempted to redesign the broader procurement process—from the awareness that a product is needed, to the development of approved vendor lists, or even to the delivery and use of the purchased product. In the future, sellers will need to look at all buyer processes in which their products are involved.

Moreover, many firms will need to help the buyer improve those processes. DuPont's concept of "effectiveness in use" as the major criterion of customer satisfaction is one leading approach to measuring the effectiveness of interorganizational processes. DuPont is motivated not simply to sell a product, but to link its internal processes for creating value in a product, to its customer's processes for using the product. This concept led DuPont to furnish EDI-provided Material Safety Data Sheets along with the chemicals it sells to its customers to ensure their safe use.

Westinghouse used an interorganizational process approach in dealing with Portland General Electric (PGE), a major customer of power generation equipment. PGE managers called upon Westinghouse's Productivity and Quality Center, a national leader in process improvement, to help them implement EDI, but the Westinghouse team asked if it could analyze the entire process by which PGE procured equipment from Westinghouse and other suppliers. They found that, while implementing EDI could yield efficiencies on the order of 10 percent, changing the overall procurement process, including using EDI and bypassing the purchasing department altogether for most routine purchase orders, could lead to much greater savings. In one case, the time to execute a standard purchase order, for example, could be reduced from fifteen days to half a day; the cost could be reduced from almost $90 to $10.

A second major type of business process is interfunctional. These processes exist within the organization, but cross several functional or divisional boundaries. Interfunctional processes achieve major operational objectives, such as new product realization, asset management, or production scheduling. Most management processes—for example, planning, budgeting, and human resource management—are interfunctional.

Many manufacturing companies that focused on quality improvement found that producing quality products and services required addressing difficult interfunctional issues. Yet most firms have never even listed their key interfunctional processes, let alone analyzed or redesigned them, with or without the aid of IT.

Two companies that recently analyzed their key interfunctional business processes are Baxter Healthcare Corporation and US Sprint Communications Company. Baxter's 1985 merger with American Hospital Supply provided the context for a major analysis of key business strategies, and the alignment of the IT infrastructure with those strategies.[23] As part of a seven-month IT planning effort, the company defined twenty-nine major interfunctional processes and analyzed the current and future role of IT in supporting them. For example, in the distribution area, the company identified order entry, inventory, warehouse management, purchasing, transportation, and equipment tracking as key processes. The success of this IT planning effort led Baxter to incorporate the process definition approach into its annual corporate planning process.

At US Sprint, well-publicized problems with the customer billing system prompted the company's IT function to develop a model of information flows for the entire business as part of a comprehensive systems improvement program. This model defined the critical information and key interfunctional processes necessary to run the business. Sprint is now assigning ownership to key processes and continuing to identify improvements—and ways to measure them—in each process. The systems improvement program raised the IT organization's composite internal quality index by more than 50 percent in one year.[24]

A major problem in redesigning interfunctional processes is that most information systems of the past were built to automate specific functional areas or parts of functions. Few third-party application software packages have been developed to support a full business process. Very few organizations have modeled existing interfunctional processes or redesigned them, and companies will run into substantial problems in building interfunctional systems without such models.

Interpersonal processes involve tasks within and across small work groups, typically within a function or department. Examples include a commercial loan group approving a loan, or an airline flight crew preparing for takeoff. This type of process is becoming more important as companies shift to self-managing teams as the lowest unit of organization. Information technology is increasingly capable of supporting interpersonal processes; hardware and communications companies have developed new networking-oriented products, and software companies have begun to flesh out the concept of "groupware" (e.g., local area network-based mail, conferencing, and brainstorming tools).[25]

Several companies, including GM's Electronic Data Systems (EDS), are exploring tools to facilitate the effectiveness of meetings and small group interactions. At EDS, the primary focus is on enhancing the interpersonal processes involved in automobile product development. The company's Center for Machine Intelligence has developed a computer-supported meeting room, and is studying its implications for group decision making and cooperative work.[26]

We should point out that IT can make it possible for employees scattered around the world to work as a team. As an example, Ford now creates new car designs using teams that have members in Europe, Central America, and the United States. Because Ford has standardized computer-aided design systems and created common data structures for the design process, engineers can share complex three-dimensional designs across the Atlantic. Similarly, a small team at Digital Equipment used the company's electronic mail and conferencing capabilities to build the core of a new systems integration business. The team was scattered around the United States and Europe and only rarely met in person.

Defining Process Objects

Processes can also be categorized by the types of objects manipulated. The two primary object types are physical and informational. In physical object processes, real, tangible things are either created or manipulated; manufacturing is the obvious example. Informational object processes create or manipulate information. Processes for making a decision, preparing a marketing plan, or designing a new product are examples.

Many processes involve the combination of physical and informational objects. Indeed, adding information to a physical object as it moves through a process is a common way of adding value. Most logistical activities, for example, combine the movement of physical objects with the manipulation of information concerning their whereabouts. Success in the logistics industry is often dependent on the close integration of physical and informational outcomes; both UPS and Federal Express, for example, track package movement closely.

The potential for using IT to improve physical processes is well known. It allows greater flexibility and variety of outcomes, more precise control of the process itself, reductions in throughput time, and elimination of human labor. These benefits have been pursued for the past three decades. Still, manufacturing process flows are often the result of historical circumstance and should usually be redesigned before further automation is applied. This is particularly true in low volume, job shop manufacturing environments.[27] Redesigners of physical processes should also consider the role of IT in providing information to improve processes; Shoshana Zuboff has described this "informating" effect in detail for the paper industry.[28]

Strangely, the proportion of informational processes already transformed by IT is probably lower than that of physical processes. True, legions of clerks have become unemployed because of computers. But the majority of information processes to which IT has been applied are those involving high volume and low complexity. Now that these processes are well known even if not fully conquered, the emphasis needs to shift to processes that incorporate semi-structured and unstructured tasks and are performed by high-skill knowledge workers. Relevant IT capabilities include the storage and retrieval of unstructured and multimedia information, the capturing and routinizing of decision logic, and the application of far-flung and complex data resources. A computer vendor's advertising videotape, for example, illustrates how artificial intelligence and "hypertext," or mixed-media databases, combine to lead a manager through the process of developing a departmental budget. The IT capabilities in the video are available today, but they are rarely applied to such information-intensive yet unstructured processes.

Defining Process Activities

Our examples of business processes have involved two types of activities: operational and managerial. Operational processes involve the day-to-day carrying out of the organization's basic business purpose. Managerial processes help to control, plan, or provide resources for operational processes. Past uses of IT to improve processes, limited as they are, have been largely operational. We will therefore focus almost entirely on managerial processes in this section.[29]

Applying IT to management tasks is not a new idea. The potential of decision support systems, executive support systems, and other managerial tools has been discussed for over twenty years. We believe, however, that the benefits have not been realized because of the absence of systematic process thinking. Few companies have rigorously analyzed managerial activities as processes subject to redesign. Even the notion of managerial activities involving defined outcomes (a central aspect of our definition of business processes) is somewhat foreign. How would such managerial processes as deciding on an acquisition or developing the agenda for the quarterly board meeting be improved if they were treated as processes—

in other words, measured, brainstormed, and redesigned with IT capabilities?

The generic capabilities of IT for reshaping management processes include improving analytic accuracy, enabling broader management participation across wider geographical boundaries, generating feedback on actions taken (the managerial version of "informating" a process), and streamlining the time and resources a specific process consumes. Texas Instruments and Xerox's corporate headquarters provide excellent examples.

Texas Instruments has developed an expert system to facilitate the capital budgeting process. Managers in a fast-growing and capital-intensive TI division were concerned that the time and experience necessary to prepare capital budget request packages would become an obstacle to the division's growth. The packages were very complex and time consuming, and few employees had the requisite knowledge to complete them accurately. The expert system was developed by two industrial engineers with expertise in both the technology and the budget process.

TI's system has radically improved the capital budget request process. Requests prepared with the system require far less time than the manual approach and conform better to the company's guidelines. One experienced employee reported a reduction in package preparation time from nine hours to forty minutes; of the first fifty packages prepared with the system, only three did not conform to guidelines, compared to an average of ten using a manual approach.[30]

At Xerox Corporation headquarters, IT has been used to improve the review of division strategic plans. Prior to the development of the company's Executive Information System (EIS), the planning process was somewhat haphazard; each division prepared its planning documents in a different format and furnished different types of information to corporate headquarters. Plans often came in too late for the corporate management committee to review them before the quarterly or annual review meeting. The EIS was developed to include standard information formats and a user friendly graphical interface enabling fast comprehension. Division plans are now developed on the EIS and delivered instantaneously over Xerox's network to all corporate management committee members. These members can now read and discuss the plans beforehand and can move directly to decisions at the review meetings. The workstations are even used in the meetings themselves, allowing revisions to be made and agreed upon before adjournment. As one manager put it, "...[the system] let us communicate at higher speed and in greater depth."[31]

Management Issues in IT-Enabled Redesign

Companies have found that once a process has been redesigned, several key issues remain. These include the management role in redesigned activity, implications for organizational structure, new skill requirements, creating a function to perform IT-enabled BPR, the proper direction for the IT infrastructure, and the need for continuous process improvements. We discuss each below.

Management Roles

Perhaps the greatest difficulty in IT-driven redesign is getting and keeping management commitment. Because processes cut across various parts of the organization, a process redesign effort driven by a single business function or unit will probably encounter resistance from other parts of the organization. Both high-level and broad support for change are necessary.

To perform the five redesign steps described above, several companies created a cross-functional task force headed by a senior executive. These task forces included representatives from key staff and line groups likely to be affected by the changes, including IT and human resources. It was particularly important that the customer of the process be represented on the team, even when the customer was external. The team composition was ideal if some members had some record of process or operations innovation involving IT.

As the redesign teams selected processes and developed objectives, they needed to work closely with the managers and staff of the affected units. Managing process change is similar to managing other types of change, except that its cross-functional nature increases the number of stakeholders, thereby increasing the complexity of the effort.

It was also important to have strong, visible commitment from senior management. Employees throughout the organization needed to understand that redesign was critical, that differences of opinion would be resolved in favor of the customer of a process, and that IT would play an important role. In many cases, the CEO communicated any structural implications of the redesign effort.

An example of the importance of the CEO's role is found at GUS Home Shopping, the largest home shopping company in Europe. GUS undertook a $90 million project to redesign its logistical processes with IT. Redesign objectives involved both cost and time: to be able to sell a product within five minutes of its arrival on the loading dock, and to be able to deliver a product to the customer's door at an average cost of sixty cents. The company's managing director commented on his role in meeting these objectives:

To change our business to the degree we have [done] demands integration. How involved should the managing director get in designing computer systems? My view is totally, because he's the one who can integrate across the entire organization.[32]

Process Redesign and Organizational Structure

A second key issue is the relationship between process orientation and organizational structure. Certainly someone must be in charge of implementing a process change, and of managing the redesigned process thereafter. But process responsibilities are likely to cut across existing organizational structures. How can process organization and traditional functional organization be reconciled?

One possible solution is to create a new organization structure along process lines, in effect abandoning altogether other structural dimensions, such as function, product, or geography. This approach presents risks, however; as business needs change, new processes will be created that cut across the previous process-based organization. This does not mean that a process-based structure cannot be useful, but only that it will have to be changed frequently.

While no firm we studied has converted wholly to a process-based structure, a few organizations have moved in this direction. For example, Apple Computer recently moved away from a functional structure to what executives describe as an IT-oriented, process-based, customer satisfaction-driven structure called "New Enterprise." The company relishes its lack of formal hierarchy; Apple managers describe their roles as highly diffuse, and team and project based.

IT-Driven Process Redesign at Rank Xerox U.K.

Rank Xerox U.K. (RXUK), a national operating company of Xerox Corporation, has undertaken the most comprehensive IT-driven process redesign we have studied. The process was led by David O'Brien, the division's managing director, who arrived at the company in 1985. O'Brien quickly came to two realizations: first, the company needed to focus on marketing "office systems" in addition to its traditional reprographics products; and second, the company's strong functional culture and inefficient business processes would greatly inhibit its growth. He began to see his own organization as a place to test integrated office systems that support integrated business processes; if successful, he could use RXUK as a model for customers.

The company began to redesign its business in 1987. In a series of offsite meetings, the senior management team reappraised its external environment and mission, then identified the key business processes needed if the company was to achieve its mission. The group began to restructure the organization around cross-functional processes, identifying high-level objectives and creating task forces to define information and other resource requirements for each process. It created career systems revolving around facilitation skills and cross-functional management, rather than hierarchical authority. O'Brien decided to keep a somewhat functional formal structure, because functional skills would still be needed in a process organization and because the level of organizational change might have been too great with a wholly new structure.

The level of change was still very high. Several senior managers departed because they could not or would not manage in the new environment. Two new cross-functional senior positions, called "facilitating directors," were created, one for organizational and business development, the other for process management, information systems, and quality. O'Brien took great advantage of the honeymoon period accorded to new CEOs, but managing the change still required intense personal attention.

Of course, this new thinking was in sharp contrast to some of the skills and attitudes of the company. We were introducing a change in management philosophy in a company that, in many ways, was very skillful and effective, but in a different product-market environment. We faced all the issues of attitudinal change and retraining that any such change implies. We were moving to a much more integrated view of the world and had to encourage a major shift in many patterns of the existing culture. This meant a very hard, tough program of selling the new ideas within the organization as well as an extensive and personal effort to get the new messages and thinking to our potential customers.*

As the key processes were identified and their objectives determined, the company began to think about how information technology (its own and from other providers) could enable and support the processes. The facilitating director of processes and systems, Paul Chapman, decided that the firm needed a new approach to developing information systems around processes. His organization used the information engineering approach discussed earlier and worked with an external consultant to refine and confirm process identification. They uncovered 18 "macro" business processes (e.g., logistics) and 145 "micro" processes (e.g., fleet management).

The senior management team reconvened to prioritize the identified processes and decided that seven macro processes had particular importance: customer order life cycle, customer satisfaction, installed equipment management, integrated planning, logistics, financial management, and personnel management. It selected personnel management as the first process to be redesigned because this was viewed as relatively easy to attack and because personnel systems were crucial in tracking the development of new skills. The personnel system has now been successfully redesigned, using automated code generation capabilities, in substantially less time than if normal methods had been used.

RXUK's financial situation began to improve as it redesigned its business processes. The company emerged from a long period of stagnation into a period of 20 percent revenue growth. Jobs not directly involved with customer contact were reduced from 1,100 to 800. Order delivery time was, on average, reduced from thirty-three days to six days. Though many other market factors were changing during this time, O'Brien credits the process redesign for much of the improvement.

Other Xerox divisions heard of RXUK's success with process redesign and began efforts of their own. Xerox's U.S. product development and marketing divisions now have major cross-functional teams performing process redesign. Paul Chapman has been loaned to Xerox corporate headquarters, where he is heading a cross-functional team looking at corporate business processes. Commitment to IT-driven process redesign by Xerox senior corporate management is also growing.

---

*David O'Brien, quoted in B. Denning and B. Taylor, "Rank Xerox U.K., Office Systems Strategy (C): Developing the Systems Strategy," (Henley on Thames, England: Henley—The Management College case study, September 1988). Other Rank Xerox U.K. information comes from personal interviews.

A more conservative approach would be to create a matrix of functional and process responsibilities. However, because of the cross-functional nature of most processes, the functional manager who should have responsibility for a given process is not always easy to identify. The company may also wish to avoid traditional functional thinking in assigning process responsibilities. For example, it may be wiser to give responsibility for redesigning supplies acquisition to a manager who uses those suppliers (i.e., the customer of the process), rather than to the head of purchasing.

New Skill Requirements

For process management to succeed, managers develop facilitation and influence skills. Traditional sources of authority may be of little use when process changes cut across organizational units. Managers will find themselves trying to change the behavior of employees who do not work for them. In these cases, they must learn to persuade rather than to instruct, to convince rather than to dictate. Of course, these recommendations are consistent with many other organizational maxims of the past several years; they just happen to be useful in process management as well.[33]

Several organizations that are moving toward IT-driven process management are conducting programs intended to develop facilitation skills. These programs encourage less reliance on hierarchy, more cross-functional communication and cooperation, and more decision making by middle- and lower-level managers. Such a program at American Airlines is being used to build an organizational infrastructure at the same time a new IT infrastructure is being built.

An Ongoing Organization

Organizations that redesign key processes must oversee continuing redesign and organizational "tuning," as well as ensure that information systems support process flows. In most companies, the appropriate analytical skills are most likely to be found in the IT function. However, these individuals will also require a high degree of interpersonal skills to be successful as the "new industrial engineers." The ideal group would represent multiple functional areas, for example, information systems, industrial engineering, quality, process control, finance, and human resources.

There are already some examples of such process change groups. Silicon Graphics has created a specific process consulting group for ongoing process management; it is headed by a director-level manager. At United Parcel Service, process redesign is traditionally concentrated in the industrial engineering function. The UPS group is incorporating IT skills in the IE function at a rapid rate, and creating task forces with IT and IE representation for process redesign projects. Federal Express has gone even further, renaming its IE organization the "Strategic Integrated Systems Group," placing it within the Information Systems function, and giving it responsibility for designing and implementing major IT-driven business changes.

Process Redesign and the IT Organization

Just as information technology is a powerful force in redesigning business processes, process thinking has important implications for the IT organization and for the technology infrastructure it builds. Though few IT groups have the power and influence to spearhead process redesign, they can play several important roles. First of all, the IT group may need to play a behind-the-scenes advocacy role, convincing senior management and process redesign. Second, as demand builds for process redesign expertise, the IT group can begin to incorporate the IE-oriented skills of process measurement, analysis, and redesign, perhaps merging with the IE function if there is one. It can also develop an approach or methodology for IT-enabled redesign, perhaps using the five steps described above as a starting point.

What must the information systems function do technologically to prepare for process redesign? IT professionals must recognize that they will have to build most systems needed to support (or enable) processes, rather than buy them from software package vendors, because most application packages are designed with particular functions in mind. IT professionals will need to build robust technology platforms on which process-specific applications can be quickly constructed. This implies a standardized architecture with extensive communications capability between computing nodes, and the development of shared databases. However, like the organizational strategies for process management described above, these are appropriate technology strategies for most companies, whether or not they are redesigning processes with IT.

Continuous Process Improvement

The concept of process improvement, which developed in the quality movement, requires first that the existing process be stabilized. It then becomes predictable, and its capabilities become accessible to analysis and improvement.[34] Continuous process improvement occurs when the cycle of stabilizing, assessing, and improving a given process becomes institutionalized.

IT-enabled business process redesign must generally be dynamic. Those responsible for a process should constantly investigate whether new information technologies make it possible to carry out a process in new ways. IT is continuing to evolve, and forthcoming technologies will have a substantial impact on the processes of the next decade. The IT infrastructure must be robust enough to support the new applications appropriate to a particular process.

Summary

We believe that the industrial engineers of the future, regardless of their formal title or the organizational unit that employs them, will focus increasingly on IT-enabled redesign of business processes. We have only begun to explore the implications and implementation of this concept, and only a few companies have ventured into the area. Many companies that have used IT to redesign particular business processes have done so without any conscious approach or philosophy. In short, the actual experience base with IT-enabled process redesign is limited.

Yet managing by customer-driven processes that cross organizational boundaries is an intuitively appealing idea that has worked well in the companies that have experimented with it. And few would question that information technology is a powerful tool for reshaping business processes. The individuals and companies that can master redesigning processes around IT will be well equipped to succeed in the new decade—and the new century.

References

The authors wish to acknowledge the support of the Center for Information Systems Research at the MIT Sloan

School, Harvard Business School's Division of Research, and McKinsey & Company. They are also grateful for the comments of Lynda Applegate, James Cash, Warren McFarlan, John Rockart, Edgar Schein, and Michael S. Scott Morton.

1. L. Gulick, "Notes on the Theory of Organization," in L. Gulick and L. Urwick, eds., *Papers on the Science of Administration* (New York: Institute of Public Administration, 1937), p. 9.

2. S. Sakamoto, "Process Design Concept: A New Approach to IE," *Industrial Engineering,* March 1989, p. 31.

3. "Office Automation: Making It Pay Off," *Business Week,* 12 October 1987, pp. 134-146. For an alternative perspective, see R.I. Kraut, ed. *Technology and the Transformation of White-Collar Work* (Hillsdale, New Jersey: Lawrence Eribaum Associates, 1987).

4. G.W. Loveman, "An Assessment of the Productivity Impact of Information Technologies" (Cambridge, Massachusetts: MIT Sloan School of Management, Management in the 1990s, Working Paper 90s: 88-054, July 1988). Loveman studied microeconomic data from manufacturing firms to estimate econometrically the productivity impact of IT in the late 1970s and early 1980s. In finding no significant positive productivity impact from IT, he argues that his findings in manufacturing raise serious questions about impacts in nonmanufacturing firms as well. Baily and Chakrabarti (1988) studied white-collar productivity and IT as one part of a broader inquiry into poor productivity growth. They found no evidence of significant productivity gain. See M.N. Baily and A. Chakrabarti, *Innovation and the Productivity Crisis* (Washington, D.C.: Brookings Institution, 1988).

5. Loveman (1988); Baily and Chakrabarti (1988). See also L.C. Thurow, "Toward a High-Wage, High-Productivity Service Sector" (Washington, D.C.: Economic Policy Institute, 1989).

6. Robert Horton, who became chairman and chief executive of British Petroleum in March 1990, argues that his major concern in setting BP's course in the next decade is "managing surprise." Horton's belief is that the external business environment is so unpredictable that surprise, rather than managed change, is inevitable. See R. Horton, "Future Challenges to Management," *MIT Management,* Winter 1989. pp. 3-6.

7. T. Malone, "What is Coordination Theory?" (Cambridge, Massachusetts: MIT Sloan School of Management, Center for Coordination Science, Working Paper No. 2051-88, February 1988); K. Crowston and T. Malone, "Information Technology and Work Organization" (Cambridge, Massachusetts: MIT Sloan School of Management, Center for Information Systems Research, Working Paper No. 165, December 1987).

8. G.A. Pall, *Quality Process Management* (Englewood Cliffs, New Jersey: Prentice-hall, 1987). Our definition also complements that of Schein, who focuses on human processes in organizations—e.g., building and maintaining groups, group problem solving and decision making, leading and influencing, etc. See E.H. Schein, *Process Consultation: Its Role in Organization Development,* Vol. 1, 2d ed. (Reading, Massachusetts: Addison-Wesley, 1988).

9. E.J. Kane, "IBM's Total Quality Improvement System" (Purchase, New York: IBM Corporation, unpublished manuscript), p. 5

10. See, for example, M.F. Morris and G.W. Vining, "The IE's Future Role in Improving Knowledge Worker Productivity," *Industrial Engineering,* July 1987, p. 28.

11. "Reference Note on Work Simplification" (Boston: Harvard Business School, HBS Case Services #9-609-0601961, 1961).

12. The relationship between business vision and IT has been explored by several researchers under the auspices of the MIT Sloan School's five-year "Management in the 1990s" research program. An overview volume is scheduled for publication by Oxford University Press in August 1990.

13. See, for example, G. Stalk, Jr., "Time—The Next Source of Strategic Advantage," *Harvard Business Review,* July-August 1988, pp. 41-51.

14. S. Zuboff, *In the Age of the Smart Machine* (New York: Basic Books, 1988).

15. E.H. Schein, "Innovative Cultures and Organizations" (Cambridge, Massachusetts: MIT Sloan School of Management, Management in the 1990s, Working Paper 90s: 88-064, November 1988).

16. Information engineering and other redesign approaches based on data modeling are necessarily limited in scope. More than data is exchanged in many process relationships. Note too that many companies have used information engineering methods without a specific process orientation.

17. Examples of IT planning approaches where high-impact objectives and/or goals are defined include critical success factors (CSFs) and business systems planning (BSP). See J.F. Rockart, "Chief Executives Define Their Own Data Needs," *Harvard Business Review,* March-April 1979, pp. 81-93; and IBM, *Information Systems Planning Guide,* 3rd ed. (Business Systems Planning Report No. GE20-05527-2, July 1981).

18. D. Goodhue, J. Quillard, and J. Rockart, "Managing the Data Resource: A Contingency Perspective" (Cambridge, Massachusetts: MIT Sloan School of Management, Center for Information Systems Research, Working Paper No. 150, January 1987).

19. J.F. Rockart, "The Line Takes the Leadership — IS Management in a Wired Society," *Sloan Management Review,* Summer 1988, pp. 57-64.

20. J.C. Henderson and N. Venkatraman, "Strategic Alignment: A Process Model for Integrating Information Technology and Business Strategies" (Cambridge, Massachusetts: MIT Sloan School of Management, Center for Information Systems Research, Working Paper No. 196, October 1989).

21. Dorothy Leonard-Barton introduced the concept of organizational prototyping with regard to the implementation of new information technologies. See D. Leonard-Barton, "The Case for Integrative Innovation: An Expert System at Digital," *Sloan Management Review,* Fall 1987 pp. 7-19.

22. R. Johnston and P.R. Lawrence, "Beyond Vertical Integration—The Rise of the Value-Adding Partnership," *Harvard Business Review,* July-August 1988, pp. 94-101. See also N. Venkatraman, "IT-Induced Business Reconfiguration: The New Strategic Management Challenge" (Cambridge, Massachusetts: Paper presented at the annual conference of the MIT Center for Information Systems Research, June 1989).

23. T.J. Main and J.E. Short, "Managing the Merger: Building Partnership through IT Planning at the New Baxter," *Management Information Systems Quarterly,* December 1989, pp. 469-486.

24. C.R. Hall, M.E. Friesen, and J.E. Short, "The Turnaround at US Sprint: The Role of Improved Partnership between Business and Information Management," in progress.

25. R.R. Johansen, Groupware: Computer Support for Business Teams (New York: The Free Press, 1988). Also see C.V. Bullen and R.R. Johansen, "Groupware: A Key to Managing Business Teams?" (Cambridge, Massachusetts: MIT Sloan School of Management, Center for Information Systems Research, Working Paper No. 169, May 1988).

26. See L.M. Applegate, "The Center for Machine Intelligence: Computer Support for Cooperative Work" (Boston: Harvard Business School Case Study No. 189-135, 1988, rev. 1989).

27. J.E. Ashton and F.X. Cook, "Time to Reform Job Shop Manufacturing," *Harvard Business Review,* March-April 1989, pp.106-111.

28. See cases on "Tiger Creek," "Piney Wood," and "Cedar Bluff" in S. Zuboff (1988); other industries discussed by Zuboff primarily involve informational processes.

29. One might consider managerial processes synonymous with informational processes. Certainly the vast majority of managerial processes, such as budgeting, planning, and human resource development, involve informational objects. Yet it is important to remember that informational processes can be either operational or managerial, so we believe that this separate dimension of process types is warranted.

30. A case study describes the process and the creation of the expert system. See "Texas Instruments Capital Investment Expert System" (Boston: Harvard Business School Case Study No. 188-050, 1988).

31. Some aspects of this process improvement are described in L.M. Applegate and C.S. Osborne, "Xerox Corporation: Executive Support Systems" (Boston: Harvard Business School Case Study No. 189-134, 1988, rev. 1989).

32. R.H.C. Pugh, address to McKinsey & Co. information technology practice leaders, Munich, Germany, June 1989.

33. See, for example, A.R. Cohen and D.L. Bradford, "Influence without Authority; The Use of Alliances, Reciprocity, and Exchange to Accomplish Work," *Organizational Dynamics,* Winter 1989, pp. 4-17.

34. See G.A. Pall (1987).

About the Authors

Thomas H. Davenport is a partner at Ernst and Young's Center for Information Technology and Strategy in Boston, where he directs research and multiclient programs. He has consulted at McKinsey & Company, Inc., and the Index Group, and has taught at Harvard Business School and the University of Chicago. He holds the B.A. degree from Trinity University, and the M.A. and Ph.D. degrees from Harvard University. His current interests include the relationship between information technology and organization, and the development of IT infrastructures.

James E. Short is Research Associate at the Center for Information Systems Research at the MIT Sloan School of Management. He is also Lecturer in Management Information Systems at Boston University's School of Management. Dr. Short holds the S.B., S.M., and Ph.D. degrees from MIT. His research interests include how information technology enables organizations to execute differential strategies and improve performance through enhanced integration and flexible, problem-focused teams and task forces.

Reprinted from the APICS 1990 Manufacturing Principles and Practices Seminar.

A Team Approach to Change
Neal S. Davis, CPIM

New Market Conditions

Going into the 1990s, our customers have an increased expectation of our performance in terms of Price, Quality, and Delivery. Not too long ago, price was often the most important factor in a purchase decision. Less than perfect levels of quality were tolerated and weeded out by incoming inspection, charging the defects back to the vendor. A wide delivery window (plus or minus a week, or more) was acceptable and as the variance could be statistically analyzed, the purchasing and the materials functions would build in the expected delivery slippage into the planned lead time.

Today, however, customers are reducing or eliminating their inspection staffs and insisting on zero defects from their vendors. With quality now a given, customers next give weight to vendors who hit their delivery promises, with special considerations to those who can deliver in shorter-than-market lead times. Low price has become simply a way of attracting the first order. Consistently high quality and reliable, quick delivery performance gain the repeat orders.

Limited Solutions

As manufacturers begin to recognize these changing priorities, they are trying to change their internal operations to accommodate them. MRP was supposed to be the answer; then came MRP II, and now JIT. We were not successful with the first, barely more so with the second, and suspect the wild claims of success from off-shore won't be duplicated in America.

If we look at these three major efforts, we find that each requires successively more organizational understanding and involvement. MRP was seen as an MIS or Materials system and not widely supported. MRP II involved more company functions and received wider participation, though mostly at higher levels of management and staff. This participation increased the number of successes and achieved benefits faster because of a more unified and coordinated effort. Shop floor personnel were included only indirectly, however, as instructions filtered down from above.

JIT is a floor-oriented philosophy of rapid product movement and elimination of waste in all forms. It relies on the knowledge, skill, and attitude of the workforce, rather than on the sophistication of technology. Based on the common-sense principles of small, incremental changes and physical observation of results, JIT techniques do not often produce hard numbers to measure interim results. This looks like smoke and mirrors to many of the managers and functional departments so used to data accuracy crusades and reports evaluation.

The two biggest problems facing the implementation of any improvement strategy are:
1. Conflicting interpretations of the business goals as they relate to the various functional groups. We might even disagree on whether we need to change anything; we might just instruct everyone to work harder.
2. Uncoordinated choosing and implementation of specific changes. Each project has its own champion whose charter it is to maximize resources available to ensure its success. This typically means fewer resources are available for other champions and projects.

We submit that the more understanding and active involvement we can get from the entire company (CEO to Janitor), the greater our chances for success in implementing these, and other, strategies for improvement.

The real solution is to agree on what has to be done, who has to do it, how it is to be done, when it needs to be done, and then do it. This is simple, but hard to do in a rigidly hierarchical organization or an environment of traditional worker-management separation. We obviously need to find a mechanism to get everyone on board the same boat and rowing in the same direction.

Form Cross-Functional Teams at All Levels

The Team Process is an organizational mechanism that prioritizes and delegates tasks to cross-functional groups who have a feeling of ownership for the business objectives and are willing to become accountable for the resolution of those tasks.

Permanent teams constantly evaluate Policies, Procedures, and Practices to identify constraints to the effective realization of the business' objectives. They are problem-finders and priority-setters.

Temporary teams are formed to work on problem-analysis, problem-solving, and solution-implementation. Members of permanent teams may participate in these ad hoc groups as their interests or abilities dictate.

Regardless of what your organizational chart says, there are only three basic levels in your company to consider when forming teams. Limiting your "permanent" team structure to these three levels greatly simplifies communication, while ensuring a large pool of people from which to recruit.
- **Strategic Level**. Sets business objectives, projects long-term resource requirements, authorizes acquisition, and establishes consistent operating policies.
- **Tactical Level**. Translates the business objectives into effective operating procedures, plans activities, and allocates resources to support the plan.

- **Operational Level.** Executes the plan, operates resources, uses safe, effective work practices, and feeds back results.

Some companies use a system of periodic rotation that might have ten people on a team drawn from a pool of fifty at that level. The individual can leave the team after a minimum period without penalty, or stay through a maximum time limit. If the team has been successful, others at that level will volunteer to participate. If more teams need to be formed at that level, these departing members can form a nucleus that can start quickly.

We recommend that no more than three levels of the formal hierarchy be present at any permanent team meeting (other than for reporting to the team). We find that too wide a spread, or a management observer, inhibits the discussion in the early stages of team formation. As the team members gain confidence, become comfortable with each other and the process, and begin to show results, they generally welcome higher- (or lower-) level observation and participation.

The cross-functional aspect of the permanent teams is to make sure that all input is considered in both identifying problems and setting priorities. A quality problem on product ABC might have a different priority if we know of a pending national promotion from Marketing, or of a change to a more reliable material from Engineering or Purchasing. Ultimately there are fewer surprises and a greater likelihood that we work on improvements that can be supported by the whole organization.

The Flow Team

A special case of permanent team at the Operational Level, the Flow Team is involved with the product from raw material release through shipment. These are the people who actually touch your products and have first-hand knowledge of what holds up their flow. This group is characterized by enthusiastic operator involvement if management listens to their ideas without prejudgment.

The Flow Team typically generates the most ideas for improvement, both "good" and "bad." It has the least patience for delay and is very action-oriented. They ask the toughest questions of management, and themselves. They expect answers, but will accept "no," if explained.

Often, other teams will be still in the problem-identification stage of a subject, while the Flow Team has tried two or three possible changes to see if they work. Since they cannot allocate major resources, these actions are of limited scope, but are surprisingly effective in improving operations.

Management's challenge with this team is to provide adequate support to keep this team running as fast as they want to. The momentum this team generates can propel the rest of the people and the company to new levels of productivity and profitability.

While other teams will be more structured in conducting meetings, the Flow Team tends to meet on the fly (on the floor, in the break-room, etc.). In order to maintain its focus, this group needs a facilitator whose major tasks are to provide a central point of communication, to give organization to the meetings, to lobby for requested resources between meetings, and to keep adequate records for the team and management.

One client formed a Flow Team and with four hours education in some analysis concepts determined a constraint in the flow. They then found ways to help the operators (three shifts) increase their output from 2,000 - 4,000 per shift to a consistent 5,000 per shift (the market rate).

Cost was less than $200 for some replacement tooling. Timing was about three weeks.

They then evaluated this step in the routing. They found it was a rework operation (resizing a hole) from some variability introduced earlier in the process. Upgrading an inspection procedure from Go/No Go gauges to variable measurement gauging before and after a plating operation targeted the vendor plating as a significant problem.

A visit to the vendor determined he was plating for bright-finish, not dimensional tolerance. Corrections at the vendor produced a significant reduction in rework, and since less plating material was needed, it bought a 5 percent reduction in costs as well. A shorter process time also allowed daily turn-around and smaller batches. Cost of gauging was less than $600. Timing was about three months into the Team Process.

Moving back up the flow, the new variable gauging and help from an SPC resource found another major quality problem at the gating operation. Inspection after this operation prevented bad parts from being worked on at any subsequent step, saving operator and machine time. Cost was nothing. Timing to set up the inspection procedures was about the end of Month Four.

The results after six months were a 40 percent reduction in cycle time and inventory, no late shipments from week ten on, a relatively empty former constraint, and a newly identified constraint whose process and set-up times have been improved from 40 percent to 75 percent. Engineering effort has been focused on the last problem mentioned and a technological break-through seems imminent.

Creating a Framework for Teams

- **Shared Vision.** State the most important business objectives in terms that can be shared with customers, employees, owners, and vendors.

Typically, the Strategic Team's first task is to arrive at a consensus on the business direction and the means they will use to get there. The CEO may have the loudest voice, but he must realize that he needs the active cooperation of all four groups to get the job done.

Hidden agendas that are detrimental to any of the above four constituencies cannot be included because the company would lose key support. Since all the other teams will be checking their actions against the Vision, only actions that best satisfy their individual and collective needs will be considered. This is obviously going to require more open communication up and down the organization and with the outside world. Consider:

At an initial team meeting composed mainly of bargaining unit shop floor operators, one of the first problems discussed was lack of people. Predictable? After some lively discussion, we came to understand that the root problem was lack of trained people. Working together, management and workers came up with a successful plan to train (and retrain) the existing workforce. The procedures worked well for new hires, as well, accelerating their ability to function in their jobs. And yes, we did need some new people, but our client wound up with quality, not just quantity.

- **Establish Direction.** Once we know where we are going, and presumably we know where we are, we need to ask a key question: What's holding us back? We may have a constraint that needs to be identified and controlled or modified.

Constraints are usually described as:

Managerial—a policy exists to handle a certain business condition, but this policy conflicts with a different condition. Example: We have adequate Engineering support for our present products and processes. Budgetary policy prevents us from training and staffing for SPC. However, we reject 10 percent of product released at various points in the routing.

Logistical—procedures that slow the flow of product or information. How many people in your company have to see a requisition for a replacement cutting tool? How many inspection steps do you have in your routing? How long does it take to get a fork-lift to move material to the next operation? Does your schedule assume a day between operations? A week?

Physical—the capacity of a resource is inadequate to handle the demand, or it is linked to the flow in such a way that a combination of resources cannot be properly scheduled.

Behavioral—operating practices that are not recognized as inhibiting the flow. Examples: 1) An operator will not start a process, before lunch, that requires his attention. 2) One combines tomorrow's work with similar work today to save set-up time, but pushes other work, required today, into tomorrow.

Also, two types of external constraints can also inhibit our throughput. Material constraints are usually temporary and a result of inconsistent supply or demand. Market demand can be a constraint and should determine the upper limit of production, and, therefore, the upper limit of material bought and released.

Understanding the effects of constraints on the flows of product and information will allow each of the teams to focus on those areas where improvements will have the greatest impact on the business.

- **Education and Training**. The Team Process must be understood before it can be used to do anything else. Once widespread acknowledgment of its potential has occurred, it can be used to ease the education burden. Group participation in a team should enhance the individual's ability to use a learning experience effectively, both as a student and, potentially, an instructor.

The team meeting is an excellent forum to conduct short training sessions. Detailed or long sessions must be held outside the regular team meeting time, but can include any, or all, of the team members plus whatever outsiders may need this particular information.

By the nature of the focusing described above, a team will request information, training, or support only for the highest priority items, things that will have quick payback.

The types of education you should expect to provide to all teams include: process and flow analysis techniques, constraint identification, problem-solving, and company-specific topics of a general nature.

Detailed or technical information sessions (SPC, SMED, scheduling techniques, etc.) should probably be approved by a permanent team at the next higher level.

- **Support and Communication**. Teams need to have a pool of people available to them who can answer questions, perform tasks, and give advice. To sustain the momentum of a team, support must be immediate and meaningful. A team can accept a "no" to a request for help, if a reasonable reason accompanies it.

We suggest that specific technical, administrative, and logistical people be designated for a finite period of time for this purpose. This rotation gets many people involved in the Team Process without any individual feeling overburdened, or conversely, left out.

A method of communicating the team's projects, priorities, progress, and problems needs to be put in place. Begin informally with short "minutes," though you may have to designate someone in each team the responsibility

of "scribe." Most teams quickly see the need for more formal methods and will jointly develop something that all can live with.

Special communications and support problems exist for a multi shift operation. Communication might be improved by overlapping shifts 10 - 15 minutes so operators can talk to each other. Support for third-shift operations might require the home phone number of a very understanding engineer or planner. If a team from one shift wants to observe on a different shift, pay them the overtime and congratulate yourself on having a motivated group. The example to others alone is worth it, even if you can't find a quantifiable result.

- **Delegation of Authority**. In order to get anyone to take responsibility for any action, it is necessary to give them sufficient authority to get the job done.

For management, this means providing sufficient training, resources and personal support to let the people know that you are serious about wanting their help. It also means that everyone needs patience for the inevitable mistakes as the Team Process is developing. Mistakes tell you that people are trying new things, and that's what you wanted, right?

Resist the temptation to direct their activities, or even their topics for discussion, away from the team's natural choices, or to reorder their priorities without knowing their thinking process. It is probable that any team's hottest item would not be management's. It is even possible that management was not aware of the team's number one item.

Let them run with their own best judgment. At first, you may have to bite your tongue and allocate resources to activities that seem unimportant. As the team and you build a working relationship, you will find that they will focus more on things of value to you. Did you change or did they? Probably you both did, through the give and take of communication.

- **Develop Measurements**. Planning for improvement is only the first step. Execution of the plan, the implementation actions, is the next. However, it is the achievement of the expected results that the Team Process was designed for.

If we have broken through a performance barrier, how will we know? It is likely that many of our current measurements will not tell us until well after the fact. It is necessary to develop measures, benchmarks, and milestones to let *us* monitor the progress of the change we are introducing.

Each company's global measurements of the health of the business must be consistent with its objectives, and all of the objectives, however intangible, must have some criteria of evaluation. Internally, each team's measurements must be tagged to the same global measures, but additionally, they must measure the local improvement. This is not an easy task, and with each of your teams, you must co-develop the solution's timing and fair measurements that describe a path from the present to your mutual expectations.

- **Monitor**. Both the progress of the teams and the Team Process have to be guided so they can be self-sustaining.

Teams develop different dynamics in approach and rate of operation. Management evaluation must allow for wide latitude in team performance. It may be necessary to reconfigure a team with a different mix of people to achieve desired results. Do so slowly, or the other teams can feel pressured and resentful.

Do not allow the teams to conceal ideas, problems, or solutions in their effort to compete with other teams. One of our clients started teams that were reluctant to talk openly with each other, and even with us, for fear of revealing their "secrets." We had to establish more friendly and constructive competition to allow the cross-fertilization of ideas.

Teams should be encouraged to estimate and commit to the timing of any action. A "monitor," whether an individual or review committee, can see if the team is realistic in the timing and scope of the action and if other support might be needed.

Typically, a temporary team communicates with its level permanent team for priorities, resource allocation, and a "reality-check." The permanent teams do the same to the next level permanent team. Since the idea is to increase the speed of problem-identification through actions-implementation, the communication mechanism cannot be rigidly tied to the "next full meeting." Provisions for interim, informal communication must exist.

If a single entity is to act as a clearinghouse for communication, his/their motivation cannot be perceived as political. The cross-functional make-up of a team generally precludes this perception, but an impartial Project Manager or internal or outside consultant may be preferable in the early stages of team development.

Two important concepts are addressed here:
Who do we tell?
I will do what you review!

Coaching the Team Process

It is expected that companies beginning a Team Process have not had much experience in using this approach for gaining Employee Involvement. It may also be that the company culture is one of confrontation and mistrust between and among management and hourly employees. These two barriers (knowledge and culture) must be evaluated objectively and provided for in your early planning to go this route. Once you have started, any slowing of momentum will cause a restart or, more likely, an abandonment as one more failed project.

Objectivity is not usual in an individual, and a steering committee may take too long to evaluate the critical issues and start. An experienced consultant can give you the jump-start you need in initial analysis, planning the process, organizing the people, and facilitating first meetings. To the extent that your own people can be perceived as impartial and can learn to be coaches to the teams and the process, a consultant's involvement will taper off.

Summary

The Team Process creates more effective lines of communication and instills an organization-wide acceptance of change.

It energizes the workforce to apply their skills and imagination to problems that challenge their achievement of the business' objectives.

The successful Team Process is characterized by the statement:
Having patience for the process, but
With a sense of urgency for the task.

A well-conceived plan avoids duplication of effort and conflicting approaches to the same problem areas.

Focusing on the important constraints allows benefits to be achieved more quickly and makes the Team Process more sustainable.

The manufacturing environment has new economic and competitive pressures. The "Factory with a Future" will be the one whose people join forces in the efforts to improve and become more responsive to the changing expectations.

About the Author

Neal Davis, CPIM, has been in the Materials and Production Control field of Manufacturing for the past seventeen years, achieving the position of Materials Manager. He has designed and implemented many priority-targeted planning and control systems, both manual and computer-based, for a variety of product lines in the commercial, consumer and government markets.

Neal has a Business Administration degree and has received Certification in Production and Inventory Management from APICS. He taught a practical approach to priorities on the shop floor for the Long Island APICS chapter for six years and has spoken often at conferences, seminars and dinner meetings for APICS and other societies.

For the past six years, Neal has used this background as an educator and consultant for a national firm, as a principal of Common Sense Manufacturing, Inc., and currently president of Planning Dynamics, Inc., Milford, Connecticut. In developing curricula and strategies for clients, Neal has been on the leading edge of planning, education, organization, and support of the integration of Synchronous Manufacturing, MRP II, JIT, OPT, Employee Involvement, SPC, and High Velocity Management through facilitated Teams.

Reprinted with permission of the Journal of Cost Management, *Winter 1996, RIA Group, Boston, Massachusetts.*

Problems with Existing Manufacturing Performance Measures

Dileep G. Dhavale

Performance measurements, evaluation systems, and reward systems are indispensable management tools. They can help motivate employees to work toward fulfilling the organization's strategic objectives. By contrast, poorly designed or poorly implemented performance measurement systems can encourage dysfunctional and sub-optimal behavior throughout an organization.

The Problems

The sections that follow discuss problems resulting from the use of traditional performance measurement and evaluation systems in advanced manufacturing environments. In particular, later sections discuss the problems of using standard costs and variances as performance measures.

Financial performance measures inappropriate at operations level. Many performance measurement systems use financial measurements that are too abstract because they are too hard to relate to activities taking place on the shop floor. Financial measurements often fail to provide information that is useful for decision making.

For example, managers may want to know how often a machine breaks down because of a certain critical part, but that information is usually unavailable because the company's information system collects only financial information. Unless the maintenance department collects data about repairs and develops an appropriate database, this information is simply unavailable. Although most companies develop and maintain financial databases well, few keep nonfinancial information with the same degree of accuracy and detail. As a result, financial performance measures are developed even when they are inappropriate simply because the information is available.

Inclusion of nonmanufacturing, allocated, or noncontrollable costs. Performance measures that include nonmanufacturing, allocated, or noncontrollable costs are distorted. A manager cannot judge the effectiveness of new initiatives and improvements because of the impact of these costs. Allocated costs create an additional problem. Changes in allocation methods change performance measures without any change in performance itself. Nevertheless, many companies continue to include allocated costs in their performance measures. The reasons for such a policy include:

- To inform lower-level managers about the additional costs so they realize the need to generate adequate revenues to cover all the costs;
- To determine "full" product costs; and
- To create an adversarial situation between staff and line managers so that line managers will exert influence to control nonmanufacturing costs.

Excessive reliance on financial measures. An excessive reliance on financial measures encourages suboptimal behavior among mangers. Inordinate emphasis on financial measures can tempt managers at the cell and focused-factory levels to improve the performance of their subunits at the expense of long-term benefits to the organization. Such suboptimal actions include:

- Starting units just before the end of a period; or
- Completing high-margin or large orders before the end of a period and ahead of their scheduled dates.

All these actions can improve the contribution margins for a cell or factory while hurting the company as a whole.

No linkage between performance measures and strategic objectives. Performance measures used to evaluate managers and employees at different levels in a organization must support its strategic objectives. Without such a linkage, the managers and employees may behave suboptimally by acting to improve performance measures that are not linked to company goals.

For example, if raises in a supervisor's salary depend on meeting production quotas, then production quotas will understandably be that supervisor's number-one objective—not improving quality or customer service, as the company's strategic objectives may require.

But, for one reason or another, organizations—from non-profit universities to for-profit companies—fail to establish these linkages. For one thing, establishing performance evaluation and reward systems is time consuming. It is difficult to change the system to reflect changing strategic objectives, then fine-tune it until it truly reflects and supports those objectives.

Moreover, few organizations have invested adequately in nonfinancial databases that will support organization-wide operational performance measures. Budgetary and other financial measures cannot adequately reflect corporate priorities.

Some organizations even resort to slogans, jingles, speeches, and campaigns in the hope that they will induce the desired response from employees. This may work in the short run, but for a lasting impact there is not substitute for having a linkage between strategic objectives and the measures used to evaluate employees.

Checks and balances among performance measures. Many complex factors and variables interact with each other in manufacturing, either implicitly or explicitly. It is often possible to show improvement in the performance of one aspect of a manufacturing system at the expense of another. To avoid suboptimization of this sort, the set of performance measures used in evaluations must provide checks and balance on each other so that a manager cannot ignore one aspect of he production process without affecting at least one of the measures.

Too few performance measures. Suboptimization also occurs when organizations put excessive emphasis on just one or two performance measures in the hope that emphasizing performance of those components will improve the performance of the system as a whole. The favorite candidates for these one or two chosen performance measures often are machine and labor use. But machine and labor utilization does not necessarily improve the performance of the system as a whole as measured by such important indicators as cycle time, customer satisfaction or on-time delivery rate. On the contrary, utilization simply increases the inventory of goods that nobody ordered.

Too many performance measures. In some companies, mangers face a reverse problem. Instead of too few performance measures, they have too many. In such a situation, managers lose sight of the main objectives; they do not know which measures are important and need to be acted upon. Having the right level of detail is more important and useful than just having more details.

Irrelevant measures displayed. The problem of too many performance measures often results from inclusion of irrelevant measures. Performance measures are irrelevant if they are not used on a continuing basis. Not all performance measures should be reported routinely, because some only distract managers' attention from what is important. Nonetheless some performance measures may be useful even if they aren't provided routinely. For example, data about frequency and cost of machinery breakdowns can be useful in negotiating purchase of new equipment and demanding higher reliability or lower prices even if this information is not provided in regular, routine reports to all mangers.

Communication of performance measures. Organizations also need to find the best way to communicate performance measures to intended users. Reports and printouts work well at high levels of management or shop-floor employees.

Visual communication techniques (e.g., graphs, charts, flags of different colors, flashing lights, spaces with painted outline of the intended item or equipment) often prove very effective. Employees can also be taught to use simple keystrokes on terminals to gain access to graphical representations of the current status of any performance measure.

Use of total production. Many current performance measures use total production or totals produced in their performance measures done so as to encourage efforts to improve quality: The emphasis is placed on production of *good* units. Such dysfunctional behavior is especially detrimental in Just-in-Time and continuous improvement manufacturing environments.

Measurement of performance and evaluation. Performance measurement is the first step, but it is not enough simply to measure performance. Performance must also be analyzed and evaluated. Evaluation of performance measures induces the desired result and behavior from employees; the mere act of measurement does not. Beyond the evaluation phase, mechanisms must be in place to check whether required actions have been taken. As straightforward as this sounds, this process is often not followed to its culmination. As a result, companies fail to reap the benefit of their performance measurements.

Use of Standard Costs and Variances

Standard cost and variances are the most widely available financial measures for shop-floor activities; they are also perhaps the most widely misused.

Standard cost systems were developed in the 1920s and were widely used during World War II. They were developed for a manufacturing system drastically different from today's manufacturing environments of cells, focused factories, and computer-integrated manufacturing.

Formerly, production occurred in large batches, and direct labor was a major component of the manufacturing cost. Since automation was minimal, production rates were determined by how efficiently labor completed it task.

Consequently, the major focus was on improving labor efficiency by using time and motion studies and other industrial engineering techniques. Standard time and the resulting standard costs were more than adequate as performance measures for that manufacturing environment.

In today's manufacturing systems, however, direct labor is not a significant component of total manufacturing cost. Speed of operation is not determined by how fast an operator can work, but by the type of automation and manufacturing system used. The sections that follow discuss specific problems with standard coast and variances systems that make them unsuitable for cellular manufacturing environments and focused factories.

Continuous improvement. According to a recent survey of cell manufacturing and focused factory systems, adoption of continuous improvement programs is one of the reasons for impressive performance. In a continuous improvement program, a process is continually improved to obtain better cycle times, quality, and efficiency. As a result, an established standard time becomes invalid as soon as the first improvement is implemented, yet—in many companies—it takes up to six months for a new standard to be put in place. Standard time is a static concept. In a continuous improvement environment, therefore, it is of limited use.

Learning curve disturbances. The learning curve phenomenon makes use of standard times even more questionable. The rate of learning is higher just after an improvement is implemented. The rate continues to drop over time until a plateau is reached, when rate changes become small.

In older manufacturing systems, it was possible to wait till the plateau phase to perform the time studies to obtain stable time standards. But because of continuous improvements in today's manufacturing environment, instead of a smooth learning curve and an eventual plateau, discontinuous learning curves occur with drops in the production rates when the new improvements are implemented. The plateau is never reached because of constant improvements, so there are no stable time standards.

Lack of timely information. Standard cost information is not timely. Variances are available only a week or ten days after month-end closings (unless the information is available on-line.) This time lag makes it impossible to take any corrective action as a batch is actually being made. In a dynamic manufacturing environment, what happened last month is ancient history.

Too much aggregation of data. Variances are generally computed for all batches completed during a time period. But a cell manager needs information by batch or by product so that problems can be pinpointed. An aggregate variance fails to inform a manager whether a problem occurred with all batches or just some.

Built-in-inefficiencies. Standards have built-in-inefficiencies. A standard material cost includes the cost of making defective units and the costs of scrap and waste. A standard labor cost includes allowances for such subjective factors as skill, effort, condition, and consistency. Furthermore, labor standards allow for job fatigue, learning time, unavoidable delays, personal needs, setups and preparation time.

Adherence to budgets. Many organizations emphasize adherence to budgets based on standard costs. To avoid either favorable or unfavorable variances, managers sometimes resort to dysfunctional behavior such as:

- Running a plant or a machine center to absorb manufacturing overhead when there is no immediate demand for the product being made;
- Misclassifying direct and indirect labor to manipulate manufacturing overhead and avoid labor-related variances;
- Purchasing low-cost, low-quality materials, or purchasing in huge lots to take advantage of volume discounts.

These actions may improve the budget-related performance of the mangers, but they hurt the performance of the company as a whole.

Direct labor emphasis. Many standard cost systems analyze direct labor costs in great detail, then compute various ratios using that cost. This is a holdover from the days when labor costs constituted a large percentage of the manufacturing cost. In today's environment, direct labor costs do not warrant such minute attention. Continued use of performance measures based on direct labor sends a confusing signal to managers at the cell and factory level.

In traditional cost accounting systems where direct labor is used to allocate manufacturing overhead, analysis of overhead often does not vary according to direct labor, so changes in direct labor use cannot explain overhead spending problems. Activity based costing has pointed this out.

Popularity of standard costs. Despite these problems, many corporations continue using standard costs and variances. Some possible explanations for this follow.

In many companies, standard costs are used for inventory valuation purposes, so the computation of variances from those data is relatively easy and inexpensive.

For some companies, it may be the only set of performance measures that could be computed for all products and departments because databases are unavailable to develop operational performance measures on an organization-wide scale.

Standard costs have been around a long time, so many middle and top managers are used to variances, which have provided a frame of reference developed over many years. It is difficult for these managers to give up something they understand (or misunderstand).

Standard cost and variance calculations are in integral part of many accounting software packages, so collection and routine processing of data to get standard cost and variance information is no added burden.

Given all the problems with standard costs and variances, however, standard cost analysis should not occur for cell manufacturing and focused factory systems. An alternative is target costs.

Different Performance Measures for Different Levels of Management

Performance measures differ substantially according to the different levels of management for which they are intended. Top management generally prefers performance measures that are finance oriented (e.g., net income, earnings per share, and return on investment.) Lower levels of management such as shop foreman, supervisors, and cell managers prefer nonfinancial, operational measures (e.g., number of idle machine and cycle times.) Shop-level managers use performance measures that cover longer periods, such as a month, a quarter, or even a year.

Between these management extremes are other levels of management—e.g., focused factory heads, department heads, and plant mangers—whose needs and requirements for performance measures fall somewhere between the extremes. Middle-level managers may use both financial and operational measures. For example, they may be interested in financial measures (e.g., contribution margin of products or payback times for cells) and also operational measures (e.g., defect rates of different cells). Exactly what kind of performance measures a middle-level manager needs depends on his responsibilities and the corporate structure.

Multidimensional performance measures. Performance measures for top management are multidimensional; they tend to summarize many functions or activities into a single measure, such as net income. Lower levels of management, on the other hand, need one-dimensional performance measures (e.g., number of defects or number of late orders.)

Performance measures used by top management are affected by many external factors, including the economy and the marketplace, whereas performance measures at lower levels mainly reflect the effect of internal changes that will show a significant impact on specific performance measures over many cells, focused factories, or plants so that changes in one cell are hardly noticeable.

Unrelated financial decisions often obscure the impact of operational changes. Savings from substantial decreases in inventories resulting from implementation of Just-in-Time programs can be overshadowed by additional taxes resulting from depletion of last-in-first-out (LIFO) inventory. The impact of improvements in operations is generally gradual and continuing; it usually takes several periods to become noticeable. Financial changes, such as changes in bad debt and pension expense, make a larger and more immediate impact on the bottom line.

Desired Properties of Performance Measures

Here is a list of properties that performance measures should have (many of which are general enough to be useful in any manufacturing system, and even in nonmanufacturing settings):

Make performance measures understandable: Performance measures should be easy to understand.

Be clear about what is being measured: Performance measures should clearly indicate what they measure (i.e., if the goal is to measure on-time delivery, the goal should not be obscured by some generic name like "customer satisfaction index," of which on-time delivery is only a part.)

Ensure that data can be collected: Data for performance measures should be easy to collect.

Make the performance measures timely: Performance measures should be available on a timely basis so that corrective action can be taken.

Link the performance measures to strategy: Performance measures should have linkages to strategic objectives.

Tailor performance measures for different levels of management: Performance measures should be appropriate for different levels of management.

Avoid allocations: Performance measures should not use allocated costs.

Encourage the good of all: Performance measures should not encourage dysfunctional or suboptimal behavior.

Make performance measures relevant: Only performance measures that an entity is responsible for should be included in its report. Avoid irrelevant and insignificant measures.

Improve communication: If budgets are used as the main communication tool, include nonfinancial performance measures in the budget.

Stress teamwork: Use performance measures for groups rather than for individual workers.

Avoid proxies and surrogates: Surrogate performance measures should be avoided unless they have very good correlations with the characteristics to be measured.

Shoot high: Performance measures and their targets should be based on external benchmarks rather than just internal standards.

Act rather than react: Performance measures should be active—i.e., designed to avoid expected problems and difficulties in the future.

Reprinted from APICS—The Performance Advantage, *September 1995.*

Delighting Customers in the 1990s: Part I

John Dougherty, CFPIM, and Blair Williams, CPIM

Almost every company drills its employees on the value and importance of customer service. Satisfying the customer features prominently in advertisements in leading publications and is included as a key strategic imperative for competitiveness. It seems that the 1990s is the decade of customer service.

How, then, does one account for an apparent gap in the P&IC body of knowledge, with so little formal instruction on how to technically manage this growing trend? What principles, practices and techniques exist in P&IC to help satisfy a customer?

The purpose of manufacturing is to make a quality product in time to satisfy a customer order. The challenge of manufacturing is to achieve this objective, while optimizing costs so that the entire operation is profitable. Customer service and customer satisfaction are the ultimate drivers of all industry.

Customer service seeks to satisfy a bundle of tangible and intangible customer-perceived needs in the process of delivering a product. The primary tangible needs are delivery, price, reliability (quality), and product options. In addition, there may be intangible needs such as responsiveness and empathy.

It must also be stressed that customer service seeks to satisfy and retain a customer on a long-term basis. Research has shown that it costs more to attract new customers than retain old ones; and moreover, retained customers buy more, cost less to serve, pay premium prices and act as a reference for new customers.

Customer satisfaction has to be strategically integrated with other business objectives, such as profitability, return on investment (primarily inventory levels) and market share. Customer satisfaction should be a company's key competitive strategy. Many companies evolve toward a customer satisfaction strategy through a total quality management (TQM) program as they seek to eliminate defects, customer complaints and customer returns.

A few anecdotal observations on the influences of customer satisfaction, provided by the Office of Consumer Affairs, are:
- Satisfied customers will tell an average of five others about their experience.
- Dissatisfied customers will tell an average of 10 others.
- Customers expect visible action within 48 hours.
- Customers will accept only one hand-off to a specialist.

Define and Measure

The four primary customer needs related to manufacturing are defined below.
- Delivery: A product is delivered or is available when required by a customer.

- Price: This is more than the sticker number. The customer must feel he has received value for the money he has spent.
- Reliability: The product performs as specified, consistently and dependably.
- Options: Customers have sufficient choices within the product line to satisfy their needs.

Precise service measurements of these elements are required to monitor performance and determine if targets are being achieved.

It is necessary to ascertain which elements contribute the most to customer satisfaction. This can be determined by asking customers and by monitoring their actual behavior. A listing of the relative importance or priority of the elements must also be compiled. For example, how will a customer choose between price and reliability? This evaluation has to be conducted separately for each product family and market. Based on the results of the evaluation, tentative objectives and measurements of customer service can be determined. It now becomes necessary to determine what level of performance is required for the elements a customer considers important. Here benchmarks are determined and used as targets to be achieved or exceeded.

To measure customer service, first decide on the criteria that will be used to measure customer service, then determine measurements for each criterion selected. Ensure that data for these measurements are accurate and easily available. The following measurements can be used for determining performance on delivery, price, reliability and options (many other criteria can be identified, as well).

Delivery

$$\text{On-Time Order Delivery \%} = \frac{\text{number of orders delivered complete on the customer's required date} \times 100}{\text{Number of orders scheduled to be delivered}}$$

Other Measurements that Track Delivery

- Order completeness or average number of shipments per order (rated 100 percent for complete orders, 95 percent for two shipments, 90 percent for three shipments, and so on)
- Orders delivered per promise date versus orders scheduled per promised date
- Number of overdue orders and extent to which (time) they are overdue (overdue aged report)
- Off-the-shelf availability—percent of items confirmed from available stock at the time of order entry

- Order cycle time—total time from placement of order to delivery Price
- Price comparison—product price compared to competition
- Revenue ($) generated through sales booking and shipment

Reliability

- Product returned—number and percent
- Warranty claims made—number of claims and dollars expended in repairing/replacing defective product
- Complaints received on product problems
- Service calls made

Options

- Number of models in a product group compared to competition

Once measurements are in place, compile a composite service scorecard by customer. This should be done by identifying the most important service criteria, assigning an importance percent weight to them, and then multiplying the actual measurement by the weight.

When the scorecards are complete, set up statistical process control limits for each of the criteria being measured (for example, lower limit for on-time delivery = 90 percent). Then monitor the process and take proactive corrective action when the process starts to deteriorate.

Continuously improve the existing process. Here the benchmarked best-in-class performance should be used as the goal to exceed.

With this measurement process in place, work to develop measurements to gauge responsiveness and empathy. These "soft" concepts are more difficult to measure. Suggested measurements may include:

Responsiveness

- Number of requests for improving delivery and number complied with
- Number of requests for delivering small lots more frequently, and number complied with
- Invoice accuracy and order accuracy
- Complaints received on "not easy to do business with"
- Number of inquiries on order status and time to respond to such inquiries

Empathy

- Number of customers retained—repeat purchases per year compared to total customer base
- Total number of customers and customer base growth

Customer Service Best Practices

Communication: Frequent and clear communication is the hallmark of good customer-supplier relationships. Among the best communication channels is electronic data interchange. Other best practices include periodic face-to-face reviews between customer and supplier, site visits, newsletters and demonstrations. It is important to make customers aware of capacity and capability, including lead times and product availability. It is also wise to keep detailed and up-to-date. This is the basis of mass customization.

Product design: It is becoming common to involve customers with the design of the product. During this design process, the customer can make tradeoffs between price, reliability and delivery. Involving the customer in the initial stages reduces the risk of making an inappropriate product that does not meet the customer's needs.

Demand planning: Demand planning entails setting up an ongoing dialogue with major customers and being informed of their changing product needs. In addition, efforts are being made to get a customer's commitment on what product will be required and when.

Reserving capacity: This is a specific form of demand planning where capacity is reserved for key customers. The customer is expected to confirm the order with a sales order at a specified period of time (usually two or three weeks before the order is due). If this is not done, the planned order is canceled and the capacity is made available.

Supply and Delivery

- Direct supply. The supply chain is shortened by dealing directly with key customers. Product is stored for, and delivered to, customers based on their requirements. This eliminates dealers, distributors, wholesalers and warehouses, and ensures an ongoing dialogue with the customer.

A Process for Establishing an Approach to Customer Satisfaction

1. Establish customer satisfaction as a strategic objective and publicize it within the organization through a vision or quality statement.
2. Ensure that top management actively supports and visibly propagates the establishment of customer satisfaction as a competitive strategy. This is probably the most critical requirement for success.
3. Establish communication channels or conduct a survey to determine the customers' needs and expectations.
4. Decide and communicate how customer service will be measured. The measurements must be aligned to the customers' needs.
5. Determine the performance of the best companies through benchmarking.
6. Set and communicate targets that are commensurate with the best in the field.
7. Train the entire organization in a customer service culture. Provide intensive training to those who have direct contact with customers.
8. Provide for excellence at the customer interface. Order entry, order inquiry, product information and after-sales service are all critical junctions.
9. Delegate decision-making authority to the customer interface level.
10. Provide integrated systems support, so that accurate on-line information is available on inventory, backlog and capacity to support on line customer promises.
11. Monitor performance. Take corrective action. Ensure that performance is aligned to the customer service vision.
12. Reinforce the focus on customer satisfaction. Remember that a company's culture may have to change.
13. Repeat the cycle. Plan. Do. Check. Act.
14. Provide training periodically, as practices and techniques for providing superior customer service evolve.

- Ship to point of use. The need to receive and inspect product is being eliminated.
- Locating product. Inventory can be stored in a warehouse close to a customer's factory or even in a customer's factory, and the customer can consume the inventory as required.
- Frequent delivery of small lot sizes. Most customers realize that frequent delivery of small lot sizes is the most effective means for them to reduce their manufacturing lead time. It also reduces the suppliers' lead time and the total investment in the supply chain.
- Packaging and delivery. Arrangements are now being made in which the supplier packages the product in the manner the customer would finally require it, thereby eliminating unnecessary double handling and packaging.

Business Arrangements

- Aggregate accounting. Numerous arrangements are established to ensure that the paperwork and accounting effort to track the product is minimized or eliminated. Product is kept on consignment at the customer's location and invoiced when used, usually by indirect means.
- Joint agreements. An agreement is entered into annually between a company and its key customers. Included in this agreement will be types of products, required quantities, how changes are made and the time limit within which change can be made. Price and escalation clauses are also agreed to for the short and long term.

Educating the customer: Many perceived service failures arise because customer expectations differ from the service offered by the supplier. This is particularly apparent in make-to-order or engineer-to-order products. To minimize this, customer communications must be handled proactively and the customer must not be subjected to any surprises. Educating the customer plays a major role in this process, and many innovative arrangements are being adopted to ensure this occurs. These include:
- Field visits to the customer's site and customer visits to the supplier's factory.

Customer Service Do's and Don'ts

Do's
1. Set up customer service measurements based on what customers consider important.
2. Ensure that top management visibly and frequently reinforces the importance of customer satisfaction.
3. Set targets based on the best in class.
4. Ensure the measurements being used are communicated to and understood by the entire organization.
5. Make a customer service composite target a part of management's incentive plan.
6. Seek direct feedback from the customer.
7. Make periodic checks to ensure that data used is accurate where necessary
8. Make important data available easily.

Don'ts
1. Establish measurements that require hard to get data.
2. Neglect to train and retrain all personnel in the customer satisfaction culture. Focus on personnel who have direct contact with a customer.

- A technical sales staff to complement the regular sales staff.
- A sales contract with the customer spelling out special requirements and capabilities.
- A customer service manual that defines the company's vision, objectives and policies, and also includes details of products, options and performance.

Linking customer satisfaction with success:
- Linking customer satisfaction and performance. For the customer service strategy to be strengthened, it is essential that the company is able to link the customer satisfaction approaches with marketplace successes. Successful practices must be identified and reinforced.
- Focusing on productive techniques. Resources and attention should be focused on successful practices. The results of such efforts must be measured. The process should be iterative.
- Reinforcing customer satisfaction successes. Successes must be communicated to all employees, thereby reinforcing their focus on customer satisfaction.

Creating a Climate of Customer Service

Company personnel, particularly those who have direct contact with the customer, must be informed of what the customer considers important and what the customer wants. Too often, surveys are conducted and an understanding of customer needs is developed, but this insight remains in the executive office or in the marketing department. It is essential that these insights be communicated to the front line staff and they be trained to develop the appropriate behavior and response to satisfy the identified customer needs.

For employees to delight customers, it is necessary that they be satisfied themselves. Customer satisfaction goals must be linked to performance evaluation, and required behaviors must be recognized and rewarded. The culture of customer service must pervade all levels of the organization. All must be trained to view their jobs from a customer satisfaction perspective.

There is need for continuous reinforcement of on-the-job performance. Trainers and observers must monitor and upgrade the performance of the staff dealing with customers. There should be frequent and visible recognition of good customer service. The reward system should complement the desired behavior. There must be an internal consistency in all the company processes supporting the service objectives.

About the Authors

John Dougherty, CFPIM, is senior partner in Partners For Excellence, which conducts private, company-focused education session on topics including MRP II, sales and operations planning, master production scheduling and inventory record accuracy.

Blair Williams, CPIM, is materials management and manufacturing engineering manager at AT&T's factory in Clark, N.J.

This article is excerpted from Blair R. Williams, *Manufacturing for Manufacturers—A Guide For The Real World*, copyright 1995 by AT&T. All rights reserved. Reprinted by permission of Addison-Wesley Publishing Company, Inc. This book is scheduled to be published in the fall of 1995.

Reprinted from APICS—The Performance Advantage, *October 1995.*

Delighting Customers in the 1990s: Part II

John Dougherty, CFPIM, and Blair Williams, CPIM

As we discussed in the first article in this series, the competitive environment of the 1990s has forced a change in focus for most manufacturing and distribution companies. Those that succeed will focus on their customers' needs and requirements and form closer relationships with their suppliers. This forces us to change how we define customer needs and set performance targets. Companies have had to revisit their internal planning and scheduling techniques to ensure that they can support the differing customer requirements.

This article focuses on the changes in the area of master production scheduling.

Master Scheduling Policy Approaches

Instead of seeking rules and techniques that support current approaches to manufacturing, planning, scheduling, forecasting and customer ordering, companies have begun to rethink this entire "information" supply chain. Leading-edge suppliers have begun to develop programs whereby the product is produced, shipped and stored in consignment, either at a customer's location or at a warehouse location closer to the customer. In some cases, this has meant more warehouse locations to satisfy a wider geographic dispersion of customers. In other cases, the approach has been to alter the shipping policies so that the same number of warehouse locations can service customers more quickly through shipping consolidation schemes, fixed shipping schedules (shipping product to given regions on given days of the week or month) and the like. Some companies have even developed approaches whereby the product can be held at a "flexible" semi-finished level, so that final configuration can be completed at a remote finishing, assembly or formulating facility closer to the customer. In some cases, these "finishing" operations are performed by the customers themselves; in other cases by local contractors or, occasionally, by the manufacturer itself

Another trend is a move away from make-to-stock environments towards assemble- or finish- or package-to-order, or even make-to-order or design-to-order. But this is necessarily being done with shorter lead times and smaller lot sizes and more frequent deliveries in mind. Manufacturers are being forced to rethink the entire manufacturing process (and product design) to better facilitate quick and easy last-minute custom configuration to customer requirements.

The master scheduling techniques to support all these new approaches have not essentially changed. However, they are being analyzed and applied in ways that increase flexibility, shorten lead time and support more custom configuration without adding cost, inventory levels or complexity to the basic processes.

Key Customer Service Techniques

In general, the approach is to find a way to plan and schedule so that near-term customer-requested changes can be more easily accommodated while minimizing their effect on profitability.

Some of these techniques would be considered improvements in a company's approach to demand management, as it directs the master scheduling process. These would include:

- Demand forecasting

Demand forecasting uses actual demand history to more accurately predict the future. Direct individual customer planning information is not usually available (either due to the number of customers or the state of their current planning systems).

Demand forecasting requires the choice and use of appropriate statistical forecasting techniques so that historical data can be projected into future forecasts. Key here is the use of "demand filters" for identifying and smoothing out the effects of unpredictable, unusual and generally nonrepeatable fluctuations in demand. Computer tools can identify these abnormal demands and then adjust forecasts.

Equally important is the summarization, analysis and "by exception" analysis of the data so that management can provide the appropriate subjective overrides to the statistical forecast projections. In an ever-changing economic environment, depending on demand to always replicate past cycles and trends can be hazardous.

- Demand time fence

The *APICS Dictionary* defines demand time fence as:

1) That point in time inside of which the forecast is no longer included in total demand and projected available inventory calculations; inside this point only customer orders are considered. Beyond this point, total demand is a combination of actual orders and forecasts, depending on the forecast consumption technique chosen. 2) In some contexts, the demand time fence may correspond to that point in the future inside of which change to the master schedule must be approved by an authority higher than the master scheduler. Note, however, that customer orders may still be promised inside the demand time fence without higher authority approval if there are quantities available-to-promise (ATP). Beyond the demand time fence, the master scheduler may change the MPS within the limits of established rescheduling rules, without the approval of higher authority.

The first definition talks about a setting within a software package so that the forecast and actual customer bookings in the short term can be combined to project total demand over the near-term horizon. This helps smooth out the effect of customer orders coming in a "lumpy fashion."

The "forecast consumption technique" is usually chosen just outside the demand time fence. It should be set at the typical customer lead time (as far as backlogs usually consume capacity and indicate "next order" promising). Inside the set demand time fence, forecasts are totally ignored and only customer orders are considered for planning purposes, since this represents the typical "backlog horizon" or "customer ordering lead time" and, for planning purposes, it is assumed that no additional customer orders will be promised inside this demand time fence. This technique is critical in assemble-to-order, finish-to-order or make-to-order environments, where the ordering patterns vary significantly from week to week.

• Available-to-promise

This calculation helps ensure that customers are promised delivery based on current inventory and schedule positions while ensuring that all future commitments made to other customers will be honored.

Available-to-promise equals beginning inventory plus schedule minus all previously committed customer orders, day by day. This does not mean that the customer can only "get it when it's ready," but that the manufacturer is constantly comparing customer requirements to current inventory/schedule/allocation positions and reprioritizing to satisfy as many customer requests as possible. Sometimes this will trigger short-term rescheduling to get more in the schedule to accommodate customer requests.

Sometimes it will trigger reshuffling of customer priorities, if some customers can accept later delivery.

Available-to-promise can sometimes represent blocks of capacity rather than actual produced or scheduled product in a given configuration. Sometimes the available-to-promise technique is used for a series of individual options, features or choices within a configurable product line.

In this case, the customer commitment date would represent the available-to-promise date of that option, which is furthest in the future.

Supply Management

Other techniques or approaches could be classified as supply management. They would include:
• Planning bills of materials

Rather than attempting to schedule and hold extra products and materials to a safety stock or minimum stock level, variability in demand can be hedged by planning for more of the variable options.

A planning bill of material would simply list all the various options along with predictions of how often each will be chosen by a customer (a product mix forecast). The scheduler can then selectively hedge or overplan those options with the greatest variability so that only those variable options need to be ordered or held in stock in large quantities. (See the APICS Dictionary definition of "hedging" below.)

The more common or stable options can be scheduled or stocked at levels closer to the forecast, allowing the manufacturer to focus extra inventory investment on those options that are most likely to vary per the customer requests. Doing this out over the planning horizon will trigger the ordering of materials based on their own specific lead times.

So, for instance, if you're working in an assemble-to-order business, and customers typically expect two- to four-week delivery, only those options with lead times longer than two to four weeks need to be held in inventory as a hedge. Extra quantities of short lead time options can provide more planning visibility to the suppliers of those options. Overplanning is a way of "hedging." The APICS Dictionary defines hedge as follows:

1) In master scheduling, a scheduled quantity to protect against uncertainty in demand or supply. The hedge is similar to safety stock except that a hedge has the dimension of timing as well as amount. A "volume hedge" or "market hedge" is carried at the master schedule or production plan level. The master scheduler plans excess quantities over and above the demand quantities in given periods beyond some time fence such that, if the hedge is not needed, it can be rolled forward prior to the need to commit major resources or produce the hedge and put it in inventory. A "product mix hedge" is an approach where several interrelated options are overplanned. Sometimes, using a planning bill, the sum of the percent mix can exceed 100 percent by a defined amount, thus triggering additional hedge planning. 2) In purchasing, any purchase or sale transaction having as its purpose the elimination of the negative aspects of price fluctuations.

• Safety stock management

In the past, companies often set blanket rules on safety stock, such as, "always hold six weeks' worth of finished goods," or "always hold four weeks' worth of raw materials." Manufacturers are now finding it more effective to stratify or segment their safety stock rules and hold varying amounts of safety stock, depending on the demand and supply variability of the products or materials in question.

• Planning time fence

By using this time fence as a set point in the future within the master scheduling software logic, it prevents the planning system from automatically adjusting or changing master schedule quantities and driving down lower level requirements. This ensures that the schedule is not changed and that lower level manufacturing priorities can be met.

The APICS Dictionary defines planning time fence as:

A point in time denoted in the planning horizon of the master scheduling process which marks a boundary inside of which changes to the schedule may adversely impact component schedules, capacity plans, customer deliveries and cost. Planned orders outside of the planning time fence can be changed by the system planning logic. Changes inside the planning time fence must be manually changed by the master scheduler.

Managing Change to Schedules and Forecasts

Obviously the more variation there is in demand (inaccurate forecasts, customer order changes, unanticipated customer orders), the harder it will be to set up and maintain a stable supply schedule. Conversely, the less reliable the supply schedule is (quality problems, yield problems, supplier reliability problems, process or capacity reliability problems, etc.), the less confident the company will feel in working to the plan as a means of satisfying customers.

Competitive pressures in the marketplace (driven by customer expectations and competitive improvements) are such that in most cases demand will continue to vary at an increasing rate. Fortunately, initiatives undertaken under the auspices of reengineering, Just-in-Time, total quality management and the like are attacking supply variability in a way that shortens lead times, increases flexibility and improves reliability in executing schedules.

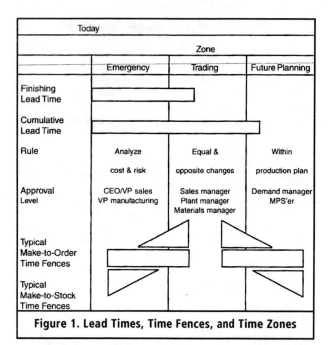

Figure 1. Lead Times, Time Fences, and Time Zones

But these trends occur at different rates, in different industries, in different marketplaces, for different companies and on different product lines within these companies. Therefore, it is critical that reasonable guidelines and rules be set up to manage and continually synchronize the demand changes to the supply plans, product by product, company by company. The use of time fences to identify "rescheduling time zones" for this is an increasingly important issue that every company needs to address.

The *APICS Dictionary* definitions of demand time fence and planning time fence refer to how the computer operates in suggesting planned master schedule orders and netting forecasts and customer orders, respectively. Each of those definitions refers to management rules or approaches to guiding, analyzing and approving changes to the schedule at various points in time (see **Figure 1**). Thus, some people would use the demand time fence to identify a boundary inside of which only emergency changes to the master schedule will be approved. This does not mean that a schedule is ever frozen, only that it is carefully controlled in the near term to ensure that the changes are necessary and feasible. Obviously there are only so many emergency changes that can be made in the short term without affecting the reliability of the schedule. This approach ensures that the proper level of management gets involved in allocating the changes possible to the right products to satisfy the right customers.

The planning time fence can also serve as a boundary between the future planning horizon, where virtually all changes in master schedule product mix are acceptable as long as they fall within the monthly production plan totals, and a "trading" zone inside critical manufacturing and purchasing lead times, where changes are counterbalanced by other changes. For instance, one product can be moved up in the schedule if a similar product is moved back by an equal amount. Or one product type can be increased if a similar product type can be decreased. It is useful for companies to establish these zones to help focus management attention on the level of change that can be accommodated over various periods of time on various products. These zones can vary by product line to reflect

the schedule changes supportable by the manufacturing and supply process.

Fences Versus Zones

Rescheduling time zones need not exactly correspond to the demand time fence and planning time fence described earlier. There may be cases where the demand time fence represents the marketplace lead time or customer backlog that is longer or shorter than the time frame in which emergency changes can be accommodated.

Likewise, a planning time fence is typically set out close to a cumulative planning lead time to ensure that constant changes inside of lead time are not triggered through the MRP system. However, if some selective hedging or overplanning of the longest lead time materials (perhaps through the use of planning bills, safety stocks or option overplanning, as described above), then the rescheduling, or trading, zones may be significantly inside the software planning time fence. If it makes sense to have the boundaries between the zones match these time fences in a given company or for a given product line, then companies should pursue that. But where it makes sense to have them differ, the difference in how they affect the master scheduling software versus the management of change to master schedules should be understood and clearly communicated. By sharing planning information with suppliers, manufacturers may be able to significantly shorten the rescheduling time zone, since key suppliers with planning visibility can react to schedule changes more easily and quickly.

Measuring Performance

The ultimate performance measurement must be on-time delivery to the customer. All other measurements should be seen as subordinate to that—if the customer isn't satisfied, short-term profitability, productivity, efficiency and reliability aren't enough to keep the customer from going elsewhere to more responsive suppliers.

Other measurements that should be tracked include:
- Forecast accuracy by family and line item. This essentially measures demand variability and gives input to the master scheduler as to which items need constant review and adjustment, overplanning, safety stocking and hedging.
- On-time performance to the latest master schedule dates and quantities. How well are you hitting your expressed plans to support the forecast and the customer?
- Master schedule stability. The percentage of changes, by product line, in different rescheduling zones as defined above.

Shared Responsibility

Whenever a customer cannot be satisfied, all departments should share the responsibility, understand the cause for the failure and identify steps to be taken to eliminate it in the future. On-time master schedule performance is a measure not only of how well a schedule is set, but how well it is followed and executed, and how well the demand management driving it is being managed.

The techniques and approaches are not new. But their importance is critical to properly scheduling a manufacturing company to better support its demanding customer and marketplace requirements in the 1990s.

About the Authors

John Dougherty, CFPIM, is senior partner in Partners For Excellence, which conducts private, company-focused education session on topics including MRP II, sales and operations planning, master production scheduling and inventory record accuracy.

Blair Williams, CPIM, is materials management and manufacturing engineering manager at AT&T's factory in Clark, N.J.

Reprinted from APICS—The Performance Advantage, *February 1995.*

Supply Chain Management in the 1990s
Bernd H. Flickinger and Thomas E. Baker

In today's customer-driven business environment, customers want a quicker response to their inquiries as to whether a product (or capacity to make the product) is available-to-promise. Soon customers will want response time to shrink to near zero. As global competition increases in the 1990s, more companies will move to such scheduling practices and bring their customers into their production processes. BASF Corp. has implemented the "Vision '96" program to reengineer their supply chains to increase speed, efficiency and product quality.

Decision-support tools for logistics management, forecasting, and production planning and scheduling play a critical role in Vision '96 and are key to servicing BASF Corp. customers reliably, responsively and at a lower cost. BASF implemented two decision-support applications prior to 1992 and four by year-end 1993. They had 15 in place during 1994 and expect to have approximately 25 by year-end 1996. However, in addition to the system elements, there are critical change components which need to be managed. These include:

- Change the processes of the supply chain.
- Change the skill level of the people involved in the supply chain.
- Change the organizational set-up to manage the supply chain.

Hence, we will focus on processes, people, organizations and decision-support tools and information systems of the future supply chains of BASF Corp.

BASF is one of the major players in the global chemical industry, a world-class company with $25 billion in annual sales of a full range of chemical-based products, including agricultural chemicals, synthetic fibers, plastics and consumer products such as recording tape. BASF is comprised of more than 100 companies active on all continents with production facilities in 35 countries and 120,000 employees worldwide.

BASF Corp. is the North American representative of the BASF Group ($5 billion in sales and 16,000 employees) with corporate headquarters in New Jersey. Vision '96 is BASF Corp.'s concept for a future business infrastructure that will provide an integrated system and process solution for all operational activities including logistics, purchasing, finance and manufacturing processes. Vision '96 is BASF's framework for implementation of a standardized and fully integrated North American transaction processing and planning system. It also provides a mechanism for supporting reengineered business processes via standard system tools, and serves as a base system environment that is functionally improved by third-party vendors.

Chesapeake Decision Sciences is a New Jersey-based computer software and professional services company which provides state-of-the-art information system technology-based enabling software for improving production planning and scheduling and supply chain optimization. Its software enables manufacturing or process industry companies to establish a high level of integration in their production planning and scheduling functions and the overall order fulfillment process. Their clients in the chemical, synthetic fiber, petroleum, lubricants, paper, food, electronics, pharmaceuticals and other manufacturing industries achieve substantial reductions in operating costs and major improvements in the delivery of products to their customers.

Change the Processes of the Supply Chain

In their pioneering book, *Reengineering the Corporation* (Harper Business, 1992), authors Michael Hammer and James Champy describe the need for radically changing the processes of the manufacturing logistics supply chain. They observe that complex business processes with scores of people in multiple departments are not flexible enough to deal with special requests or to respond immediately to customer inquiries or changes. They conclude that companies must change the processes of the supply chain and then organize around the processes, or the collection of activities that create value for the customer.

The Iacocca Institute at Lehigh University has coined the phrase "agile manufacturing" to describe a manufacturing enterprise in which "information flows seamlessly among inventory, sales and research departments and between the organization and its suppliers and customers."

Change the Skill Level of People in the Supply Chain

A supply chain manager at BASF Corp. must understand the business, negotiate with suppliers, satisfy the diverse needs and wants of various customers by meeting and exceeding all of their expectations, deliver Just-in-Time (and not ahead of time or behind time), expand time as needed, and take some time for family and community (which is why they are spending all this time shortening time).

Finding people to do this well is not easy. Now that Michael Jordan has retired, players that can do it all don't exist. Education and training are key and the process entails awareness, training the leaders and then mass education/training. Perhaps one benefit of corporate downsizing (615,000 layoffs in 1993 according to *Business Week*) is that most companies now have fewer masses to educate and train. However, those that remain are so busy running the business they may not have the time or the energy for training.

Lt. General William G. Pagonis, has described some of the lessons in leadership and logistics from the Gulf War in his book *Moving Mountains* (Harvard Business School Press, 1992). He offers practical real-world advice on the role effective management and strong leadership and training play in the success of any large undertaking. He provides insights on setting goals and direction as well as providing education and training. Once the immediate situation is under control (10,000 troops arriving per day with no place for them to go, no way for them to get there, and no food for them to eat or water to drink once they do finally get there) he describes how a trained team needs to pull out of the day-to-day what it is and focus on the what it will be (what are all these troops going to need while they are here to do what they've come to do, and how are we going to get them home safely where they belong when they are done).

Change the Organizational Setup to Manage the Supply Chain

Most companies are currently organized around the stages of production, the division of labor concepts established during the industrial revolution, or on jobs, people or organizational structures. BASF Corp. and many other large corporations have evolved into the "silo management syndrome." Companies are organized by functional areas including purchasing, manufacturing, finance, logistics and sales/marketing. Information, work and advancement moves nicely up and sometimes down the silo.

However, when marketing locates a customer with a need for X, and sales promises to deliver X to the customer on day Y, purchasing has to gather the raw materials, manufacturing has to make X, finance has to do whatever it is they do to make sure the customer pays for X and that the supplier earns enough money from X to R&D X2 which the customer will no doubt want next week, and logistics has to move X from the supplier to the customer.

Hence, the value to the customer comes from moving concurrently across functions while corporations value, promote and reward based on work and information moving sequentially and vertically within functions.

Systems Requirements in the Supply Chains of the Future

Decision-support tools for supply chain optimization are key enabling information technologies. These interactive, quick-response scheduling applications require large amounts of both static and dynamic information. The static data would include plant production rates and capabilities, recipes and routings, and facility preferences. The dynamic data, on the other hand, involves forecasts, orders and current deliveries. Using all of this information to solve the quick-response scheduling problem is virtually impossible with a single technology, though all the data can be readily obtained from existing information systems through SQL calls to various relational databases

Technologies such as expert systems, simulation, optimization, communications and graphics are typically required for supply chain optimization. Allen Spence, an associate partner with Andersen Consulting, has expanded this list and defines 10 qualifiers for decision-support software:

1. SQL interface—Efficient relational databases are required to handle the vast amount of forecast, order, inventory, process and product information. The decision-support tool must serve as a data concentrator and have an SQL interface for direct links to common relational databases.

2. Expert system rules—Once the data has been gathered and a schedule produced, the scheduler interprets the schedule and determines its validity. Expert systems technology can capture some of the scheduler's expertise. The expert system can apply and test the validity of production rules-of-thumb, analyze the schedule and recommend policy changes that yield cost savings.

3. Scheduling algorithms—The scheduling tool should be able to develop a schedule based on the information in its database. The process of generating the schedule involves determining what should be made, when, how much, and on what production units. The scheduling tool should contain algorithms based on traditional operations research algorithms including capacity balancing, materials explosion, sequencing, lot sizing, Just-in-Time scheduling and material flow adjustment.

4. Linear programming capabilities—The software tool should have the capability to formulate any linear, nonlinear or mixed-integer model. Direct links should be available to the best commercially available optimizers. Special algorithms and approaches are needed for large-scale nonlinear problems and decision-making under risk and uncertainty.

5. Blocked scheduling—Blocked operations defy most algorithmic approaches, especially when transitions involve significant sequence-dependent setup costs and losses. Examples of blocked operations that are particularly difficult include chemical reactors, plastics extruders, paper machines, continuous blenders, packaging lines, printing presses and some flexible manufacturing processes. A combination of linear programming and expert system rules is particularly effective.

6. Multistage/multisite scheduling—Multiplant and multistage processes are encountered routinely. Linear programming can allocate production across plants and optimally distribute products to warehouses and demand centers. The information or data required includes: raw material availability and costs, transportation costs, inventory storage costs, and plant capacity and capabilities. Multistage processes can be handled within the bill of material structure, which provides for different recipes and routings for making a product at each distinct stage of production.

7. Graphical user interface—A powerful graphical user interface (GUI) is needed to provide facilities for the on-line creation of custom windows and dialog boxes, pull down menus, presentation graphics and hypertext help. These capabilities enable new applications to be built in just a few days and user interfaces constructed quickly and easily.

8. User definable database—Every scheduling application has unique attributes which need to be defined in the form of large matrices, bills of materials, product flows, etc. The database should be user definable and have an object-oriented flavor with frames, methods and inheritance. Extensive data manipulation capabilities should be provided via set and matrix algebra, a macro language and an integrated expert system shell that operates directly on the database.

9. Available-to-promise—In today's customer-driven business environment, customers want a quicker response to their inquiries as to whether a product or capacity is available-to-promise. Soon customers will want response time to shrink to near zero. As global competition increases, more companies will move to such scheduling practices and bring their customers into their production processes.

10. Demand management—Demand management is the operational management of demand information for planning purposes. In every supply chain there are operations that need to be planned based on predicted demand. The specific operations, including production of intermediates, purchase of raw materials and production of finished goods are a function of asset flexibility and market lead times. The issue is not just forecasts, but how to generate forecasts, manage them, reconcile new information with the forecasts and constantly keep them up-to-date.

Success Factors in Supply Chain Management

BASF has discovered five success factors for supply chain management. First is the selection of partners, such as Chesapeake Decision Sciences, that can supply leading edge technology and also assist with the implementation. Second is the need for full-time resources—part-time help while you are doing your everyday job will not work in this type of undertaking. By definition, cross-functional empowered teams are required to break out of the hierarchical silos. Communication of information and ideas from the top down and the bottom up is essential. There is a natural dichotomy and debate that exists surrounding where the leadership will come from. While strong leadership from the top of the organization is essential to create the vision, someone once observed that when the people lead—the leaders (eventually) will follow. The organization has to be willing and ready to change (often dramatically, sometimes radically) and to embrace what Michael Hammer calls out-of-the-box thinking.

Measurable Benefits

BASF Corp. has already seen the benefits of supply chain optimization. In those areas where they have applied these methodologies, they have improved customer service levels to 95-99 percent, improved on-time delivery to at least 97 percent, reduced invested inventory by 30 percent and reduced administrative effort to make it all happen by 50 percent. Other economic benefits and significant cost reductions in computer hardware, software and manpower are expected from using a standard tool set that will be selected as the various pieces of the puzzle are defined as part of Vision '96.

Supply Chains of the Future

Fortunately, each of the identified technologies is sufficiently well-developed to be readily implemented within an integrated software package that links together the sales force, order management and production scheduling. Properly applied, the results from such interactive, quick-response scheduling can be enormous. For most companies, the principal gain is immediate customer response. Your sales and customer service people can query the systems remotely and provide immediate feedback and delivery commitment to the customers. Further, these new commitments are immediately visible in the production schedule. Everyone wins in this new domain of interactive, quick-response scheduling. The customer gets an immediate delivery promise, the salesperson can make the commitment with certainty, the plant promptly knows of the commitment, and the schedules drive the low-cost manufacturing/distribution solution.

References

1. Baker, T. E. and G. W. Cleaves, "World-Class Performance Through Improved Planning and Scheduling Integration," *APICS—The Performance Advantage*, October, 1991.
2. Baker, T. E. and D. E. Collins, "Using OR to Add Value in Manufacturing," *OR/MS Today*, December, 1989.
3. *Business Week*, "The Information Revolution: How Digital Technology is Changing the Way We Work and Live," 1994.
4. Flickinger, B. H., "Supply Chain Management at BASF Corporation," Keynote Address at the Chesapeake MIMI User Group Meeting, April, 1994.
5. Hammer, Michael and James Champy, *Reengineering the Corporation*, Harper Business, 1993.
6. Iacocca Institute at Lehigh University, "Agile Manufacturing" from the MESA International Glossary of Terms, Pittsburgh, PA.
7. Pagonis, William G. and J. L. Cruikshank, "Moving Mountains: Lessons in Leadership and Logistics from the Gulf War," Harvard Business School Press, 1992.
8. Stevens, Tim, "Success Runs on Schedule," *Industry Week*, August 15, 1994.

About the Authors

Bernd H. Flickinger is senior vice president, purchasing and logistics at BASF Corp., Parsippany, N.J., where he is responsible for all purchasing and logistics functions in BASF North America.

Thomas E. Baker is president and founder of Chesapeake Decision Sciences, Inc., New Providence, N.J., a computer software/consulting firm specializing in production planning and scheduling and supply chain optimization.

Reprinted with permission from CIM Review.

A Primer on Quality Function Deployment

Ronald M. Fortuna

Although the need for better designs is well recognized, practitioners have received relatively little guidance on the how-to aspects. The purpose of this article is to introduce the reader to quality function deployment (QFD), a leading-edge method that many companies have begun using to help them design more competitive products in less time, at lower cost, and with higher quality. It addresses the need to start the design process with clear objectives for a product—objectives that if met will not only satisfy the customers' wants but actually excite or delight them.

QFD also emphasizes the need to know as much as possible about a product before it is introduced to the manufacturing process.

Ronald M. Fortuna is a manager in Ernst & Whinney's Manufacturing Excellence practice in Chicago. He provides education and support for the total quality control efforts of many companies, including statistical process control (SPC) training and implementation assistance, and has helped several companies begin using QFD. Fortuna is a member of the American Production and Inventory Control Society (APICS) and is a certified quality engineer with the American Society for Quality Control. He received his BS and MBA in production operations management from the University of Michigan.

This article is based on Fortuna's presentation for APICS at its "Interfaces in Manufacturing: APICS Just-in-Time seminar," July 11 - 13, 1988, San Francisco.

Many leading authorities on the just-in-time. (JIT) philosophy of manufacturing have long recognized the importance of product design. Robert W. Hall stated this very succinctly in his landmark book Zero *Inventories*: "Excellence in stock-less production begins with the design of the product "[1] More recently, Mr. Hall has written that design efforts must be integrated—they must include both design engineering and marketing and manufacturing expertise, "otherwise, production is a turmoil of conflict and engineering change."[2] In his book *The Spirit of Manufacturing Excellence*, Ernest C. Huge states that designing with consideration of producibility and quality is one of the "pillars of the philosophy" of manufacturing excellence.[3]

Control Methods

We are happily reaching consensus on the meaning of JIT. During the early 1980s, much of the focus was on JIT production, with a corresponding emphasis on inventories and product flow. Therefore, we leveled schedules, balanced operations, reduced setup times, pulled instead of pushed, configured into cells, and perhaps browbeat our suppliers into keeping it at their place. Of course, most soon discovered

that quality is the linchpin that keeps the whole house of cards from falling down.

Thus, JIT is now most often viewed as part of a higher-level concept (e.g., manufacturing excellence or value-added manufacturing) that includes a comprehensive quality improvement initiative such as total quality control (TQC) and, also by necessity, employee involvement.

However, few people understand what the total means in TQC. Many view it to be a broad manufacturing-level quality improvement effort or to be nearly synonymous with SPC. To be effective, TQC must have much more breadth and depth; it should cut across functional lines and begin long before a product is manufactured or a service is offered.

As observed by Dr. Kaoru Ishikawa, the world-renowned quality expert, what we are seeing is the evolution of quality activities into a new generation. The first two generations, inspection and manufacturing process control, are gradually giving way to a third—product and process design improvements. In other words, many companies are moving from manufacturing-process quality control to product-development quality control. QFD is at the forefront of this movement.

Reliance on SPC

Companies should undertake SPC to prevent defects and to improve quality by reducing variation. To that end, many have achieved remarkable improvements in quality and productivity. SPC is a preventive measure but only to a point. It addresses only the variation owing to the many variables in the production process itself. In a broader sense, it is still reactive in nature and represents after-the-fact problem solving. That is, SPC involves fixing what is wrong and attempting to reduce variation after a product has been released for production. Prevention and reduction of variation can and should begin much earlier in the life of a product.

QFD gets the product and process correct from the outset. Quality function development is aimed at detecting and solving quality problems at a much earlier stage than SPC— getting the product and process right from the outset. It is easier and less costly to correct a defect right after it occurs during manufacture; it is even more beneficial to improve product and process design before manufacture—protection against environmental variables and product deterioration can be built into a product at the design stage. Furthermore, optimization during the product and process design is becoming more important in determining the quality and performance variation and manufacturing cost of a product.

QFD: Translating the Voice of the Customer

We know by experience that the product development process is rarely the same for any two products, causing longer design cycles, more product problems, and higher cost. One of the keys to shortening the process and producing competitively superior, more producible designs is to better define the product and better document the design process. It takes longer to define the product using QFD, but total design time is reduced because priorities are focused early on and documentation and communication are improved.[4] Through the use of some structured planning tools, a discipline is introduced to the process. The net result is elimination of much redesign on critical items and a great reduction in overall engineering changes.

First used by Mitsubishi's Kobe Shipyards in 1972, the discipline and structure of QFD is a natural for product development. It solves many problems such as shared responsibilities, interpretation differences, long development cycles, sub-optimization, and personnel changes. Visual documents that can be easily interpreted by those downstream help prevent things from falling through the cracks of the process. Multi-functional teams put much of the reasoning behind product and process decisions on these documents. This reduces the chance that the right hand won't know what the left hand is doing, which is so often the case in the development of complex products.

Although many definitions of QFD are possible, the following captures the essence of the concept for our purposes: QFD is a means of ensuring that customer requirements (needs, wants, demands) are accurately translated into relevant technical requirements throughout each stage of the product development process.

In other words, we can trace a clear path from customer requirements at the start of product planning down to the most detailed instructions at the operating level. This necessitates that the ends and means are linked at each stage—that we have a system.

The voice of the customer is the point of departure for QFD and drives the process. Listening, understanding, interpreting, and translating what the customer says forms the philosophical heart of QFD. It is important that the members of a QFD team share a common understanding and knowledge of a product's objectives based on this expanded product definition step. Extraordinary efforts to collect and understand the unsolicited comments of potential and current customers are a hallmark of successful Japanese applications of QFD.

The Structure of QFD

QFD starts with a positive statement of what the customer wants and needs. In other words, what are the product objectives or the ends to which we are working? These are often referred to in QFD as the whats. These are not necessarily product specifications but may be more general in nature. For example, a commercial printer may tell his paper supplier that he wants no tears while it is running on a rotary press.

However, we know that we can't act specifically or directly on such general requirements. Therefore, we must specify, in our own internal technical language, what means we will use to accomplish our ends. At the product planning stage, these are often called substitute characteristics or design requirements. More generally in QFD, we call them the hows. So, for our example, we might translate the customer's requirements of no paper tears into design requirements for thickness, width, and tensile

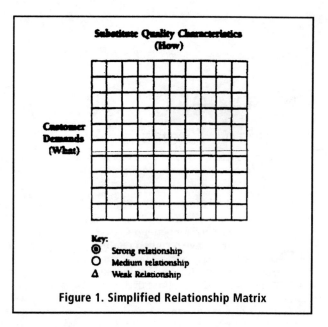

Figure 1. Simplified Relationship Matrix

strength. We should also determine objective target values that are as specific as possible. Width and thickness might then be assigned targets measured in millimeters and tensile strength assigned targets measured in pounds of force.

Except for the simplest of products, the relationships between the whats and hows can quickly become very confusing. One way to solve this problem is to form a matrix from the lists of whats and hows and to show the relationship between them by the use of various symbols. **Figure 1** shows a simplified conceptual picture of this most basic QFD tool.

The matrix is, of course, a simple concept, but it is a disciplined way to compare two sets of items. It provides a logical in-depth look at many of the critical aspects of any product or service. We can focus on the customer and consider a widespread number of correlations and relationships. In short, it helps to ensure that things don't fall through the cracks.

Although this matrix represents the basic logic of all QFD charts, many options and enhancements are commonly used. For example, importance-weighting systems are frequently used and can help systematically and successfully apply the Pareto principle, that is, elaborate the details at one stage, then select the most important items for the next stage. Thus, QFD can tell where to concentrate the engineering effort and, just as important, where not to invest time and money.

Another option for product planning is to make competitive evaluations of the whats and hows:

- Ask customers how well you fare against the competition on their most important requirements.
- Ask your engineers how you rate against the competition on the technical requirements that are specified for the product.

Together, these evaluations can often help pinpoint how to gain a competitive advantage and where improvement may be most needed.

A correlation matrix, in which the hows are compared against each other may also be used to identify conflicting design requirements. For example, the design requirements for a diesel engine may include targets for acceleration and particulate emissions. These two requirements might have a strong negative correlation in the

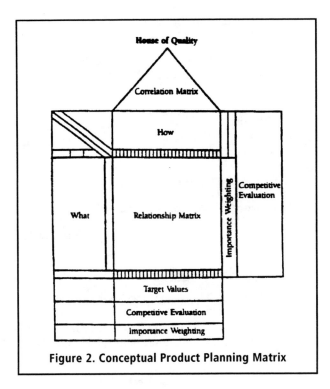

Figure 2. Conceptual Product Planning Matrix

Phase 1. Product Planning —————————→ Customer Requirements

Substitute Characteristics (Design Requirements)

Phase 2. Product Design —————————→

Critical Part/Mechanism Characteristics

Phase 3. Process Planning —————————→

Key Processes

Phase 4. Process Control Planning —————————→

Control Methods

Figure 3. Discrete Phases of an Assembled Product's Process

sense that as the emissions improve, the acceleration worsens. This type of exercise helps detect possible trade-offs early on—a primary goal of QFD.

Figure 2 shows a conceptual product planning matrix that includes all of the enhancements previously described. This is often referred to as the house of quality, and it is almost always the first chart to be completed in a QFD study.

This exhibit identifies a handful of key customer requirements and substitute characteristics that will become the focus of the rest of the QFD study. In general, these characteristics are transferred onto subsequent charts to be explored in more detail.

The number of phases (or translations) needed to move from general customer requirements to highly specific production process controls varies with the complexity of the product. As with much of QFD, there are no absolute rules—you should use as much or as little as needed to ensure that key customer requirements will be met each and every time. In this regard, there are two general rules:

• Use what makes sense to you.
• Do not make things foreign to people.

Many managers find it useful to think of QFD in somewhat discrete phases. The phases for an assembled product are generally described in a fashion similar to the

scheme shown in **Figure 3**. It does not mean that there would be only four charts. In fact, many more charts might be involved in phases two, three, and four.

This process seems rather complicated, but the potential rewards are great. Many U.S. companies are becoming convinced that it is worth the extra up front effort in planning, execution, and top management involvement. As mentioned earlier, the magnitude of these benefits is often large. Toyota and NGK, for example, report that their design cycle has been reduced by one-third. Toyota further reports that startup costs on one product line were reduced by 61% over a seven-year period that covered four startups. Aisin Warner claims that the number of engineering changes and their design cycles have been halved. Komatsu MEC, a manufacturer of heavy equipment, used QFD to introduce 11 new products within a 2 _-year development cycle, five of them simultaneously. These products met with a high degree of customer acceptance and resulted in substantial gains in market share.

QFD has also been applied successfully to mature products. For example, the Tokyo Juki Kogyo Co. used QFD to help direct the redesign of its line of sewing machines. It began by taking extraordinary measures to collect and comprehend information from the market, including detailed observations and discussions with machine operators and evaluation of complaint reports. One key customer demand was the ease with which cloth could be handled at the start of a sewing operation. The company's technical analysis and customer survey of competitors' machines further revealed that improvement in this area would provide a significant competitive advantage. The QFD process guided it to target key design characteristics such as bed cross section and holding height for intensive engineering effort.

The result of this effort was that the machines materially improved their customers' quality and productivity and sales increased despite a long-term decline in the sewing machine market.

Although many Japanese companies are using QFD, including all Toyota suppliers, the first US case studies only emerged in early 1986. However, interest is very strong. All of the Big Three domestic automakers have begun training and applications. Ford is strongly encouraging the use of QPD by its suppliers. Other automotive suppliers have already completed case studies and are using QFD on an ongoing basis. Non-automotive users include such diverse companies as Omark Industries, Digital Equipment Corp., and Proctor & Gamble.

Applications in the US thus far have generally been more modest in scope and impact than in Japan. Nevertheless, success stories are already emerging. For example, the QFD coordinator for an automotive supplier reported that a QFD team uncovered a problem with a glove compartment design that would likely have gone undetected for another year.

One of the reasons that QFD is so powerful is that it helps determine and rank critical items to which quality technology and engineering effort should be applied. In addition, QFD will often identify conflicting design requirements. In these instances, the use of methods of experimented design, including the Taguchi methods, can provide some remarkable results. In fact, many Japanese companies would attribute more than 50% of the total improvement in quality over the last 10 years to the use of the Taguchi methods. However, they also give credit to the use of QFD as a planning mechanism that helps them get the biggest bang for the buck. Those serious about QFD should learn more about experimental design and other tools commonly used with QFD, such as fault tree analysis (FTA), failure mode and effect analysis (FMEA), and other general planning tools.

Summary

Competitive JIT requires a first-class design process. In fact, product and process design improvements should form the heart of a TQC effort. Although manufacturing-level quality improvement efforts are necessary and valuable, the leverage from improvement is much greater during design.

SPC should be an important element of a company's goal to achieve world-class quality and productivity. However, the responsibility for quality must be extended to all functions of the business. Quality efforts should begin at the very inception of a product, using the voice of the customer as a constant guide. QFD is an appropriate mechanism to integrate this voice into guides that eliminate waste and foster continuous improvement.

Every organization already has some means of eventually incorporating customers' presumed requirements into a final product. In this sense, QFD certainly does not represent a totally new or radical idea. However, through QFD, companies do this in a very disciplined, structured, and methodical manner (most often through the use of a series of charts or matrices) as a means to achieve specific product objectives and translate customer requirements into requirements that people within the organization can understand and act on.

Given that the main objective of any company is to preempt the competition by bringing products to market sooner with improved quality, lower cost, and greater customer acceptance, those companies that embrace QFD and related tools may well distinguish themselves as the leaders in the worldwide battle for market share.

References

1. R.W. Hall, *Zero Inventories* (Homewood IL: Dow Jones-Irwin, 1983), p. 180.
2. R.W. Hall, *Attaining Manufacturing Excellence* (Homewood IL: Dow Jones-Irwin, 1987), p. 140.
3. E.C. Huge, *The Spirit of Manufacturing Excellence* (Homewood IL: DowJones-Irwin, 1987), p. 25.
4. B. King, *Better Designs in Half the Time—Implementing QFD in the USA* (Lawrence Growth Opportunity Alliance, 1987).

Recommended Reading

Ealey, L. "QFD—Bad Name for a Great System," *Automotive Industries (July* 1987), p. 21.
Fortuna, M. "Quality Function Deployment: Taking Quality Upstream," *Target,* Association for Manufacturing Excellence (Winter 1987), pp. 11 - 16.
Ishikawa, I. *What is Total Quality Control? The Japanese Way* (Englewood Cliffs NJ: Prentice-Hall, 1985).
Kogure, M. and Akao, Y. "Quality Function Deployment and CWQC in Japan," *Quality Progress* (October 1983), pp. 25 - 29.
Sullivan, P. "Quality Function Deployment," *Quality Progress* June 1986), pp. 39 - 50.

Reprinted from the 1995 APICS International Conference Proceedings.

Concurrent Engineering: A Building Block for Total Quality Management

Donald N. Frank, CFPIM, CIRM

Total Quality Management (TQM) can be defined as the process by which all non-value-added activities are identified and then systematically eliminated. TQM can be used to address engineering activities as well as those in the manufacturing arena. Concurrent Engineering (CE) is a concept that allows the users of the design to participate in it from the inception. With the strong focus on Quality, American industry has started to adapt CE as a tool to increase global competitiveness.

Concurrent Engineering has proven that it can substantially reduce the time it takes to complete a new design. It has also demonstrated its ability to increase the quality of the design to the point that CE has become an integral part of TQM. Even Aerospace and Defense companies and the Government are now trying to implement CE in order to get more product on line faster in a period where the budget for defense spending is being drastically curtailed.

The major topics addressed here are the current, or traditional, approach to engineering design, the elements of CE, how engineering uses CE, what manufacturing and materials management contribute to the CE design process and what benefits can be expected from successful implementation of a Concurrent Engineering program.

Perhaps the best way to start is to state what Concurrent Engineering is not. It is not Computer Aided Manufacture (CAM), Computer Aided Design (CAD), or Computer Integrated Manufacturing (CIM), and it certainly is not Artificial Intelligence (AI). Any of these tools can be used as part of the CE design process, but Concurrent Engineering is a concept, not a tool.

Traditional Approach

Traditionally, once a new design project is authorized, research determines what technology(s) will be used; development defines the application of the technologies to the specific products being designed. Product designers then determine the detailed design of all the components, subassemblies, parts, etc., that make up the product. The process designers then determine how the product will be made. At some point, drawings are released to manufacturing and industrial engineers review the design and structure the product (and perhaps are forced into a major redesign) in order to allow the product to be made manufacturable at a reasonable cost.

After engineering, in all its aspects, has completed the design (by their definition) the drawings are turned over to manufacturing so that the planners can enter manufacturing bills of material (perhaps going through another restructuring) and routings into the manufacturing database. Then, and only then, can the manufacturing planning process of master scheduling and detailed planning (MRP/

CRP) begin to plan and schedule the manufacturing activities so that the shop can make the product. This is known as the OTTER principle (Over The Transom Engineering Release).

Two things normally happen once manufacturing starts to plan and make the product from the engineering drawings. First, the project is already behind schedule because engineering has used up all of the quoted lead time. Second, a wave of engineering changes is required to get the designs through the manufacturing process. Both commercial manufacturing and Aerospace and Defense companies suffer from the large number of engineering changes and for late deliveries that result. Another sad, but true, result of this traditional scenario is that the cost to make usually far exceeds that of the original targets.

Concurrent Engineering Approach

In order to break this cycle of late deliveries of low quality products with both cost and delivery overruns, companies have turned to Concurrent Engineering. CE is not a new concept.

Under one name or another, it has been around for at least 25 years. It has only achieved prominence in the 1980s when American manufacturing started recovering from its inferiority complex caused by the Japanese manufacturing miracle. It derives its strength in the recognition that the *customer* of engineering is manufacturing, and that the product to be delivered to this customer is timely, accurate documentation of how manufacturing can convert the design into quality products, delivered on time and at reasonable cost. A recent definition [1] of Concurrent Engineering is

> A systematic approach to the integrated, concurrent design of products and their related processes, including manufacturing and support ... intended to cause the developers, from the outset, to consider all elements of the product life cycle from conception through disposal, including quality, cost, schedule and user requirements.

How does Concurrent Engineering work? It starts by defining the set of responsibilities that have to be managed in order for the design to be successful. These include Project Management for the overall design process, Product Design, Process Design, Firmware and Software Design (traditional engineering design functions), Quality Assurance, Program Management, Cost Management, Material Planning, Production Process and Facility Planning, Customer Logistic Support and Production and Inventory Management. What makes Concurrent Engineering different is that all of these people participate in the

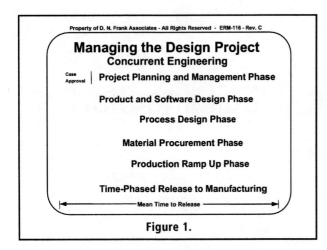

Managing the Design Project
Concurrent Engineering

Case
Approval | Project Planning and Management Phase

Product and Software Design Phase

Process Design Phase

Material Procurement Phase

Production Ramp Up Phase

Time-Phased Release to Manufacturing

Mean Time to Release

Figure 1.

design from its outset. The old domino approach of each discipline getting into the act after the previous one had hardened its design is replaced by a tandem team approach. **Figure 1** shows major activities that proceed together with the objective of a time phased release of information to the manufacturing, documentation and field support organizations.

The approach is to set up a project team with each of the disciplines represented by an individual with clout and credibility. As soon as the functional design specification is drafted, it is reviewed by this committee to see that all areas of concern are covered in the design plan. As issues come up that impact each of the disciplines, a small task force of subject matter experts address each problem and bring a solution to the project team for review and acceptance. This process continues until the design is finished, released for manufacture, delivered and supported throughout its useful life.

Implementation Issues

Concurrent Engineering is not implemented by purchasing software. It is a continuous process of people empowerment that once started, makes small but significant improvements constantly. Measurement of success is in seeing teamwork develop new attitudes, in fewer manufacturing delays due to engineering changes and in fewer returns from customers.

One need not wait for new designs to implement concurrent engineering projects. There are opportunities to apply concurrent engineering principles to the upgrading of existing designs where the product or the process (or both) need attention in order to improve quality or cost performance.

Perhaps the most significant implementation issue is to establish the correct cross-functional team for the pilot project. Remember that concurrent engineering is not just design engineers working with manufacturing engineers. Getting the right people together to work on a project that has a high potential of early and significant results is a sure way of gaining and keeping management commitment.

One can take a page out of the Just-In-Time implementation strategy. It does not matter where you start, as long as you start, now.

Examples

Let us examine a few specific cases of how the process works.

Example No. 1. Electrical design determines that a new part is needed. There is no supplier readily available because the specification is new. The first cut is review the design to see that an available part cannot be used. If a new part is really needed, purchasing is called in to help identify potential suppliers who are both financially stable and capable of supporting volume production requirements. If samples are required, they are procured within the manufacturing procurement system, with part numbers assigned, so that lead times and budgetary costs can be determined. In many cases, suppliers are called in to give their expert opinions. This often results in a less costly part with shorter delivery lead time.

Example No. 2. Process design determines that the prototype and pilot runs will have to be done using manufacturing facilities. The master scheduler is called in to work out a preliminary bill of resource so that when the work arrives on the shop floor, the critical capacity requirements have been properly allocated. As the design matures, planned releases are made to manufacturing, using the manufacturing database to prove out the design in pilot and/or first production runs. At the same time, the ability of manufacturing to plan effectively and build from the engineering documentation is also proven out.

Benefits

Manufacturing and industrial engineers, by participating in the design process, ensure that the product can be made, has the correct product structures (subassembly breakdown) for manufacturing, using known production facilities and that value engineering and other cost reduction methods have been included in the initial design.

Quality engineers work with the design group to insure that the design has sufficient stability to reduce rejections and rework to a minimum, while the product and process are being designed.

The master scheduler has started the process of scheduling all the deliverables so that, as the design progresses, each purchased part and subassembly can be planned and scheduled in accordance with the latest engineering release information. The new designs impact on the critical resources is defined to the Rough Cut Resource Planning (RCRP) file so early warning of constraints is made visible.

Where this scenario has been used, mean time to engineering release to manufacturing has been cut as much as 50%. The volume of engineering change has been brought down to acceptable levels. These dramatic improvements do not happen just from doing the design in tandem, rather than serially. The team approach results in a significant increase in design productivity and product quality. All of this has the effect of not just reducing the engineering design time, but also of reducing the manufacturing cycle time because of all the up-front planning. The overall benefit is getting a competitive product to customers while the window of opportunity is still open.

Nontraditional Applications

One of the major results of this Concurrent Engineering process is in a whole new view of the configuration management activity. Traditionally, the as-designed, as-planned and as-built were conceived to be discrete, sequential phases in the design and manufacturing process. Concurrent Engineering allows the as-planned to commence much earlier in the design process and allows the as-built to conform to the as-designed without horrendous modification. **Figure 2** illustrates this comparison

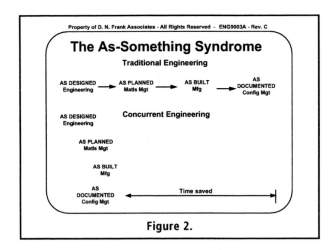

The As-Something Syndrome

Traditional Engineering

AS DESIGNED Engineering → AS PLANNED Matls Mgt → AS BUILT Mfg → AS DOCUMENTED Config Mgt

Concurrent Engineering

AS DESIGNED Engineering

AS PLANNED Matls Mgt

AS BUILT Mfg

AS DOCUMENTED Config Mgt

Time saved

Figure 2.

Concurrent Engineering Approach

Project Budget Approval → Research and Development ← ··· Engineering Change Request

Structured Bills of Material → Start Product Design

Manufacturing Routings by Work Center → Start Process Design → Start Software Design

Documentation and Approval

Release to Manufacturing

Figure 3.

and shows the potential for reducing overall design and production times.

A logical extension of the Concurrent Engineering concept is to document the design into the manufacturing database, and only into the manufacturing database, as a part of the design activity. The manufacturability function becomes part of the initial design so the product structures are correct at the outset. The need for separate engineering and manufacturing bills of material is eliminated [2]. The process can be documented directly into manufacturing routings and into valid manufacturing work centers. **Figure 3** illustrates this concept. All of the costly errors of transferring information from one group to another, often using unfriendly databases, is eliminated. The cost of data maintenance is drastically reduced by only having one place to make changes.

Once one accepts the discipline of documenting the design into the manufacturing database, the job of master scheduling, part procurement and manufacturing scheduling becomes easier and due dates become more realistic. The benefit is that, having all the resource contentions in one master schedule, the due dates of all the activities can be monitored and validated and the costs monitored so that overruns can be flagged before they become severe financial and contract compliance problems [3].

It has become increasingly apparent over the last few years that this concept of documenting designs into the manufacturing database and using its master schedule is a good cost/schedule performance measurement tool. Perhaps the major benefit from this approach is to provide management a highly visible linkage between the engineering design activity and the anticipated manufacturing delivery schedule. Another benefit that is starting to be utilized is the use of this technique to manage non-recurring engineering activities, even those that do not result in a hardware shipment.

Conclusion

In conclusion, Concurrent Engineering is larger than an engineering activity. It is a concept of developing a team approach to designs to shorten lead times, reduce cost and increase product quality. As we approach the 21st century, Concurrent Engineering is taking its place along with Total Quality Management (TQM) in our journey toward manufacturing excellence. In commercial manufacturing the viability of the company may depend on the successful implementation of Concurrent Engineering principles. In the Aerospace and Defense industry, it is the viability

of our country, our life style and our survival as an industrial nation that is at stake. The only obstacle in our way is the traditional separation of engineering and manufacturing into armed opponents, rather than partners in peaceful coexistence.

References

1. Institute for Defense Analysis IDA Report R-338, November 1988: *The Role of Concurrent Engineering in Weapon Systems Acquisition.*
2. Frank, Donald N. *You Do Not Need Two Bill of Material Systems.* Proceedings of the 1988 LA-ADSIG Conference.
3. Frank, Donald N. *Managing Non-recurring Engineering Activities Within the MMAS.* Proceedings of the 1991 APICS A&D SIG Symposium.

About the Author

Mr. Frank is President of D. N. Frank Associates. He holds a B.S.E.E. from Newark College of Engineering, 1959, and is APICS Certified at the Fellow level in Production and Inventory Management and in Integrated Resource Management. Since 1971 he has been helping companies in the selection, design and implementation of computer-oriented manufacturing systems and associated educational programs. His current practice includes companies moving toward Concurrent Engineering, MRP-II and Just-In-Time environments in such diversified fields as aerospace, electronics, semiconductor fabrication and plastics processing.

Don is active in the APICS New Jersey Chapters, served on the Steering Committee of the APICS Aerospace and Defense Specific Industry Group (A&D SIG) and is the designated instructor for its MMAS Standards and Manufacturing Excellence in A&D Courses both at public and contractor locations. He is a member of the CIRM Customers and Products Committee of the APICS Curricula and Certification Council, previously served on the CPIM Material and Capacity Requirements Planning Committee and teaches Certification training courses at client locations and for APICS Chapters in the Northeast. He is a frequent speaker on the professional society circuit and is well known in the literature for his papers on the interface among engineering, manufacturing and the database.

He is a member of IIE, CASA of SME, Project Management Institute and was a charter member of the Industrial Advisory Board for the Materials Management Program of Bloomfield, N.J., College.

Reprinted from the 1992 APICS International Conference Proceedings.

How to Integrate Engineering and Manufacturing through Concurrent Engineering

Thomas W. Gillen, CFPIM, and Larry Roubidoux

Concurrent Engineering is an effective method for managing Engineering and Manufacturing as one function to develop and produce high quality products quickly. Engineering and Manufacturing as one function is achieved by controlling and managing Engineering and Manufacturing as a continuum of tasks and activities. Once this continuum is established, the next step is to arrange the tasks and activities in parallel to compress cycle times. Establishing the Engineering/Manufacturing continuum requires the Engineering Resource Planning discipline. Arranging Engineering/Manufacturing tasks in parallel and compressing lead times requires the Concurrent Engineering discipline.

In this presentation, traditional engineering methods and the problems with traditional engineering methods will be described. Concurrent Engineering will be defined and introduced as an improvement over traditional engineering. Engineering Resource Planning will be described, and introduced as an improvement over traditional methods for planning and controlling engineering activities. The requirement to manage Engineering and Manufacturing as a continuum of tasks and activities driven by a common Master Schedule will be developed. How this continuum is realized through the integration of Engineering Resource Planning with Manufacturing Resource Planning will be shown. Finally, this presentation will describe the results achieved and the implementation process a company actually used to implement Engineering Resource Planning and Concurrent Engineering.

Traditional Engineering

In traditional engineering, the product is designed, documented and released to manufacturing where process design takes place. The traditional method for product design and release of design information is basically a serial process with many handoffs involving approvals among many functions. Requirements are developed in systems engineering, and transferred to equipment engineering, where the design is created. The design is transferred to drafting for documentation. The design documentation is transferred to checking and following approval, transferred to the release process. The release process often involves a serial approval procedure among such functions as Configuration Management, Contracts, Programs, Manufacturing and Quality Assurance. The traditional engineering outputs are drawings, specifications and the As Designed Bill of Material.

In traditional engineering, Manufacturing Engineering uses the engineering drawings, specifications and bills of material to:

1. design the build process,
2. create "as planned" bills of material, and
3. produce manufacturing planning.

Typically, many problems are found at this point. Unfortunately, just as typically, when these problems are cycled back to Engineering, the design people are working on a new project and there is not a lot of receptivity to Manufacturing requested changes.

Problems with Traditional Engineering

Traditional engineering results in a high degree of change following release. Opportunities for improved product manufacturability and supportability are difficult to realize using this traditional process. The traditional practices have resulted in the following problems:

1. Design accountability is poor because, to get into production, the design passes through many hands. Take Bill of Material accountability as an example. Engineering may be accountable for the accuracy of the As Designed Bill. In some cases, Engineering is not responsible and Configuration Management is responsible for the As Designed Bill. Manufacturing Engineering is accountable for the As Planned Bill and Quality Assurance is accountable for the As Built Bill. Who is responsible for the complete package?
2. Engineering is isolated from the effect of design practices on downstream functions and as a result, is not motivated to change design practices to improve the downstream functions. Further, there is a moving finish line for Engineering. The engineer thinks he is complete when the design is documented. Yet the downstream approvals create changes.
3. Lack of Manufacturing involvement in the design stages results in a high change rate following release. A high change environment increases product cost and increases obsolete inventory risk.
4. The serial design process coupled with multiple approvals "eats" lead time. This is lead time that Manufacturing and Engineering could use to meet customer commitments. Over consuming lead time in release and approvals forces Manufacturing and Engineering to work under compressed lead time conditions. This lead time compression coupled with a high change environment results in many changes done "on the fly." Changes done "on the fly" increase production and quality difficulties.
5. Adding to the lead time difficulty is the lack of Procurement and Materials Management participation in the early stages of design. A knowledge of sourcing and lead time problems is not considered when the design is created.

Control Problems

There are three major difficulties in traditional methods for controlling engineering activities.

- **Lack of Focus on Resource Requirements.** Traditional methods adequately determine the task sequence needed to accomplish engineering work. However, there is universally poor performance among engineering companies in estimating the resources required to accomplish these tasks. Typical of the "rule of thumb" methods is the practice of estimating requirements on the number and size of drawings that are to be produced. This approach overlooks issues such as technical risk, level of analysis required to support designs and software requirements.

- **Narrow Focus on Release Related Events.** A good deal of change activity involves design documentation, checking, configuration management, and release approval cycle activities. In many cases, design activity is an insignificant activity compared to the control of design activities. Unfortunately, the practice in many cases is to assume that all changes can be estimated and controlled through release related events and fundamental activities such as system architecture, system requirements definition, systems functional analysis, etc., are handled internal to the product engineering function.

- **No Common Engineering and Manufacturing Schedule.** Because of the separation of engineering activities from manufacturing, it is difficult in traditional engineering to establish a common schedule. Typically, scheduling starts by presenting a manufacturing need date to engineering. Just as typically, this date is rejected by engineering as being unachievable. A negotiation and expediting sequence follows and the expediting continues for the length of the project.

Concurrent Engineering

Concurrent Engineering is designed to address the problems of the traditional design and build process. The objectives of concurrent engineering are the following:

1. Reduce design through build cycle times.
2. Improve the quality of product designs.

Concurrent Engineering, as the name implies, converts the serial product and process design sequence into a concurrent, parallel process. Concurrent Engineering represents the application of the Just-in-Time philosophy to engineering. JIT's relentless pursuit of reduced inventory forces improved factory Quality. Concurrent Engineering's relentless reduction of cycle times forces improvement in design Quality.

A working definition of Concurrent Engineering is the following:

The integrated production of all the technical data needed to design, manufacture, test and support a product.

Concurrent Engineering comprises three main components.

- Teamwork
- Automation
- Analytical Tools.

Teamwork involves viewing product design and process design as a single design problem to be solved by multi-disciplined, cross-functional teams. Further, process design involves both the build process and the material acquisition process. Automation involves use of CAD, CAE, CASE, and CAM methods to support design and process integration. Analytical methods are used to optimize the product and process design through the use of formal techniques such as the Design of Experiments (DOE) and Design for Manufacturing (DFM).

Teamwork

Concurrent design teams comprise Design Engineering, Manufacturing Engineering, Test Engineering, Quality Engineering, Material Planning and Buyer functions. These functions comprise the core teams that stay intact during the product life cycle. Leadership of a team shifts as a function of the product life cycle. For example, in the early stages, when the emphasis is on requirements and product design, the Design Engineering representative would lead the team. Even though Design Engineering is leading the team, all the functions are involved in the early stages of the design. Because of this involvement, the ability to procure quality parts will influence the design, the ability to meet tolerances in production will influence the design, improvements in production capability needed to build the design will be started early so as to be ready when the design is released. As the design proceeds through its life cycle, leadership of the Concurrent Engineering team shifts. As pilot production starts, for example, the team would be led by Manufacturing Engineering. As the production sourcing and initial buy take place, the team could be led by Procurement. By keeping core teams intact throughout the life cycle, handoffs outside of the team are minimized. Product designs created in a Concurrent Engineering environment, because of this teamwork approach, represent designs that have been developed from considerations of customer functional requirements, manufacturability, testability, and procurability. One company, who is utilizing Concurrent Engineering, assigns all parts and assemblies on its product data base to a Concurrent Engineering team. Each Concurrent Engineering team has a team code that is used much in the same way a planner code is used. If a change is requested, the change is handled based on the Concurrent Engineering team code. In this company, the Concurrent Engineering teams comprise design engineering, manufacturing engineering, material planning and buying functions.

Analytical Tools

The analytical tool aspect of Concurrent Engineering improves the quality of both product and process design. Analytical tools include Design of Experiments (DOE), Quality Function Deployment (QFD), Statistical Process Control (SPC), and Design for Manufacturability (DFM). Process Capability (Spec Width/Process Width) is an important link between product design and process design. Design of Experiments and Design for Manufacturability help define the product parameters and tolerances that are critical to performance. Statistical Process Control determines the process width of the processes that create the important product parameters. Improved quality of design reduces the high change rate experienced with the traditional serial design methods. Further, improved tools reduce design cycle times that further reduce the change rate. Quality of product and process design improves Manufacturing's ability to work to both the design and the build plan, diminishing the need for substitution, alternates, and deviations.

Simplification and Complexity

Concurrent Engineering simplifies the post release process by insuring that manufacturing process requirements are incorporated in the product design. Concurrent Engineering complicates the pre-release process by requiring an increase in the number of tasks that must be performed prior to release and requiring that these tasks be executed in parallel.

Engineering Resource Planning

Definition and Scope

Engineering Resource Planning is a methodology for the planning and scheduling of the engineering resources needed to produce an engineering product. It is a methodology that is integrated with the Manufacturing Resource Planning (MRP II) system. Engineering Resource Planning involves the adaptation of MRP II principles and techniques to plan, schedule and control all the engineering activities needed to meet a company's sales and operation plans.

Engineering resources are not limited to design or product engineering but can include manufacturing engineering, test engineering, applications engineering, etc. Engineering products or deliverables include:
- Product drawings and specifications
- Tooling drawings and specifications
- Manufacturing process specifications
- Design studies and analysis
- Product and process software.

Engineering Resource Planning involves the application of the following Manufacturing Resource Planning (MRP II) Priority and Capacity Planning principles to engineering activities.
- Dependent demand and due dates equal to need dates
- Capacity requirements driven from a master schedule
- Required capacity equal to demonstrated capacity plus or minus planned changes
- Input/output control and dispatch lists.

Utilizing Engineering Resource Planning results in improved performance to schedule and improved engineering resource productivity.

Functional Overview

Engineering Resource Planning starts with the completion requirements for engineering deliverables, an Engineering Master Schedule. A product structure is developed that defines the engineering products and product sequence needed to meet the master schedule. The product structure and the deliverable requirements are combined in Engineering Planning to derive the completion dates for the products needed to meet the engineering master schedule. The product completion requirements are compared to available resources in Resource Planning. Once a proper match has been achieved between completion requirements and available resources, a resource plan and dispatch list are produced for each engineering work center. In Resource Tracking, resource consumption and progress to schedule is monitored and compared to plan. Delays and capacity problems are fed back to the Engineering Planning function or, if necessary, back to the engineering master schedule for resolution.

Engineering Resource Planning: A Concurrent Engineering Enabler

Enabling through Control

Engineering Resource Planning is a formal system for controlling engineering activities. This level of control must be in place prior to making fundamental changes in how engineering work is accomplished. Engineering Resource Planning provides the following three capabilities that enable the implementation of Concurrent Engineering.
1. Engineering Resource Planning formally links engineering and manufacturing to a common master schedule.
2. The Engineering Resource Planning integration of engineering and manufacturing activities improves the basis for teamwork.
3. Engineering Resource Planning can simulate the change from traditional engineering to Concurrent Engineering.

The Common Master Schedule

In manufacturing companies, engineering products are scheduled to meet a manufacturing need date. The manufacturing need date is when manufacturing must have engineering output in order to meet a customer commitment. For example, before parts can be ordered, drawings and specifications must be sent to suppliers. The manufacturing need date defines when the drawings and specifications must be released so that there is enough time to procure the parts. The need date is derived from the customer commitment date by backwards scheduling through the product lead time.

In the Class A company, all of the engineering activities in support of a customer commitment are integrated with the Manufacturing Planning and Control system. Engineering Resource Planning is the method for achieving this integration. Achieving this integration means that there is a company master scheduler instead of a master production scheduler. By using Engineering Resource Planning for engineering activities, engineering and manufacturing activities are planned and controlled using a common method. Following a common method means that engineering and manufacturing activities can be managed as a continuum. In this continuum, the manufacturing need date is derived from the master schedule using MRP. This manufacturing need date is compared to the engineering release date that is the output of the Engineering Resource Planning system. When operating to a common master schedule, discontinuities between the engineering output date and the manufacturing need date are resolved by the company master scheduler.

Traditional methods of planning and controlling engineering work don't directly link engineering activities and resources to a company master schedule. Traditional methods rely on the informal system of expediting to insure engineering output supports customer commitments. Informal systems do not handle change well. Concurrent Engineering requires that both engineering work content and sequence be changed. A change of this magnitude can easily overwhelm an informal control system. Implementing Concurrent Engineering without first ensuring that engineering activities and resources are formally linked to the company master schedule puts the company in danger of missing customer commitments.

Engineering and Manufacturing Integration

Traditional engineering shields much of the design activities from manufacturing problems and priorities. In the traditional engineering approach, manufacturing interfaces with engineering through the release function and perhaps some low level participation in design reviews. The Engineering Resource Planning integration of engineering and manufacturing activities in support of the company master schedule is an important step in fostering engineering/manufacturing teamwork. In an Engineering Resource Planning environment, the impact of both engineering and manufacturing on the master schedule and on meeting customer commitment is highly visible. Further, the impact of each function on the other function's ability to meet master schedule commitments also becomes visible. This visibility and working toward a common goal sets the basis for the manufacturing/engineering teamwork needed for successful Concurrent Engineering implementation.

Piloting Concurrent Engineering

The change from the traditional organization of engineering to Concurrent Engineering is a major change in how a company operates. From successful MRP II and JIT implementations, we have learned the value of simulating change and learning how to work in the new environment through the use of controlled pilots. Engineering Resource Planning can be used to simulate operation in the Concurrent Engineering environment by incorporating the following.

- **Product Structure**. Define Concurrent Engineering teams' output.
- **Templates**. Develop sequences of activities within Concurrent Engineering teams.
- **Work Center Definition**. Create work centers and define work center capacity based on the Concurrent Engineering environment.

The new Product Structure, Templates and Work Center definitions can be incorporated into the Engineering Resource Planning system. When the system is run, the Concurrent Engineering priorities and resource loading requirements can be determined. A portion of the company can be selected as a pilot and Engineering Resource Planning Resource Tracking used to compare predicted to actual performance and thus validate the Product Structures, Templates and Work Centers. By following this approach, the Concurrent Engineering environment can be simulated and pilots used to insure that the implementation approach is workable before the whole company is changed to Concurrent Engineering.

Engineering Resource Planning and Concurrent Engineering

Engineering Resource Planning applies Manufacturing Resource Planning priority and capacity planning techniques to engineering. Engineering Resource Planning integrates engineering activities in support of a customer commitment with the manufacturing planning and control system. Through Engineering Resource Planning, a company can manage both engineering and manufacturing from a common master schedule. This integration of engineering and manufacturing activities through a common master schedule leads logically to Concurrent Engineering. Once engineering and manufacturing activities are managed as a continuum, it is a logical next step to rearrange the work sequence to shorten cycle times and improve design quality.

Concurrent Engineering focuses on improving product and process design and cycle times by changing both the nature of the task performed and the sequence in which they occur. Concurrent Engineering is based on the performance of cross functional teams. Concurrent Engineering represents a major change in the way a company does business. To insure that the transformation from traditional engineering to Concurrent Engineering is managed and successful, Engineering Resource Planning should either be in place prior to the start of Concurrent Engineering or should be developed as the first step in Concurrent Engineering implementation.

A Company Implementation

Engineering Resource Planning

Engineering Resource Planning was implemented as part of the Martin Marietta Strategic Systems Company's successful effort to achieve the Class A level of performance as certified by the Oliver Wight Company. Strategic Systems produces Missile Systems. The company is very much engineering driven and reaching Class A required that engineering be heavily involved. Often, reaching Class A performance is seen as strictly a manufacturing department responsibility to be achieved through implementing an MRP II system as opposed to a process for achieving a specified level of performance. Class A achievement requires that all operating departments contribute to improving operating performance. Involving engineering required defining engineering's contribution to Class A performance and then providing engineering with a tool for improving engineering performance. That tool is Engineering Resource Planning.

In an engineering-driven company, Engineering must provide a significant contribution to Strategic Planning and Business Planning and be strongly involved in the Sales and Operations Planning process. New product introduction activities and engineering activities in support of a customer order must be integrated with manufacturing planning and control. Engineering must support properly structured bills of material and contribute to a 98% bill accuracy and contribute to an effective process for planning and controlling changes to existing products. Engineering must continually improve design quality, involve Manufacturing and Purchasing in product design and continually reduce product cycle times.

Martin Strategic Systems utilized Engineering Resource Planning to meet the requirement that new product introduction activities and engineering activities in support of a customer order must be integrated with manufacturing planning and control. Since implementing Engineering Resource Planning requires the involvement of Engineering management and involves a detailed analysis of how Engineering conducts business, Engineering Resource Planning was chosen as the lead activity for involving Engineering in the company's Class A process.

The Martin Strategic Systems implementation approach was to build on a manual system of Engineering Work Plans and to grow into Engineering Resource Planning. The plan started by automating work plan creation and performance tracking functions. Further, Martin expanded the scope of Engineering Resource Planning beyond that of the work plans to include all engineering activities, not just those associated with release.

The Engineering Resource Planning functional flow was used to define the software functional requirements. A

Personal Computer based Critical Path Method (CPM) tool called "Open Plan" was chosen as the software to implement Engineering Resource Planning. Using a CPM based tool as opposed to working with MRP software turned out to be an important choice. Engineering is accustomed to working with CPM tools and was not asked to adapt to MRP software and output.

The Engineering Resource Planning implementation was managed as a spinoff task force within the MRP II implementation. Education in priority and capacity planning principles was a major implementation effort and an Engineering Resource Planning conference room and live pilots were completed prior to going live. The live pilot was a bit more live than originally intended. The Engineering Resource Planning tool was used to handle the redesign associated with a launch problem.

Work started in April of 1990 when the Engineering Resource Planning implementation team was formed. A detailed review of Class A requirements for Engineering Resource Planning was completed in May. Education and training and software evaluation were started in May. A detail review of engineering work flow and estimating methods was started in April and continued for the duration of the project. This effort was the first to yield results as a review of engineering work flows resulted in several process improvements. The software selection was made in July and three months were spent with two programmers defining and implementing modifications. Initial piloting began in September and in December the live pilot was successfully completed by using Engineering Resource Planning to plan and control a quick response redesign. By the end of December, Engineering had met the Class A requirements and the whole company was certified Class A in April of 1991.

Implementing the Common Master Schedule

Strategic Systems established the operating structure needed for a common master schedule as pan of reaching Class A. Engineering management is fully involved in the company Sales and Operation Planning process and involved in establishing the Common Master Schedule as previously described. Martin uses MAC/PAC/D for MRP II software and as mentioned previously, a Martin modified version of the PC-based "Open Plan" for Engineering Resource Planning. Manufacturing need dates are calculated in MAC/PAC. An extract of need dates is fed down to a PC file. The engineering deliverables completion dates are calculated in the Engineering Resource Planning "Open Plan" and compared to the manufacturing need date extracted from MRP II. Engineering Administration and Master Scheduling continually monitor completion dates versus need dates and operate to resolve differences. Master Scheduling is a combined Engineering Administration and Master Production Scheduling function. Consideration is being given to creating a consolidated function but for now Engineering Administration working with Master Scheduling is providing satisfactory results.

Concurrent Engineering

Implementing Concurrent Engineering involves a high investment of time and money. Concurrent Engineering involves major culture changes. For these reasons, Martin chose not to implement Concurrent Engineering on mature projects. Instead Martin chose to establish Engineering Resource Planning on mature projects to get the tool operating and to develop proficiency in its use. Concurrent Engineering was to be implemented on new work. That is exactly what is happening. Larry Roubidoux, this paper's co-presenter and the architect of the Martin Engineering Resource Planning system used in Strategic Systems, is in the process of applying Engineering Resource Planning in conjunction with implementing Concurrent Engineering on a new project.

The Martin Company has gained proficiency with the Oliver Wight method of achieving operational improvement, namely:
- Top Management commitment and involvement
- Education
- Performance Specification
- Proven Path Implementation

The Oliver Wight methodology is being applied to Concurrent Engineering implementation. Top management is involved, education in Concurrent Engineering, Engineering Resource Planning, Design for Manufacturability and High Performance Work Teams is occurring. A version of the ABCD Checklist has been created to establish the performance to be achieved and a steering committee, project team operation established.

Conclusions

The present competitive business climate requires that product and delivery cycle times continually improve. To meet this requirement realistically, Engineering and Manufacturing must be managed as a continuum of tasks and activities executed in a Concurrent Engineering process. To be managed as a continuum, Engineering and Manufacturing must have common scheduling and capacity management tools. For some time, Manufacturing functions have been using MRP II tools for priority and capacity planning. Through the implementation of Engineering Resource Planning, Engineering can apply MRP II priority and capacity planning principles to managing Engineering.

Managing Engineering and Manufacturing utilizing common priority and capacity planning tools means it is now possible to create a common master schedule to drive and control both functions. Implementation of this capability requires that both Engineering and Manufacturing change some business practices. Implementing the common master schedule as part of an overall improvement project designed to bring the company to the Class A level of performance will insure that the needed changes are made successfully. The common Master Schedule establishes the engineering and manufacturing continuum. The next logical step once the engineering and manufacturing continuum is established is to compress the lead times within this continuum. This compression in turn leads logically to Concurrent Engineering.

The Martin company is following this logical progression of Engineering Resource Planning, Common Master Schedule, Engineering and Manufacturing Continuum, Concurrent Engineering to reduce product lead times drastically and improve design quality.

References

1. Edison, Norris, "Engineering Resource Planning Principles," APICS National 1991.
2. Gillen, Thomas, "Engineering Resource Planning an Enabler of Concurrent Engineering," LA-ADSIG 1991.
3. Gillen, Thomas, "Integrated Engineering/Manufacturing Scheduling," APICS National 1991.

4. Gillen, Thomas, "Common Master Schedule and Concurrent Engineering," LA-ADSIG 1992.
5. Gillen, Thomas, "Concurrent Engineering Answers Bill of Material Ownership Issues," A & D Washington Symposium March 1991.

About the Authors

Larry Roubidoux is Chief of Engineering Planning and Administration for the Strategic Systems Company, a Denver based division of the Martin Marietta Corporation. Larry has been responsible for developing the Engineering Resource Planning concepts, selecting the software and leading the Engineering Resource Planning implementation for Strategic Systems. Larry has been responsible for ensuring that the Engineering Resource Planning effort supported the overall Strategic Systems Class A achievement. Larry is also in charge of ensuring that Engineering Resource Planning and Scheduling supports the company Sales and Operations Plans and is compatible with the master production schedule. Larry is now developing the Engineering Resource Planning system to support the Concurrent Engineering implementation on a new project for Martin Marietta.

Larry has spent the last eleven years working for the Martin Company in various capacities and assignments.

Larry has a Bachelor of Arts degree from Western New Mexico University.

Tom Gillen is an Oliver Wight principal, a founder of two electronics companies and has over 20 years of engineering, operational and executive experience. Tom helps companies compete effectively and achieve superior operating results. Tom assists companies with the following:
1. Operating Strategy development and implementation paying particular attention to Product Development and Engineering and Manufacturing integration.
2. Continuous Improvement of Cycle Times, Asset Returns, Operating Margins and Customer Satisfaction through the application of Class A Product Development principles and techniques, such as Concurrent Engineering and Engineering Resource Planning, and the application of TQM, JIT and MRP II principles and techniques.

Tom has worked with such companies as General Dynamics, Martin Marietta, Xerox, Beckman, Solar Turbines, Singer-Kearfott, ITT, and Square D. Tom has a Bachelor's degree in Electrical Engineering from Manhattan College and a Master's degree in Industrial Management from the Polytechnic Institute of Brooklyn. He is certified at the Fellow level in Production and Inventory Management by the American Production and Inventory Control Society.

Reprinted from the 1987 APICS International Conference Proceedings.

Integrating Planning and Execution Through Contemporary Handling Systems

John M. Hill

Dramatic changes have occurred in the U.S. material handling market since 1979. These changes are due in large part to a broader understanding within the user community of the impact of material handling throughout manufacturing, warehousing and distribution. The relative size of the large scale automated storage system market has diminished in the past five years with the trend toward lower inventories and "just-in-time" delivery. Users and suppliers now think in terms of modular systems that link such tools of automation as guided vehicles, carousels and transporters in smaller configurations that are more adaptable to changing business conditions and product mix. Further, recognizing that increased throughput, tighter inventory control and lower per unit handling costs are keys to survival, conventional warehouses as well as manufacturing stores operations in the U.S. are adopting new packaged information and control systems that can be installed, modified and expanded quickly and less expensively.

Background

The most significant development in the United States material handling market in the past fifteen years is user recognition of improved inventory control as a tangible basis for handling system investment. Control of raw materials, work-in-process and finished goods inventories from warehouse receipt to customer shipment is fundamental to effective operations management in any industry—in any country. Tighter stock control leads to faster order turnaround, improved use of people, facilities and equipment, lower inventory investment, and reduced costs.

The foregoing is not a new perspective; nor is inventory management a new concept. What has changed in the past few years, however, is American industry's understanding of the impact of improved inventory management on corporate profitability—the growing evidence that the impact can be quantified—and that material handling can play a critical role in the equation. Although handling systems suppliers, academicians and consultants have agreed on this point for years, the majority of U.S. investment in these systems has been justified on the basis of space and labor savings alone. Why is the pattern changing?

Knowledgeable U.S. managers have recognized for some time that material handling represents from 30% to 80% of typical operating costs. Until recently, however, handling had been viewed as an unavoidable adjunct to value-adding processes—a necessary evil that all too frequently took last place on the capital budget priority list. This perception was inadvertently reinforced in the late 1970s with the flood of reports in the trade and business press on declining U.S. productivity. Articles focused almost exclusively on the manufacturing sector, its aging facilities, outmoded machinery and techniques, and a de-motivated U.S. workforce. An average annual productivity growth rate of .4% during the 1970s supported the concern. Indeed, during the same period, U.S. warehousing productivity averaged .5%. While some talked of the inevitability of continued erosion of the United States' industrial base, others set out to find solutions.

Next, we heard glowing reports from overseas about Kanban, Just-in-Time and the Automatic Factory that promised:

"An unmanned, unlighted, marginally heated plant that devours raw materials delivered moments before they are needed and converts them into finished products that are immediately loaded for customer shipment."

With the help of Hollywood, "reprogrammable, multi-function manipulators" or robots soon joined the list of solutions. And, of course, everyone had to have one. From the data processing sector, material requirements planning or MRP emerged as the answer for the inventory control portion of the equation; and many companies plunged forward with adoption, ill-prepared for the costs associated with faulty implementation, inaccurate forecasts, production miscues, day-, week-, or month-old reports, etc.

During this period, little press was given to the potential contribution of material handling systems except for the more exotic applications of guided vehicles and the massive AS/RS installations of the mid-1970s. Similarly, the concept of integrated systems, though intellectually within grasp, was infrequently emphasized as a fundamental goal for productivity improvement programs. The three-year period from 1980 to the end of 1982 was a difficult one for a good portion of American industry. Budgets for capital expenditures were particularly tight and payback criteria stringent. During this period, U.S. material handling equipment sales dropped more than 40% (from approximately $10 billion to under $6 billion). At the same time, however, robotic equipment sales grew from under $50 million to $190 million and MRP sales exploded to over 3000 systems with a total of $1.35 billion. The statistics support my contention that, in the rush to turn the corner on declining productivity, many users looked to specific pieces of value adding equipment or batch oriented, not real-time, data processing systems, i.e., piecemeal solutions that addressed part, not all, of the problem.

The result? Isolated islands of automation and/or output from data processing too old to be useful for real-time management of actual operations. I do not mean to suggest that managers were unaware of the benefits of integration of a fuller complement of equipment and systems, but, rather, that limited budgets and narrowly focused payback criteria forced them to allocate funds to those areas where apparent savings could be more readily identified. As these partial solutions were implemented, it became clear that:

- Although initial attempts at solving the productivity problem may have produced marginal returns, the time-worn alternatives of "more inventory" or "more people"—even if economically feasible—were simply no longer acceptable;
- No MRP system can deliver the expected benefits without real-time visibility of actual transactions at receiving, in storage, in production and at the shipping dock;
- No amount of equipment or systems can obscure omission of the fundamentals of materials management in the development of any industrial automation project;
- The value of increased throughput on production machinery is a direct function of the adequacy of the delivery system that supports it;
- Flexibility, integration and control would be the cornerstones of future systems designed to meet the needs of fast-moving manufacturers in an increasingly competitive world market.

With a better appreciation of the foregoing, both the press and users began to talk in terms of computer-integrated manufacturing (CIM), flexible manufacturing systems (FMS) and, more recently, computer-integrated logistics (CIL) and flexible material management (FMM). In each case, flexibility, integration and control provide the framework for the particular technologies that form the discipline—and material handling plays an increasingly prominent role by providing the disciplined environment critical to effective implementation of the integrated system.

In the following pages, the impact of this shift in perspective upon various segments of the U.S. material handling industry will be examined. As a baseline, it should be noted that industry sales have rebounded from the 1982 low point, growing some 40% since that time, but with a considerably different composition. As painful as the 1980-82 period was for the typical supplier, the opportunities for those survivors and newcomers who have adapted their products for contemporary integrated manufacturing systems have never been greater. Indeed, the installed base of major automated handling systems in the factory is expected to grow from 700 in 1984 to 5805 in 1990, a compound annual growth rate of 58.2%. Further, these developments have positive implications for those charged with warehousing and distributing raw materials and finished products to and from not only the "just-in-time" manufacturer, but also all of those manufacturers who recognize the bottom-line value of the concept.

MH Systems Focus: Discipline

Trends toward shorter production runs, lower inventory levels and "doing the job right the first time" preclude operations management on the basis of historical performance reports. Given realistic productivity, product quality and customer service goals, the difference between success and shortfall will be heavily influenced by:

- The administrative discipline provided by the systems and procedures used for order processing, production planning, purchasing and related corporate functions;

- The process discipline provided by computer-aided design, computer-aided engineering, statistical process control and other subsystems and equipment that target upon lower cost, higher quality production;
- The material management discipline provided by the handling system that receives, moves, stores and controls "assets in process" throughout the entire operation;
- The accuracy and timeliness of information exchange between the handling, process and administrative disciplines—and, the speed and quality of response to anomalies, exceptions and opportunities for improved performance.

Material handling equipment and system developments in the past few years have been highlighted by enhancements that not only improve control of physical material flow, but also management visibility of real-time operations. Developments fall into one or more of the following areas:

- Identification: Bar code, RF, machine vision, radio data terminals
- Movement: Conveyors, guided vehicles, lift trucks, robotics
- Storage: AS/RS, mini-load, carousel, tote stacker
- Controls: Sensors, computers, programmable controllers, packaged and custom software

Of particular significance is the attention given to the three driving forces mentioned earlier: flexibility, integration and control. Equipment modularity and the thrust toward standardization are also characteristics of the new family of systems and equipment. The following paragraphs highlight some of these trends.

Identification

Bar Code

Few technologies have had as long a gestation period as automatic identification. About the same time Wiley Post made his solo flight around the world (1933), initial patents covering the use of optical sensors for automatic package sortation were issued in Switzerland. For the next thirty years, the primary focus of identification technology was in the area of direct machine control—from conveyor line sorting to automatic bobbin replenishment in textile mills. In the early 1960s, pioneering efforts associated with optical systems for railcar identification and automatic checkout at grocery supermarkets suggested the information potential of such systems for item tracking in factories, warehouses and distribution centers. Initial applications of these early code reading systems in industry (Volkswagen, 1969 and General Motors, 1971) were justified solely on the basis of labor savings associated with production counting—not the value of increased inventory accuracy—and usage grew slowly. A second constraint on growth was supplier reluctance to collaborate on code or symbol standards for industrial applications. The situation began to change in the late 1970s with user-initiated pressure for standards. Today, formal standards have been promulgated by the U.S. Department of Defense, the American National Standards Institute and such industry organizations as the Automotive Industry Action Group, the Health Industry Bar Code Council, the National Association of Wholesaler Distributors, etc. The standards include specifications for the alphanumeric "Three of Nine" code and the numeric "Interleaved Two of Five" code. It is estimated that the industrial market for these systems is now growing at a better than 30% annual rate with industry associations, user groups, seminars, shows and conferences adding fuel to the fire. Primary developments in the bar code area include:

- **Autodiscrimination**: the ability of decoding electronics to automatically recognize, read and verify multiple symbol formats.
- **Hand-Held Laser Scanners**: light weight, non-contact portable code readers that provide greater operator flexibility.
- **Omnidirectional Laser Scanners**: fixed-position readers capable of reading a code regardless of its orientation.
- **Expanded Coding Capabilities**: from computer-controlled dot-matrix printers to laser-etching for printed circuit boards and castings when standard printing or labeling cannot survive the process environment.

Other Identification Technology

The growth of bar code reading systems as important tools for productivity improvement has rekindled interest in a variety of non-optical techniques for automatic and operator-driven real-time data entry including radio frequency, surface acoustical wave, magnetic stripe and voice recognition systems as well as mobile radio data terminals. Further, in concert with the growth of robotics, machine vision is rapidly emerging as a potential alternative for a number of applications.

Identification systems are a vital element in the mix of solutions available for improved factory and warehouse productivity. As such and in that they provide the window for management on operational performance, their careful consideration in the early stages of design can make significant contributions to operational control and system integrity.

Movement

The variety of alternatives available for moving materials could fill a library. Our focus in the following paragraphs will be on those developments that bear directly upon providing users with tighter control of inventories, flexibility and the potential for more fully integrated systems.

- **Lift Trucks**: Lift truck sales in the U.S. have not recovered from their plunge from 109, 000 units in 1979 to 62, 000 units in 1982. Although considerable press has been given to the encroachment of overseas competition, the fact is that users are now turning to other means of horizontal transportation. To meet the challenge, U.S. manufacturers are adding:
- **Two-Way Mobile Radio Data Terminals** (RDTs) that permit computer-controlled dispatching and operator performance monitoring;
- **On-Board Controllers** that permit automatic height positioning and other features that allow integration of conventional operations with computer-based systems.
  Given these enhancements and the demands for flexibility, we see a continuing significant role for narrow-aisle vehicles that present a cost-effective alternative to aisle-captive automated storage and retrieval systems. Further, these enhancements offer current users the opportunity to upgrade existing operations without major new capital outlays.
- **Automatic Guided Vehicles**: The AGV market in the U.S. is currently growing at a 30% annual rate after more than twenty years of relatively modest growth. Primary reasons include AGV flexibility and the relative simplicity

of its integration with computer-based systems. Trends highlighted in a recent report include:
- Growing use of AGVs as mobile work platforms that carry work to various assembly stations.
- Fork-equipped vehicles that lift and stack loads to various heights.
- Special-purpose designs for applications in specific industries, e.g., newsprint handling, "clean room" handling in disk drive and semiconductor production.
- Other designs that integrate on-board robots, manipulators, conveyors, turntables and other devices to fit the user's particular requirement.
- Significant improvement in the cost and reliability of control software including user-friendly routines that minimize the complexity of guidepath or vehicle routing changes.

We also expect to see increasing progress on off-the-guidepath travel and related installation cost reduction. Accordingly, there's little question of continuing growth for AGVs as flexible alternatives to fixed path systems.

- **Conveyors**: Flexibility, integration and control have been the watchwords for U.S. conveyor industry development of new family of modular systems to support kitting and small parts assembly in the electronics and other industries. These systems—often called transporters—are characterized by:
- Chain or belt driven bi-directional transport conveyors;
- Microprocessor-controlled, single or double air-transfers that can be easily moved or interchanged;
- Preassembled modules (i.e., beds, transfers and workstations delivered with integral air, electrical and communications lines) to speed installation and simplify maintenance as well as adaptation for new requirements;
- Low noise level and "clean room" compatibility;
- Direct communication with operator workstations and user host computers.

The integration of these systems with contemporary small parts storage systems has led to significant improvement in throughput control, inventory reduction and space utilization for such companies as Priam (disc drive manufacturer), Westinghouse and others.

Storage

While the trend towards just-in-time delivery has lessened demand for large scale automated storage systems in the manufacturing sector, it has also fostered growth and innovation in other storage system approaches including mini-load, micro-load, tote stackers and vertical and horizontal carousels. Further, demand for unit load systems for finished goods warehousing has held fairly constant and computer control has found a niche in conventional flow rack picking systems. Let's briefly review some of the more significant trends.

- **Unit Load AS/RS**: Primary developments in this area are those associated with optimization of throughput or transaction rates through simulation and software that maximizes productivity on the basis of operation-specific requirements; e.g., first-on, last-off trailer loading, etc. There is also a move towards upgrading or retrofitting older storage systems with contemporary software, automatic identification equipment and interfaces with automatic guided vehicle subsystems.
- **Mini-Loads, Micro-Loads, and Tote Stackers**: With smaller inventories, parts and kit control for manufacturing operations has never been more critical. Primary

users in the United States today are the automotive, airline and electronics industries although appliance manufacturers, parts distributors and others are showing increased interest. Current trends include:

- Increased reliability: 97% uptime and six to seven years before major overhaul is normally required.
- Lateral as well as end-of-aisle input and output stations for assembly operations.
- Lower software costs with increased focus upon "velocity loading" and higher transaction rates.
- Standardization or "preengineered" hardware and software modules targeted at reducing costs and delivery time.
- Designs that are somewhat easier to relocate than earlier versions.

• **Carousels**: Often characterized as "the poor man's AS/RS," vertical and horizontal carousels are quickly becoming an important element in integrated systems. In fact, in a recent survey of some thirty applications where miniload or carousels could have been used, the carousel generally offered a higher return-on-investment. Like the competitive alternatives, carousels offer significant productivity improvement potential by bringing the "pick location" to the worker. Combining carousels with transporters, robotic loaders and unloaders and other devices offers not only faster, more efficient material flow to kitting and production, but also the tighter stock control that permits reduction of inventory.

Other features that assure carousels of a continuing role in contemporary manufacturing and distribution include:

1. Low maintenance costs—often as little as .1 % of the unit's original cost per year;
2. Modularity and flexibility—systems can be installed, relocated and expanded (through module additions) more readily than other AS/RS;
3. The appearance of innovative designs such as the horizontal carousels whose tiers move independently for increased throughput;
4. Continued developments in basic controls, interfaces and standard software.

Controls

The evolution of controls for material handling and material management applications in the past few years has been mind boggling. In addition to refinement of sensors, motor starters, communication links, etc., for direct machine control, the advances in computer hardware and software have been significant; and, their role in future systems solidly assured. Indeed, the demand for automated handling systems mentioned earlier is expected to produce the following results for suppliers of programmable logic controllers and minicomputers:

Installed Units	1984	1990
AMH Systems	700	5805
Prog. Controllers	5531	29438
Minicomputers	1000	7508

Given the foregoing, there is little doubt that the growth of automated handling systems is intimately linked with the growth of real-time information systems in the plant or warehouse environment.

As impressive as the projections may be, however, there is one other important consideration. The installed base of MRP systems in the United States is expected to grow from about 21, 000 to over 143,000 units. Although an over simplification, one could come to the conclusion that by 1990 well over 100,000 MRP users will be managing their inventories without the discipline provided by an integrated, computer-controlled handling system or the benefits of real-time feedback such a system can provide. This conclusion ignores the probability of installation of identification subsystems, radio data terminals, etc., in conventional facilities for inventory transaction monitoring, but even if the numbers are discounted by 50%, it highlights the fact that user awareness of the benefits of integrated systems is still in its infancy.

Part of the problem has been the apparent simplicity of batch-oriented MRP systems and their implementation. As experienced practitioners have learned, the converse is more frequently true. Furthermore, MRP may not be the best solution for every company—consider its utility for companies with new products with undefined demand—but material control certainly is!

The primary distinction between batch-oriented systems and real-time systems is that the former emphasize planning and scorekeeping, while the latter focus upon execution and winning the game. Effective material control depends upon the accuracy and timeliness of information exchange at and between the operations level and other elements of the corporate hierarchy. In the absence of standards for such exchange, it is not difficult to understand the appeal of early MRP systems that ran on existing and familiar data processing hardware and provided more useful output than had been previously available. Constraints on the growth of integrated, real-time material control systems have included:

• Computer hardware capacity and costs;
• Incompatible communication interfaces, protocols and standards;
• Resistance from corporate data processing personnel who were persuaded that batch approaches were sufficient;
• Lack of top management support.
• Myopic payback criteria.

Further, early attempts at implementing integrated material control systems were hampered by:

• The cost, complexity and delays associated with custom real-time software development,
• Problems with systems that combined machine control and inventory management on undersized computers with low transaction processing speed, and
• Little system flexibility to accommodate changes in product mix, scheduling, routing, etc.

No one denies that the availability of flexible standard software packages for real-time material control will substantially reduce the risks and accelerate adoption. Indeed, such packages are fundamental to extension of the benefits of this control beyond the limited set of larger companies now enjoying them. Given a family of modules from which a user can select those features that address his particular needs, we should expect to see a dramatic increase in integrated systems usage for years to come.

The practical challenge to standard package development has been definition of and agreement upon the basic functions that such packages should include and, then, the optional features that would extend their utility to a broader group of prospective users. Given the availability of such packages, the next issue is user willingness to unemotionally assess the trade-offs between a packaged system that may address 80% to 90% of his requirements and the custom alternative, tailored just for him, but at substantially higher cost. Considerable progress has been made on both fronts in the past couple of years. Let's take a look at a couple of these systems:

- **Conventional Warehouse Systems**: The genesis of packaged real-time material control software was in the conventional warehouse. A primary reason for this was that such a system could provide measurable benefits on its own without the need for direct linkage to a corporate host computer. Orders and shipping instructions were manually entered and operations summary reports printed on site for subsequent transfer to corporate management.

The focus of these systems is upon tracking materials from receipt to storage, stock location record maintenance, pick generation and inventory adjustment upon shipment. In the conventional facility, communications with supervisory personnel are generally via printers and CRTs, and with order pickers via hand-held or lift truck-mounted radio data terminals (RDTs). Most of the systems being installed today do have a batch or real-time communications link to the user's host computer.

In operation, the systems accept orders from the host while stock receipts are entered via CRTs at receiving. The systems organize daily activities and allocate work on the basis of demand and available resources. Operators receive tasks via RDT to store, move or pick materials. They confirm completion of each task before the systems will assign the next activity. Inventory files are updated by item and location upon completion of each transaction. Reports are generated routinely and on demand for supervisory personnel. All transactions are recorded on an inventory transaction log that is periodically transferred to the host.

Other features of these systems are:
- System or operator selection of storage location
- Shipment planning
- Item reservation and quarantine
- Batch or single order picking
- Kit picking
- Stock relocation
- Forward pick area replenishment
- Cycle counting
- Back-order and cross-dock handling
- Lot control
- Productivity analysis

System benefits include the ability to interleave material storage, picking, replenishment and inventory checking on a single lift truck cycle, thereby eliminating deadheading and increasing operator and vehicle productivity. Reductions of better than 30% to 40% are not uncommon. The elimination of paperwork and increased inventory accuracy are also cited as primary sources of payback. The modular construction of the systems permits the addition of both software features and hardware to meet expanding requirements with minimal disruption of operations. Further, most systems permit the user to generate additional reports peculiar to his specific requirements. Initial installations of these systems suggest potential cost savings of 30-40% when compared with custom alternatives, and delivery times are as short as three to four months.

- **Material Control Systems and Mechanization and Manufacturing**: In the past year, the functions we've just reviewed have been repackaged for use within the manufacturing environment. As opposed to communicating with lift truck operators via RDT, these systems communicate with the programmable controllers and micro-processors that control the storage and delivery of materials to and from workstations or the assembly line. Characteristics of these systems include the applicable warehouse system functions noted above and the following:
  - Work-order check-in and release,
  - Workload allocation,
  - Workstation communications and control,
  - Routing optimization, and
  - Material handling device control.

Essentially, these systems provide a real-time bridge between batch-oriented manufacturing planning or MRP and the factory floor. They are not a replacement for MRP, but rather the complement to it that closes the loop on fully integrated material control.

Conclusions and Caveats

Fifteen years ago at a material handling seminar, a speaker stressed the importance of totally integrated manufacturing and distribution operations, noting that the materials handling system for the future must be able to respond to automatically generated material management commands—and that the response must be fast enough to satisfy the particular requirements of the overall operation. Later, at a packaging show, a plant manager warned that success in automating and speeding material flow had too often been dimmed by the absence of a parallel effort aimed at obtaining real-time information and operation status from the line.

Borrowing a word from the manufacturing sector, I submit that the catch phrase for the next fifteen years and beyond will be Flexible Material Management—and, as you have heard, that the tools now exist to profitably manage both information and material flow—for small companies as well as large—for warehouse managers as well as plant superintendents.

Make no mistake, however. These systems are not solutions for inadequacies in requirements analysis or system design; nor are they a substitute for basic discipline in current material or information flow—or slipshod management.

In dealing with control of assets-in-process, objective analysis may point towards full or selective automation—or, in some cases, hardly any automation at all. The issue is simply what combination of people, equipment and systems will provide you with the level of flexibility and control your operation demands. In other words, whether user or supplier, pioneer or apostle, each of us has an obligation to keep an eye on the basics and our feet on the ground in our headlong rush towards the factory or warehouse of the future.

About the Author

John M. Hill is Chairman of Logisticon, Inc. As 1980 President of the U.S. Material Handling Institute, Inc., he has also served as president of the Material Handling Education Foundation, Inc., an officer of The International Material Management Society and a member of the College Industry Council on Material Handling Education. Logisticon is a California-based developer of real-time material control systems.

Reprinted from the Production and Inventory Management Journal, *Fourth Quarter, 1992.*

Process Flow Scheduling in a High-Volume Repetitive Manufacturing Environment

Darryl T. Hubbard, CPIM, Sam G. Taylor, Ph.D., and Steven F. Bolander, Ph.D.

Process flow scheduling (PFS) is a technique that uses the process structure to guide scheduling calculations for groups of products. Taylor and Bolander [2,6] recently introduced and documented process flow scheduling concepts with case studies from Scott Paper, EG&G, Eastman Kodak, and Coors Brewing. These process industry cases formed the foundation for a statement of PFS principles [7]. In this article, the use of PFS principles in a repetitive manufacturing environment will be illustrated.

Scheduling Environment

The Sylvania Lighting Division—U.S. is part of GTE Corporation's Electrical Products Group. Sylvania Lighting produces a wide range of lighting products including incandescent, fluorescent, quartz, high intensity discharge, and various other specialty lamp types. The scope of this article is limited to a representative group of straight fluorescent lamps that are produced on a high-volume line at the Danvers, Massachusetts, lighting plant. The basic concepts described are applicable at all the lighting plants, with some variation expected due to the characteristics of each product line's process structure.

The Product

Schematic drawings of a fluorescent lamp are shown in **Figure 1**, which illustrate how a low-pressure mercury vapor arc is used to generate invisible ultraviolet energy. This energy is absorbed by the phosphor coating on the inside of the glass tube that transforms the energy into visible light.

The subject production line is dedicated to a specific base configuration and produces over 100 end items of varying lengths, light output, and color. For each length lamp, ranging from as small as two feet to as long as eight, there are two light output levels offered (denoted as either option "A" or "B" in this example). The "A" or "B" light output of a certain length lamp is determined by the mount assembly, which consists of the cathode, lead-in wires, stem press, and exhaust tube, illustrated in Figure 1. Mount assemblies for operation "A,"

which represents over 85% of the line's volume, are made on in-line equipment and coded as phantom assemblies. Mounts for option "B" are made off-line and inventoried.

This line and its products are a "family group" in Sylvania's planning systems. The lamps in this family share the same base style and are all one and one-half inches in diameter. Using group technology (an engineering and manufacturing philosophy that identifies the sameness of parts, equipment, or processes), the family group is divided into twelve "manufacturing groups" based on the length of the lamp and its rated light output level (option "A" or "B"), which facilitates effective planning and scheduling. Manufacturing groups may also be separated into subgroups by color (cool white, warm white, daylight, etc.) or by packing quantity to further increase scheduling efficiencies on the line. Individual lamp types are represented at the lowest level of this product planning hierarchy.

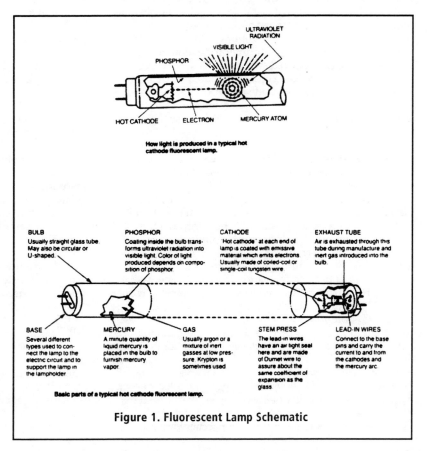

Figure 1. Fluorescent Lamp Schematic

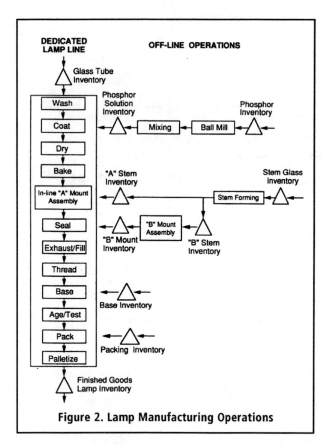

DEDICATED LAMP LINE

Glass Tube Inventory

Wash

Coat

Dry

Bake

In-line "A" Mount Assembly

Seal

Exhaust/Fill

Thread

Base

Age/Test

Pack

Palletize

Finished Goods Lamp Inventory

OFF-LINE OPERATIONS

Phosphor Solution Inventory — Mixing — Ball Mill — Phosphor Inventory

"A" Stem Inventory

Stem Forming — Stem Glass Inventory

"B" Mount Inventory — "B" Mount Assembly — "B" Stem Inventory

Base Inventory

Packing Inventory

Figure 2. Lamp Manufacturing Operations

Process Description

Sylvania Lighting's high-volume operations are excellent examples of repetitive manufacturing. The APICS Dictionary [1] defines repetitive manufacturing as the "production of discrete units, planned and executed to a schedule, usually at high speeds and volumes. Material tends to move in a continuous flow during production, but different items may be produced sequentially within that flow."

The production process consists of the dedicated line with in-line mount equipment and several off-line operations. As shown in **Figure 2**, the line is an integrated operation designed for the high-volume assembly of a specific lamp family. Two or three shifts of production are scheduled per day based on need, with lamps being produced at the rate of roughly 40 per minute. The projected replacement cost of this line would be well in the millions of dollars.

Sylvania Lighting has used some JIT concepts in the design and operation of its high-volume production lines and is continuing its efforts to achieve the JIT goals of low cost, flexible production. Materials flow through the lines in a JIT manner with no decoupling inventory between operations. This permits the entire line to be scheduled as a single unit or cell, although it consists of many machines and personnel performing various assembly operations.

A principal difficulty in implementing JIT is setup reductions. Although the benefits of fast changes are well recognized and efforts to reduce setup times have been undertaken, setup times must still be considered in the planning and scheduling process. Changing the lamp length for the entire line may take several hours while changing the light output level (for mount assembly "A" or "B") within a given length requires a fraction of an hour. Changing among colors or packing to produce the individual lamp types takes several minutes. These setups, which can negatively impact capacity, efficiencies, and quality, follow the group technology structure

previously described. However, when the timing and sequence of setups are optimized, the line's cost performance is at its best. Following this strategy allows manufacturing to produce high-quality lighting products with the lowest possible unit costs.

Planning and Scheduling Systems Development

Sylvania Lighting's planning and scheduling systems were being developed while the MRP crusade was still largely focused on the discrete order, job-shop environment where every end item was planned independently of the others. Early job-shop MRP systems were designed to primarily plan and control materials, with capacity (assumed to be infinite and/or highly flexible) being considered as an afterthought. Adopting those rules to the group technology environment with its dedicated high-volume production lines would have threatened Sylvania Lighting's product quality and low cost objectives. It was also felt that the volume of transactions needed to plan and control production via job-shop methods would require an inordinate amount of clerical support and result in more reams of paper.

For the above reasons, Sylvania Lighting aggressively pursued the development of proprietary planning and scheduling systems that recognized both the capacity constraints and competitive advantages unique to high-volume repetitive manufacturing. This evolutionary process, which now includes commercial software where advantageous, has resulted in the systems configuration described herein. The challenge for the 1990s is to continue total quality and JIT programs and provide a computer-integrated logistics planning system from order entry, through the distribution network, to manufacturing that will reduce the investment in finished-goods inventory while still maximizing customer satisfaction.

Production Planning Practices

Production and inventory planning, a centralized responsibility of marketing's customer-support function, manages the aggregate inventory levels for all product lines by participating in the sales and operations planning process. Planning at the end-item level is also done by this group, with high-volume lamp types planned for weekly production to minimize inventory carrying costs and to maintain a flow through the distribution pipeline. Lower volume types are planned in monthly buckets and cycled to achieve the lowest sum of carrying and setup costs. Minimum inventory levels for each lamp type are planned by the distribution planning system, taking critical customer-service measures into account.

Run lengths for each manufacturing group are planned based on customer demands, production rates, setup times, and inventory carrying costs. Planned runs for a group may be rounded to full-shift increments to increase operating efficiencies in the plant. Distribution network requirements are used to determine if a lamp type needs to be produced in the given planning period. If so, a production run for the lamp's manufacturing group is planned, though all types in the group may not need to be replenished. The specific quantity of each type to be run in the planned setup is determined based on current and future network requirements, economic minimum runs, and manufacturing group cycles.

Quantities are calculated so that the runout time for all items being run in the joint setup is equalized. This procedure is similar to that described by Taylor and Bolander

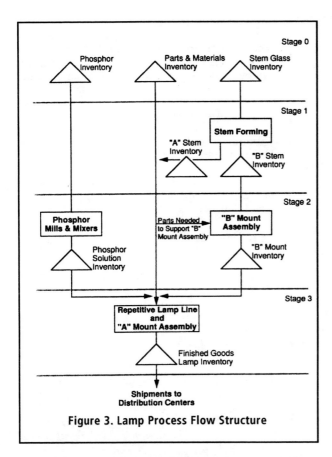

Figure 3. Lamp Process Flow Structure

[5]. More importantly, this tactical use of joint replenishment with equal runout optimizes the total of setup, run, and inventory carrying costs for the group while still meeting the critical business goal of having the right products available to provide customer satisfaction throughout the distribution network.

Due to the high degree of commonality in components, labor and equipment resources used by the family/manufacturing groups, the production plans may be net changed to respond to the demands of the marketplace. The next step, production scheduling at the plants, is primarily concerned with developing detailed schedules that will meet each item's planning requirements on time, in an efficient manner.

Production Scheduling Practices

Sylvania Lighting's production scheduling practices incorporates some of the basic principles of process flow scheduling [7]:

1. Scheduling calculations are guided by the product's process structure.
2. Single stages are scheduled using processor-dominated scheduling (PDS) or material-dominated scheduling (MDS) approaches.
3. Process trains are scheduled using reverse-flow scheduling, forward-flow scheduling, or mixed-flow scheduling.

Sylvania Lighting's planning and scheduling systems use reverse-flow scheduling to backward schedule through the process structure that is shown in **Figure 3**. All operations in Figure 2 whose schedules are not decoupled by inventories are combined into a single scheduling unit in the process structure. A flow-chart for Sylvania Lighting's production scheduling procedure is given in **Figure 4**.

A commercial, interactive scheduling program [3] is used to assist the scheduler. Using known sequencing rules and the weekly and monthly production requirements from production planning, Gantt charts are used to finite forward schedule the lamp line in daily increments. Inventories are projected and displayed with a line graph. Problems are highlighted when the inventory for any item drops below its planned requirement.

Scheduling is an interactive process using the scheduler's knowledge of planning's priorities and the production process along with the computer's computational and graphical capabilities. Since the lamp line is the most critical resource, it is scheduled first by finitely loading the available capacity. Setup and .run costs are reduced by minimizing changes in lengths and/or light output levels when scheduling the manufacturing groups. This leads to a natural sequence that moves back and forth between long and short groups scheduling adjacent size setups, whenever possible, given production planning's priorities. Component inventories are then checked for feasibility. This is possible due to the high degree of commonality in material requirements within the manufacturing groups and because the planning horizons extend beyond vendor lead times. This scheduling procedure is called "processor-dominated stage scheduling" [7], since the processor (lamp line) is scheduled before materials.

It should be noted that the production planning system has performed rough-cut capacity analyses for the equipment at all stages to prevent overloading the weekly and monthly plans. The use of dedicated routings, shallow bills of material, and little investment in WIP inventories makes these rough-cut analyses very accurate prior to performing the actual MRP explosion. In this environment, having capacity planning precede material planning provides significant cost advantages to operations.

After developing an acceptable schedule for the lamp line (stage 3), earlier process stages are scheduled. In stage 2, phosphor coatings and B mounts are scheduled. Requirements are determined by exploding the lamp schedule (stage 3) into a schedule of material requirements for the stage 2 outputs that feed stage 3.

In contrast to the lamp line, the stage 2 equipment is somewhat more flexible and not generally constrained by capacity. Thus, a "material-dominated scheduling" [7] approach may be used. Material requirements are calculated and planned based on the lamp line's needs. If conflicts do arise when developing daily schedules, components may be expedited, overtime may be added, safety stocks may be used, or the material requirements may be altered by revising the stage 3 daily lamp schedule. In rare cases, the weekly/monthly production demands for end items may need revision.

After developing stage 2 schedules, a similar procedure is used to develop stage 1 and 0 schedules for the internally produced stems and the purchased parts and materials, which are managed by the material requirements planning system.

Summary and Conclusions

This case is an illustration of the use of process flow scheduling in a high-volume repetitive manufacturing environment that produces a high number of end items on dedicated equipment. Sylvania Lighting's planning and scheduling systems are designed to efficiently utilize expensive equipment in the lamp lines. A reverse-flow scheduling technique is used to first schedule the final assembly lines and then schedule the upstream stages that produce parts and

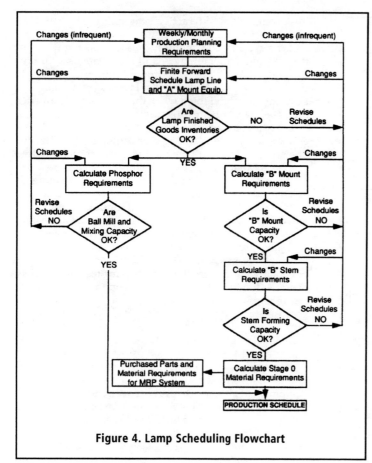

Figure 4. Lamp Scheduling Flowchart

required parts and materials and to provide the well-documented benefits of an integrated manufacturing planning and control system. Implemented together, PFS and MRP can provide greater competitive advantage to repetitive manufacturers than would either method used alone.

Acknowledgment

The authors wish to acknowledge James Holleran, Manager of Inventory Management, and the many other professionals within GTE's Sylvania Lighting Division who were instrumental in the development and implementation of the planning and scheduling concepts referenced in the article.

References

1. *APICS Dictionary*, 6th ed. Falls Church, VA: American Production and Inventory Control Society, 1987.
2. Bolander, S.F. and S.G. Taylor. "Process Flow Scheduling: Mixed Flow Scheduling Cases," *Production and Inventory Management Journal*, Vol. 31, No. 4 (1990),1-6.
3. *Schedulex*. Toronto, Canada: Numetrix, Ltd., 1990.
4. Taylor, S.G. "Are Process Industries Different?" *APICS 23rd Annual Conference Proceedings* (1980), 94-98.
5.— and S.F. Bolander, "Scheduling Product Families." *Production and Inventory Management*, Vol. 27, No. 3 (1986,: 47-55.
6.—, "Process Flow Scheduling: Basic Cases." *Production and Inventory Management Journal*, Vol. 31, No. 3 (1990), 1-4.
7. —, "Process Flow Scheduling Principles," *Production and Inventory Management Journal*, Vol. 32, No. 1 (1991), 67-71.

About the Authors

Darryl T. Hubbard, CPIM, is Materials Manager for Sylvania's domestic coil operations, a part of GTE's Precision Materials Group that supplies components to the lighting divisions and other industrial users. He has over ten years experience in planning systems development and various production and inventory management functions, the majority of that with the Sylvania Lighting Division, U.S. His professional interests include intercompany logistics and integrating the operations and marketing functions. He has a BBA in management, is APICS certified, and is pursuing and MBA in marketing/operations management.

Sam G. Taylor, Ph.D., is a professor of operations management in the College of Business at the University of Wyoming. His research interests are in planning and scheduling systems for process industries. Prior to his academic career, Sam worked eight years in the oil and chemical industries. He has a BS and an MS in chemical engineering and a Ph.D. in industrial engineering.

Steven F. Bolander, Ph.D., is a professor of management at Colorado State University where he teaches undergraduate and graduate courses in production management. Steve's research interests are in production and inventory management. Formerly he worked as manager of manufacturing systems development and as a program manager for Rockwell International. He has a BS in chemistry, an MBA, and a Ph.D. in manufacturing management.

assemblies off line. In this manner, the stage 3 schedule for the lamp line "pulls" material requirements in as needed to consume critical capacity, instead of having a traditional material requirements plan schedule critical capacity after the fact, and perhaps inefficiently. This strategic use of a capacity-oriented master production schedule is very common among process and repetitive manufacturers [4].

Sylvania Lighting's approach illustrates both processor-dominated and material-dominated scheduling. The lamp line uses finite forward scheduling software that first schedules the capacity of the lamp line and then checks inventories for feasibility. A material-dominated technique is used for scheduling the other stages.

An important process flow scheduling concept illustrated is the development of the feasible capacity and material plans for the lamp line before any upstream stages are scheduled. This stage-by-stage reconciliation of capacity and material is an important feature of process flow scheduling systems.

PFS, like MRP, is a scheduling philosophy with many variations. As illustrated in this case, PFS can be utilized in production environments where the schedules of sequential stages in a process flow are decoupled by inventories. Also illustrated was the use of finite forward scheduling to effectively schedule a high-volume production line that produces a repetitive mix of end items that are most efficiently manufactured using group technology concepts and optimal sequencing rules.

Finally, this case is a demonstration that PFS and MRP can be complementary scheduling techniques: PFS being used to schedule the capacity of critical manufacturing operations to ensure the lowest total cost of logistics; and MRP being used to schedule the timely procurement of

Reprinted from the 1997 APICS International Conference Proceedings.

Transforming Your Manufacturing Organization into a Learning Organization

Karl M. Kapp, CFPIM, CIRM

The Opportunity

It's not altruism, goodwill, or kindness that transforms a manufacturing organization into a learning organization. It's bottom line results. Manufacturing firms that implement training programs increase productivity by an average of 17 percent [1].

In the 21st century, the only sustainable competitive advantage will be an organization's ability to learn faster than its competitors. A study by the Washington, D.C., Brookings Institution revealed that 60 percent of an organization's competitive advantage is derived from internal advancements in knowledge, innovation, and learning [2]. If your organization is going to thrive in the 21st century, it must transform from a manufacturing organization into learning organization.

Unfortunately, few manufacturers emphasize knowledge, innovation, or learning. Employers spend one-ninth as much on formal training as they do on durable equipment purchases. [3] The average number of training days per manufacturing employee is a mere three. [3] In 1995, the United States spent less than 2 percent of its total payroll wages on training expenditures. [3] The average employer is just not interested in developing a competitive advantage through corporate learning.

However, organizations that do place a high value on organizational learning have achieved dramatic results. Laser Drive, Inc., a Pittsburgh-based manufacturer, used learning organization techniques to achieve a market share of 70 percent. Motorola, who Fortune Magazine characterized as the "gold standard of corporate training" estimates that for every dollar spent on problem solving and statistical process control training, 30 dollars are returned to the corporation. [4] Several companies have reported a training return on investment of over 1,000 percent. [5]

More manufacturing firms need to be aware of the tremendous potential of focusing on learning and training within their organizations. Fortunately, there are clearly defined steps to becoming a profitable and productive learning organization. The first is to understand the definition of a learning organization.

What Is a Learning Organization?

A learning organization is a group of people who have woven a continuous, enhanced capacity to learn into the corporate culture, an organization in which learning processes are analyzed, monitored, developed, and aligned with competitive goals. A learning organization generates knowledge and learning faster than competitors and turns that learning into a strategic advantage to outmarket, outmanage, and outsell competition.

A learning organization moves beyond simple employee training into organizational problem solving, innovation, and learning. For instance, in a learning organization, when a product is bad, instead of just scrapping it, the employees find the cause of the problem and develop solutions to prevent it from happening again. In a learning organization, the focus is on a company's only appreciating asset—its people.

The Five Disciplines

The idea of building a flexible, profitable learning organization appeals to CEOs, corporate presidents, and other executives seeking an advantage in today's competitive environment. Interest in developing learning organizations has propelled the book, *The Fifth Discipline: The Art and Practice of The Learning Organization,* into a national best seller. The book was written by Peter Senge, the Director of the Center for Organizational Learning at MIT's Sloan School of Management. *The Fifth Discipline* outlines five areas, or disciplines, necessary for an organization to be classified as a learning organization: Personal Mastery, Mental Models, Shared Vision, Team Learning, and Systems Thinking [6].

The first discipline involves an individual's ability to know what he or she wants and to work toward that goal. In a learning organization, creating an environment in which members can develop themselves toward the goals and purposes they choose encourages Personal Mastery.

Mental Models, the second discipline, are an organization's and individual's internal picture of the world—a paradigm. Paradigms must be constantly evaluated, analyzed, and clarified to ensure they are as accurate as possible. Too many organizations get caught in an old paradigm and cannot react quickly enough to a changing market.

Shared Vision is building a sense of commitment in an organization by developing shared images of the future. This includes developing the principles and guiding practices used to reach the goal. In many organizations the mission or vision statement is often a tangible symbol of the shared vision.

Team Learning is geared toward developing collective thinking skills. These skills enable members of a group to reliably develop intelligence and abilities greater than the sum of the individual members' talents.

Systems Thinking is a way of thinking about and understanding the forces and interrelationships that shape the behavior of systems. This discipline helps organizations to see how to change the systems more effectively and to act more in tune with the larger processes of the natural and economic world.

While the five disciplines are vital, they do not in themselves provide much guidance on how to begin the journey of building a learning organization. In order to implement these five disciplines, an organization must commit resources to learning, establish a learning infrastructure, institutionalize learning, appoint a corporate learning officer, and conduct extensive soft-skills training.

Once those items are in place, the organization must implement an evaluation program to measure the effectiveness of the training. A good evaluation program ensures that the training within the organization is effective and positively impacting the bottom line. The final step is for an organization to openly encourage employees to pursue personal growth and development.

The Transformation

What is the first step to becoming a learning organization? Ask Tom Peters. In his 1987 book *Thriving on Chaos*, Peters urges American managers to "consider doubling or tripling your training budget in course of the next 24 to 36 months." He goes on to say "less serious consideration means a failure to come to grips with both the nature of the problem and the magnitude of the opportunity" [4] However, simply conducting thousands of hours of highly expensive training will not produce a learning organization. The entire company must institutionalize learning and hold it up as a corporate priority.

Does anyone in your organization have the word "learning" in his or her job description? Is "learning" in your corporate mission statement? Every recruiting effort, new hire, succession plan, incentive dollar, and promotion must involve recognition and appreciation of learning. A learning urgency must "ooze" from the organization.

For example, your CEO or president must conduct as well as attend training classes. Your CEO doesn't have the time? Roger Enrico, CEO of a $30 billion dollar company with more than 300,000 employees, spends over 100 days a year conducting workshops for senior executives. [7] If the CEO of Pepsi can do it, your CEO can do it.

A dramatic step toward becoming a learning organization is to appoint a Chief Training Officer (CTO) or a Chief Learning Officer (CLO). Many organizations claim to value human resources, but how many have a human resources representative involved in discussions about R&D commercialization, new product development, the strategic vision of the company, or increasing shareholder value?

The job of the CTO is to monitor internal training practices, position training to support the strategic direction of the company, participate in succession planning, develop a learning infrastructure, and champion organizational learning and employee growth and development. The corporate asset of "employees" must be planned and monitored with as much care and attention as the purchase of major capital equipment.

The CTO needs to establish a corporate-wide training curriculum tied directly to corporate goals and objectives. The learning infrastructure developed by the CTO should consist of several interrelated systems encouraging learning and providing information on an as-needed basis. Many hi-tech and low-tech tools are available for building a learning infrastructure.

Intranets are excellent hi-tech tools for providing a common location for learning materials. An Intranet can serve as a collective corporate memory, capturing and distributing policies, procedures, and centralized training. A collective corporate memory helps your organization to avoid relearning the same information over and over again. These electronic networks can distribute computer-based training and provide a central exchange and discussion of ideas, competitor actions, and new product launches.

Low-tech solutions include a corporate lending library holding trade journals, competitive information, audiotaped seminars, and an old-fashioned pushpin bulletin board. Brownbag lunchtime training sessions serve as excellent forums for the exchange of knowledge and information.

In learning organizations, much of the training focuses on soft-skills as opposed to hard-skills. Hard-skills or technical skills such as computer usage or machine operation are important but do not provide a sustainable competitive advantage. Hard-skills become obsolete and are typically not transferable from one situation or project to another. Training in problem solving, decision-making, leadership, and needs analysis provide skills useful in a variety of circumstances and are easily transferable. Non-learning organizations spend all their time and money on hard-skills training and ignore the more important soft-skills.

For example, choosing a new enterprise resource planning (ERP) system is a half-million dollar decision impacting the entire company for the next five to ten years. Yet few selection committees receive any training in team building, decision-making, needs assessment, or any other soft-skills. Prior to making this huge decision, the selection committee should be trained how to analyze corporate needs, how to work together, and how to make a group decision. In a typical organization, the selection committee never receives this type of training—that's a little scary.

But the really scary part is that once this untrained selection committee chooses the ERP system, they will implement it with little or no soft-skills training. Not only will soft-skills training improve and simplify the ERP implementation but, once learned, soft-skills are transferable to other corporate improvement projects. Make an organizational or a departmental commitment to soft-skills training today.

While it is important that organizations institutionalize learning, appoint a Chief Training

Time Savings	
• Shorter lead time to reach proficiency	(hours saved x dollars per hour)
• Less time required to perform an operation	(hours saved x dollars per hour)
• Less supervision required	(supervisory hours saved x supervisory pay per hour)
• Better management of time	(hours freed x dollars per hour x opportunity cost of freed hours)
Increased Productivity	
• Faster work rate	(dollar value of additional units, sales etc.)
• Time saved by not waiting for help	(hours saved x dollars per hour + hours of helpers time saved x dollars per hour)
• Decreased downtime	(dollar value of reduced nonproductive time)
Improved Quality	
• Less scrap produced	(dollar value of scrap x decreased scrap level)
• Fewer rejects	(dollar value of reject x decreased reject level)
• Improved market share	(percent increase in market share x dollar value of increase)
Better Personnel Performance	
• Less absenteeism/tardiness	(hours of increased production x dollars per hour)
• Reduced grievances, claims, accidents	(dollars saved on paperwork, actions, medical claims, and lost time)
• Avoiding the need to hire new employees	(salary and benefits savings)

Table 1. Quantifying the Benefits of Training [10]

Officer and allocate the proper funds for learning, it is equally important that training positively impact the bottom line. Training's impact on the bottom line can be determined by continually monitoring and improving the training through an established evaluation program.

Four Levels of Training Evaluation

The most common evaluation method of training programs was presented in 1959 by Donald L. Kirkpatrick, then a professor at the University of Wisconsin. [8] He developed a four-level classification scheme for the proper evaluation of training programs. The Kirkpatrick levels are an excellent framework for the Chief Training Officer or an interested manager to continually and effectively monitor the training within an organization. If measurements aren't taken at each level, it's difficult to attribute any improvements to training.

Level 1 evaluations are conducted by handing out questionnaires at the end of the training session. Was the presenter knowledgeable? Did the presenter carry himself well? Were the ideas clearly presented? Some training professionals sneer at these "smile sheets." These professionals insist that end-of-course evaluations only measure the entertainment value of a course and not its quality. Not entirely true—what is actually measured is initial customer satisfaction. And initial customer satisfaction is an important measurement. The only time Level 1 evaluations become sneerworthy is when they are used as the only evaluation of training.

A *Level 2* evaluation tests participant learning. At this level, the evaluation can involve anything from a pencil-and-paper test to a full-fledged skill demonstration. The idea is to see if the participant can pass a test demonstrating what he or she learned. If you have ever taken a final examination for a class, you've been through a Level 2 evaluation. The APICS CIRM and CPIM exams are examples of Level 2 evaluations.

The *Level 3* evaluation checks to see if the skills taught in the training class are actually being used on the job. Is the employee exhibiting behaviors that were discussed and learned in the classroom? Did behavior change as a result of training? A Level 3 evaluation can be conducted by observing an employee on the job or by interviewing the employee's supervisor or customers and asking them if they noticed a difference.

The *Level 4* evaluation attempts to measure the bottom line result of training. Did the training positively affect the company? Are trained workers producing more subassemblies per hour, with fewer defects, than untrained workers? Have sales increased because the salespeople are using the new closing techniques taught to them in a training class? A Level 4 evaluation compares the monetary benefits of the training with the costs. This level of evaluation is difficult to obtain but must be measured to ensure that the company is not wasting its training dollars.

Two common formulas for calculating return on investment are a benefit/cost ratio and ROI. To find the benefit/cost ratio, you divide the total dollar value of the benefits by the cost as shown in the following formula:

$$\text{Benefit/Cost Ratio} = \frac{\text{Total Dollar Value of Benefits}}{\text{Cost of Training}}$$

ROI is determined by subtracting the costs from the total dollar value of the benefits to produce the dollar value of the net benefits, which are then divided by the costs and then multiplied by 100 to develop a percentage:

$$\text{Costs of Training} - \text{Total Dollar Benefits} = \text{Dollar Value of Net Benefits}$$

$$\frac{\text{Dollar Value of Net Benefits}}{\text{Costs of Training}} \times 100 = \text{ROI}$$

For example, a training program at Magnavox produced benefits of $321,600 with a cost of $38,233. [9] The benefit/cost ratio is 8.4. For every dollar invested, $8.40 in benefits is returned. The net benefits are $321,600 - $38,233= $283,367. ROI is $283,367 ∏ $38,233 x 100 =741 percent. Using the ROI formula, for every dollar invested in the training, there was a return of $7.40 in net benefits.

Identifying the costs of training is easy: course development expenses, material expenses, instructor salary, and course fees. Quantifying the dollar value of the benefits is more difficult. There are four areas that can be quantified in terms of accessing the benefits of training: time savings, increased productivity, improved quality, and better employee performance. The quantification of these items is contained in **Table 1.**

Conducting a four-level evaluation of the corporation's training programs will ensure that training is contributing to the competitive position of the company. Conducting evaluations will focus the offerings of the training department and help shape the learning infrastructure of the organization. It is the job of every person within the organization to help ensure that a training evaluation program is in place and that the training is positively affecting the bottom line.

Encouraging Personal Growth

Unfortunately, most organizations do not conduct the four levels of training evaluation or even seem to value learning. Typically when personal growth and an increase in the training budget are mentioned in most organizations, the old "what if we train our people and they leave?" question arises. It's a silly question. Participation in employer-sponsored training actually reduces the likelihood of an employee leaving. [3] At a truck leasing firm, turnover was reduced by more than 6 percent as a result of employee training. [10] Only stagnant organizations should worry about employees leaving after being trained.

Growing organizations ask a far more important question, "what if we don't train our people and they stay?" Without training, employees don't even know what they don't know. Do you use any Microsoft products? If you do, what percentage of the product do you use? Most people admit to using less than 70 percent. Even more disturbing is that most people don't even know all of the features available. Training, if nothing else, exposes employees to previously unknown possibilities.

The futurist Daniel Burrus stated at the 1996 APICS conference that no consumer ever asked for a self-cleaning oven. Why? Do people like to clean ovens? No. It's because they didn't know a self-cleaning oven was possible. Organizations can't expect employees to remain competitive, cut costs, and improve productivity if the employees don't know what's possible. The reason training is so important is because it provides organizations and individuals with a "taste" of the possible.

If your organization is not a learning organization then you must take the learning initiative yourself. How do you do this? By becoming a knowledge broker. Carnegie Mellon University conducted a study to find out why some employees of Bell Labs (now known as Lucent Technologies) were "stars" while others were just good, solid middle performers. [10] Obviously, IQ did not separate stars from middle performers since a high IQ is simply a point of entry for a position with Bell Labs.

The researchers found that star performers were members of an informal knowledge network in which ideas and information were bartered for more ideas and information. The star performers indicated that to be accepted into the knowledge network, an individual first had to become knowledgeable in a particular area and then freely share that knowledge. In other words, star performers are a kind of knowledge broker, exchanging ideas with colleagues in exchange for more ideas and more knowledge.

Star performers within an organization build their own informal learning network. You can start to build this network by subscribing to industry magazines and sharing what you learn with others. You don't have time to read more magazines? No problem. Do not read the entire magazine. Simply scan the advertisements and the table of contents every month. Nothing tells you more about the state of an industry than vendor advertisements. You will learn new industry buzzwords, new industry techniques, and pick up on future trends.

Now that you are a knowledge broker, photocopy articles of interest and pass them onto colleagues. Even if you don't have time to read the article, place a note on the article with a message "Hey, thought this looked like something you'd be interested in. I haven't had time to read it because I wanted to get it to you as soon as possible. Let me know if it was helpful." This technique will help you to gain access to the star performer network.

Knowledge brokers take time to share their knowledge with others. They present at APICS meetings, write articles for the local APICS newsletter, teach CPIM and CIRM classes, and become known as an expert in a particular area. Knowledge brokers spend time every day on personal growth.

Conclusion

An organization can transform itself into a learning organization by first understanding the tremendous competitive advantage that can be gained by the transformation. Once the advantage is realized, the organization must appoint a Chief-Training-Officer and empower him or her to develop a corporate learning infrastructure. The next step is to conduct evaluations of all the organizational training to ensure that corporate goals are being met.

However, above all else, a learning organization must encourage individual learning and development. Even though CEOs, presidents, and corporate managers are all interested in large scale corporate learning, there is no corporate learning without individual learners. Grand, expensive programs are not necessary for the learning organization transformation to begin or to be sustained. Simple, incremental steps toward organizational learning will succeed in helping you and your organization learn faster than competitors and transform your manufacturing organization into a learning organization.

References

1. Bartel, A.P. "Training, Wage Growth, and Job Performance: Evidence from a Company Database." *Journal of Labor Economics*, 1995, vol. 13, No. 3. pp. 401-425.
2. Carvenale, A.P. "Learning: The Critical Technology." *Training and Development*, 1992, vol. 46, No. 2. pp. s2-s16.
3. Bassi, L.J., A.L. Gallagher, and E. Schroer. *The ASTD Training Data Book*. American Society of Training and Development. 1996.
4. Peters, T. *Thriving on Chaos*. HarperPerennial, New York. 1987.
5. Phillips, J.J. "ROI: The Search for Best Practices." *Training and Development*, 1996, vol. 50, No. 2. pp. 42-47.
6. Senge, P. et al. *The Fifth Discipline Fieldbook: Strategies and Tools for Building a Learning Organization*. Doubleday, New York. 1994.
7. Tichy, N.M. and C. DeRose, "The Pepsi Challenge: Building a Leader-Driven Organization." *Training and Development*, 1996, vol. 50, No. 5. pp. 58-66.
8. Gordon, J. "Measuring the Goodness of Training." *Training*, vol. 28, No. 8. pp. 19-25.
9. Phillips, J.J. "ROI: The Search for Best Practices." *Training and Development*, 1996, vol. 50, No. 2. pp. 42-47.
10. Kelley, R. and J. Caplan, "How Bell Labs Creates Star Performers." *Harvard Business Review*. July-August 1993. pp. 128-139.

About the Author

In his current position as training manager at Telesis Computer Corporation, Karl M. Kapp, CFPIM, CIRM, is responsible for the development and delivery of a training curriculum intended to help individuals and manufacturing organizations deal with the complex changes brought about by the implementation of the TelesisMFG ERP system. He has conducted ERP training classes at dozens of different manufacturing plants, including such Fortune 500 companies as Lockheed Martin and Eaton Corporation.

He earned his doctorate of education in instructional design and technology from the University of Pittsburgh. The field of Instructional Design and Technology is the study of the application of technology and adult learning theory to the design, development, and delivery of instruction to adults. He uses his knowledge of adult learners to provide manufacturing and management education.

Mr. Kapp conducts APICS CPIM and CIRM courses for the Pittsburgh chapter and has published articles in such manufacturing trade magazines as *APICS—The Performance Advantage*, *Manufacturing Systems*, and *The EDI Forum*.

As a practicing knowledge broker, Mr. Kapp frequently speaks to APICS Chapters, colleges, universities, businesses, and nonprofit organizations. He is a dynamic and experienced speaker—his presentations motivate individuals and organizations to promote quality, contribute to learning organizations, and embrace change.

Reprinted from the Production and Inventory Management Journal, *Fourth Quarter, 1996.*

Outsourcing Strategy and a Learning Dilemma

Brian Leavy, Ph.D., CFPIM

The make-or-buy decision has always been a central concern of production and inventory management. However, in the context of today's more dynamic and volatile economy, driven by the increasing globalization of competition and the unprecedented rate of change in product, process and materials technologies, such decisions have never been more strategic in their significance for many companies. Often, what is at stake is not just short-term advantage but longer run competitiveness and survival. In many industries, from automobiles to computing and from athletic footwear to earth-moving equipment, the growing range and sophistication of the supply segments offer increasing opportunities to outsource high level subsystems as well as more basic components. In short, strategic outsourcing now offers many companies more interesting and varied routes to competitiveness than ever before.

However, the main theme of this article is that at the heart of the decision on whether or not to outsource, and how extensively, lies a learning dilemma. To fully appreciate the nature of this dilemma and how it might be tackled, it will first be useful to review briefly the growing influence that the concept of learning is having on our understanding of how competitiveness is developed and enhanced in the modern enterprise. Following this review, the remainder of the article will examine the learning dilemma in strategic outsourcing and discuss its implications for company strategists. In brief, a central issue facing strategists in outsourcing is which opportunities for future learning to retain and which to forgo.

Learning in Strategy and Competitiveness

The importance of learning as a source of competitiveness has long been recognized in the production and strategy fields. The notion of the experience curve represents the most enduring association between learning and strategy to date. This concept, based on the earlier but narrower notion of the production learning curve, first came to prominence in the 1960s when the Boston Consulting Group, under the leadership of Bruce Henderson, demonstrated that in many industries unit costs could be seen to decrease with cumulative volume in a predictable and exponential way [6]. In the then emerging semiconductor industry, for example, the price per unit fell from $25 to $1 over the 1964-72 period as the cumulative volume produced by the new industry grew from 2 million to 2 billion units. Henderson and his colleagues believed that the primary advantage enjoyed by market leaders was a cost advantage based on cumulative experience, and many companies, like Lincoln Electric in arc-welding, Bausch and Lomb in contact lenses and Texas Instruments in calculators were successful in building and sustaining market leadership based on experience-curve strategies. Experience-based pricing (aggressively tracking the exponential reduction in unit costs with cumulative volume) also proved to be a very effective way for early movers like BIC Corporation, in the disposable ballpoint pen industry, to maintain market leadership and deter competition.

Since the 1960s, however, the business literature has also been full of examples of experience-based strategies that failed to live up to expectations. In some cases, like Monsanto in the acrylonitrile industry, this was because the strength of the experience effect was overestimated and the level of anticipated cost reduction simply never materialized [4]. However, a more serious limitation with traditional experience-curve thinking is the implicit assumption that all competitors learn from their experience at the same rate, so that the effect is seen to be related mainly to volume rather than time. This assumption was recently challenged by Ray Stata of Analog Devices: "How else can we explain the success of the Japanese automobile industry which learned faster than the U.S. industry with substantially less cumulative volume [14]." The Japanese, with more active learning strategies (as reflected in continuous improvement programs), were the more efficient learners. Stata went so far as to suggest that "the rate at which individuals and organizations learn may become the only sustainable competitive advantage [14]," especially in industries that are knowledge intensive, as most industries are nowadays [2]. In short, competitiveness based on learning appears to be related to both cumulative volume and learning efficiency.

The current interest in the concept of core competencies (or capabilities) reflects a widespread belief in the growing importance of learning-based advantages in modern competitive analysis. Recent theorists, like Hamel and Prahalad [11], agree with Stata that endproduct market share is an unreliable indicator of real competitive strength, but their analysis of the reason takes us beyond the time versus volume issue. For them, 80% of the learning advantages that really matter are associated with 20% of the components in products of any complexity and sophistication. World manufacturing share of those core products or subsystems that embody key technologies with diverse applications is often a better indicator than market share of where the most important economies of experience are to be found. Honda, Philips, Canon, Intel and Sony are all examples of companies whose competitiveness across a diverse range of industries is more accurately reflected in their global manufacturing shares of core components and technologies than in their market shares of end products. For example, Honda competes across a variety of sectors, including automobiles and outdoor power equipment, but is market leader in only one, motorcycles. Yet it is highly competitive in all of them, due in large measure to its position as the world's leading manufacturer of small engines and power trains, the core components of all motorized equipment. In outdoor power equipment, for example, the real competitive battleground has been between Honda engines and those of Briggs and Stratton, as well as between Honda mowers and those of Toro and Snapper (Briggs and Stratton's original equipment manufacturers [OEMs]).

According to Hamel and Prahalad, core products, like Honda engines, are the tradable parts of the more fundamental levers of learning in determining present and future competitiveness, a company's core competencies. A company's core competencies are more than just technologies. They reflect "collective learning" in how to "coordinate diverse production skills and integrate multiple streams of technologies [11]." It is this deep embeddedness in the overall social fabric and processes of the organization that make them so difficult to imitate. For example, Canon's core competencies lie not just in its discrete skills in semiconductors, fine optics, fine chemicals and precision mechanics, but in its ability to integrate these technologies and the engineering, production, procurement and marketing systems that it has developed to fully leverage them. Firms that build their future competitiveness on the basis of carefully selected core competencies, like Canon, focus on how to match depth in firm-specific learning with breadth in its commercial application, since few companies are likely to excel in more than five or six fundamental competencies [11]. Learning advantages, based on depth in core competencies, are not confined to manufacturing companies alone. Wal-Mart, for example, has been successful in leveraging its depth of experience in core logistical capabilities across a diverse range of retailing and wholesaling formats [13], while Banc One's successful institutionalization of its "share and compare" learning philosophy has been the cornerstone of its sustained competitiveness in the U.S. retail banking sector [15].

The Learning Dilemma in Outsourcing Strategy

Outsourcing strategies are becoming more prevalent in the current economic environment. This is reflected in the recent trend away from vertical integration in the computer industry, where during the latter half of the 1980s, companies like Sun Microsystems, using extensive outsourcing, outperformed the then vertically integrated leaders like IBM and Digital Equipment Corporation in productivity, growth and return on investment. This trend has not been unique to computing. For example, in the early 1950s the *Fortune* 500 accounted for eight million employees and 37% of the United States's GNP. By the late 1970s these figures had risen to 16 million and 58%, respectively, as major industries became more concentrated and leading firms more vertically integrated. Since the early 1980s this trend has been largely reversed, to 12 million and 40%, respectively [10], as the economic "rules of the game" have since changed to favor more nimble players, more extensive outsourcing, and more sophisticated intermediate markets for key components, subsystems and services [17].

The core competency approach to building competitiveness, and the organizational learning perspective that underpins it, are providing some of the strongest arguments for outsourcing in modern strategic analysis. More and more, companies are being advised to concentrate in-house on those activities that are core and to outsource much of the rest, particularly where suitable intermediate markets

exist. Of course the main challenge posed by such a strategy is how to identify which activities to outsource and which to retain in-house. Quinn and Hilmer suggest that a company should consider outsourcing any activity except those where "it can achieve definable preeminence and provide unique value for customers," or for which it has a "critical strategic need [12]." Ravi Venkatesan, of Cummins Engineering, advises manufacturing companies to concentrate on proprietary components that are pivotal to product differentiation (like NIKE sole inserts, or Benetton dyes), and to outsource commodity-like components with mature technologies that add nothing to the qualities that customers consider important [16]. Building competitiveness on what is ultimately depth of know-how requires clear and consistent focus. According to Venkatesan, his company and too many others have, in the past, systematically overinvested in expensive and time-consuming world-class manufacturing programs, like TQM, JIT and CIM, that were misdirected at commodity parts, when the effort should have been primarily concentrated on "proprietary components that could have become sources of competitive advantage [16]."

Advantages of Outsourcing

There are many advantages to be gained from strategic outsourcing, including the ability to achieve market scale without bureaucratic mass. When combined with a policy of close partnership with suppliers, perhaps the greatest advantage is the opportunity to harness the complementary core competencies of an array of sophisticated suppliers in the creation of value for customers, and to deepen a company's own core competencies through the wider access to learning and new ideas that such relationships can provide. As Quinn and Hilmer argue, strategic outsourcing can offer a company "the full utilization of external suppliers' investments, innovations and specialized professional capabilities that would be prohibitively expensive or even impossible to duplicate internally [12]." Furthermore, by following a policy of codeveloping two main supplier-partners for each major subsystem, the outsourcing firm can retain some of the benefits of competition and market discipline throughout its supply system, thereby producing "more overall learning and innovation than would occur in a highly integrated, bureaucratic firm [3]."

Dangers of Outsourcing

However, there are dangers associated with strategic outsourcing that are also learning related. Critics of outsourcing point to the risk of losing key skills and mortgaging the future to secure what may be, at best, only a fleeting competitive advantage. Companies that outsource their manufacturing to lower-cost suppliers may be able to protect the competitiveness of their current products, but at the expense of their ability to create new ones. As the "integrated resource management" perspective now consistently emphasizes, engineering and manufacturing are not so much discrete activities as related bundles of skills. Cutting off one from the other, through the outsourcing of all or part of manufacturing, can damage both. Core competencies are synonymous with neither discrete functions nor technologies but are deeply embedded in the collective know-how that is reflected in their integration. The most proprietary and strategic elements of any core competence are usually rooted in shared tacit knowledge and intuitive understanding. For example, at Cummins it is the "combustion recipe"—a recipe based on "many detailed understandings" of the linkages between user requirements, system parameters, and component specifications, "intuitively developed in countless conversations"—that makes the company's medium-duty engine the best in its class, "even though all competitors may use identical components such as fuel systems or pistons [16]." That is why many companies that are extensive users of outsourcing, like NIKE, often retain some manufacturing capability and closely tie it to engineering, in order to protect and develop the underlying cross-functional competencies that are the key to their future success. Even in the most traditional of industries, companies that seek to consciously build their competitiveness on deeply layered learning capability see the integration of engineering and manufacturing as key to this process. At Chaparral Steel, for example, Gordon Forward recently described his company as a learning organization in which "everybody is in research and development" and "the plant is our laboratory [9]."

To Outsource or Not To Outsource

Competing for the future is closely tied to competing for today's learning opportunities. When a company like Canon offers itself as an attractive source of laser printer "engines" to Hewlett Packard and Apple, it is increasing its own control over the learning opportunities provided by this key subsystem, and borrowing the end-product markets of its OEMs to do so. With a global manufacturing share of over 80% in this key subsystem, a position nowhere near reflected in its own market share, Canon seems to be well in control of the future technological trajectory of the small printer market. Companies with strategies like Canon are developing and deepening the competencies that will be key to the future of their industries in "the race to learn" and to "capture investment initiative from firms either unwilling or unable to invest in core competency leadership [5]." In this way outsourcing can result in the unintended transfer of the most significant part of an industry's experience curve from the OEM to its supplier. This happened to General Electric in its outsourcing relationship with Samsung in microwave ovens, and to Bulova in its relationship with Citizen in the watch industry [8]. Even in the closest of outsourcing relationships, the partners will always remain potential future competitors [7], and in such cases, the one with the most efficient learning capability across the partnership interface may prosper at the ultimate expense of the other.

For companies like Hewlett Packard and Apple, the strategy to outsource some high-level components to Canon may make sense, if the learning afforded by the manufacture of today's laser printer engines is marginal to the development of their own core competencies. However it can be notoriously difficult to know when particular opportunities to learn in the present might be more crucial to future competitiveness than they now seem. For example, several years ago Eastman Kodak decided to exit the camcorder business altogether when there was little prospect of its ever becoming a major commercial activity for the company. Years later it came to look back at this decision as a lost opportunity to develop skills in key components of the camcorder with potentially much wider future applications. In the same vein, few in the 1970s could have foreseen how many of the key competencies on which the future of the computer industry came to be built would have passed so quickly from those of IBM and Digital to those of the upstream suppliers like Intel and Microsoft. This is always a risk in outsourcing. As Lei and Slocum have argued, many firms that rely on outsourcing to improve their competitiveness "may find their internal skill sets deteriorating as they become 'locked out' from learning new skills and technologies critical to participating in industry evolution [8]."

The risk is all the greater in the new economy, where many of the growth markets of tomorrow will be found in the convergence of what were once considered to be disparate competencies and technologies. Canon is itself an extensive user of outsourcing. However the company continues to manufacture many of its own semiconductor devices for current products, though it readily acknowledges that it cannot compete with the major players in the VLSI semiconductor industry in terms of cost or experience. It might reasonably be tempted to outsource these components in an activity that remains marginal to its current competitiveness. However, it retains this capability, and the learning opportunities that it engenders, because it sees its future lying in the anticipated convergence of optics and electronics. This convergence will not only be key to its future in office products, where electronic imaging is set to have a growing influence at the expense of the more traditional chemical kind, but may allow it to become a credible competitor to IBM and NEC when, as it now confidently expects, optoelectronics soon becomes the dominant underlying technology in mainframe computing [1].

Conclusion

Today's economic environment offers more interesting, varied and valuable opportunities for strategic outsourcing than ever before. The growing popularity of outsourcing strategies reflects the concurrent growth in influence of the partnership approach to supplier relations, popularized by the successful diffusion of the JIT management philosophy. It also reflects the increase in influence of strategy concepts like core competencies that encourage companies to compete for the future through a concentration on developing depth of learning in carefully selected core activities, and creating value for customers through a network of supply partnerships with other similarly focused firms. The strategic logic of this perspective is that focused partners with complimentary competencies can create more value for customers than the equivalent resources concentrated within a vertically integrated company. However, the dilemma facing any company attracted to such a strategy is the risk that it helps its supplier-partners to deepen their competencies at its own expense, which, in the competition for learning opportunities today, will be crucial in the competition for tomorrow's key markets. In short, outsourcing companies need to consciously think through not just which parts they can outsource with profit today, but what learning opportunities they may be foregoing, and which competencies they may be fragmenting in the process. This kind of caution will be crucial if long-term competitiveness is not to be carelessly sacrificed for short-term advantage.

References

1. Ackenhusen, M., and S. Ghoshal. "Canon: Competing on Capabilities." *INSEAD*, Case #392-031-1 (1992).
2. Beck, N. *Shifting Gears: Thriving in the New Economy.* Toronto: Harper-Collins, 1992.
3. Dyer, J. H., and W. G. Ouchi. "Japanese-Style Partnerships: Giving Companies a Competitive Edge." *Sloan Management Review* (Fall 1993): 58.

4. Ghemawat, P. "Building Strategy on the Experience Curve." *Harvard Business Review* (March-April 1985): 143-149.

5. Hamel, G., and C. K. Prahalad. *Competing for the Future.* Boston: Harvard Business School Press, 1994: 167.

6. Henderson, B. "The Experience-Curve Revisited: The Growth Share Matrix of the Product Portfolio." *Perspectives.* Boston Consulting Group, 1992.

7. Leavy, B. "Two Strategic Perspectives on the Buyer-Supplier Relationship." *Production and Inventory Management Journal* 35, no. 2 (1994): 47-51.

8. Lei, D., and J. W. Slocum "Global Strategy, Competence Building and Strategic Alliances." *California Management Review* (Fall 1992): 81-97.

9. Leonard-Barton, D. "The Factory as a Learning Laboratory." *Sloan Management Review* (Fall 1992): 29.

10. Peters, T. "Rethinking Scale." *California Management Review* (Fall 1992): 7-29.

11. Prahalad, C. K., and G. Hamel. "The Core Competence of the Corporation." *Harvard Business Review* (May-June 1990): 79-91.

12. Quinn, J. B., and F. G. Hilmer. "Strategic Outsourcing." *Sloan Management Review* (Summer 1994): 43.

13. Stalk, G., P. Evans, and L. E. Shulman. "Competing on Capabilities: The New Rules of Corporate Strategy." *Harvard Business Review* (March-April 1992): 57-69.

14. Stata, R. "Organizational Learning: The Key to Management Innovation." *Sloan Management Review* (Spring 1989): 64 and 69.

15. Uyterhoeven, H. E. R., and M. Hart, "Banc One—1993." *Harvard Business School.* Case #9-394-043 (1994).

16. Venkatesan, R. "Strategic Sourcing: To Make or Not to Make." *Harvard Business Review* (November-December 1992): 99 and 102.

17. Verity, J. "Deconstructing the Computer Industry." *Business Week* (November 22, 1992): 44-52.

About the Author

Brian Leavy, Ph.D., CFPIM, is AIB Professor of Strategic Management at Dublin City University Business School. He is also course director of the school's executive program in production and inventory management run in association with the Irish Production and Inventory Control Society to prepare participants for APICS professional certification. His research interests span the strategy and PIM fields and his new book, *Key Processes in Strategy*, was published by International Thomson in early 1996.

Reprinted from the 2000 APICS International Conference Proceedings.

Gaining Competitive Advantage Through Kaizen

J. Michael Lemon, CFPIM, and Bradley T. Hanpeter

"Kaizen" translated means "good change." Many companies use kaizen as a tool to promote rapid, team-based positive change. It is a plant manager's dream come true. As past plant manager, I can tell you firsthand. I walked through my operation daily. In doing so I tried to remain open to those things that could increase our effectiveness as an organization. Often I would see an operation or process that I knew could be improved.

The recognition of improvement opportunities is the easy part. Follow-through is the difficult part. Regardless of our personal titles and the roles we play in manufacturing, we all generally have a full plate. Let's assume for a minute that you have identified an area in your operation that is ripe for improvement. Now let's pretend that you have been able to retain your thoughts long enough to make it back to the office to write down your thoughts.

Where do we begin to improve that area of the operation? Perhaps we call in the engineering manager and explain our observations to her. We instruct her to collect some critical data. These might include actual run times, travel distances, current throughput, current lead times, space, or square footage currently consumed by this process. We further request additional data such as current levels of WIP and standard hours of queue. Before we go any further, we are gently reminded that this data could be better provided by production control. By the way, you may also want to get planning and marketing involved to supply information pertaining to customer demand, she says in a helpful way.

We agree that other departments are required to get this thing started. Next I put out a memo to all department heads. "We will meet in the conference room next Thursday to discuss plans to improve the process in machining cell X." We have our first meeting, which, as usual, takes several hours of dialogue. At the conclusion of this meeting, every department head has the objective of going back to their departments and reviewing current projects and assignments. We will meet again next Thursday so that each department can report on their availability to support this undertaking.

Are you beginning to get the idea? This is the way we have always done things. By the time all the meetings have taken place—by the time all the schedules have been arranged—by the time all the data has been collected—by the time arrangements have been made with outside concerns (electricians, plumbers, machine technicians, etc.)—we are now ready to start taking action. I forgot to mention that several weeks ago we took one of our best support people off their job to become temporary project manager. After four to six months, we have probably completed the work.

Now we start up production. It goes without saying that the operators in the machining cell were never asked for their input. Not only do they have some wonderful ideas that we never thought of, but we find there is no feeling of ownership or buy-in from them. So we back-pedal and implement some of their ideas. We can't implement all of them because it would require a complete redo of the entire project. We have improved the process, but not to the level we could have. The operators never do embrace the change as their own.

What I have described to you is the best case. All too often our plans for improvement never get implemented at all. The daily battle and fire fighting often get in the way. We tend to dread the thought of establishing another committee. We don't look forward to another six months of extra meetings and project management. So while good intentioned, it's business as usual.

What if I told you that most opportunities for improvement could be accomplished in one four-day cycle? Bigger projects, maybe two or three four-day events. The truth is, improvement never ends. Therefore, a cell or department may have a kaizen event every six months, constantly improving the process. Before too long the environment has been transformed into one of constant change and improvement. The employees not only buy in to the change, they lead it.

Today's session will be broken into two major sections. The first section will be led by Mike Lemon. Mike will demonstrate what kaizen means to a plant manager and the affected organization. Mike will review required preparations, team participation, event planning, and execution.

The second section will be led by Brad Hanpeter. Brad has facilitated in excess of 75 events. Brad will share with you the basic educational material that takes place during the first day of an event. This will give you a glimpse at the simplistic, commonsense approach that is used in making positive change. Brad will then share with you actual results from some of the events he has facilitated.

If you have used kaizen as a tool yourself, you may find it very interesting to benchmark your own results against another practitioner. If you have never used kaizen as an improvement vehicle yourself, then hold on to your hats. You won't find it easy to believe the dynamic results that can be attained by such a simple process.

Plant Management's Role

The Kaizen Process

The first thing management must do is to provide a road map, that is, a list of potential kaizen events. That's easy enough. Are there any processes or departments where you think there is the potential for improvement? Next rank them in order of where you feel the most gain can be made. This is the order your events should follow.

One word of caution here. Your first event should have a very high probability of success. When going over your list of potential kaizen events, select one that is not extremely complex. Remember the momentum you establish with your first event will provide the catalyst for future excitement among your employees. Once you have made your selection, you are ready to begin.

The first step is to select a facilitator. This selection is critical. It is suggested that an experienced kaizen facilitator be selected. There are consulting groups that are available with vast experience in the field. If you do not want to use an outside source, then proceed slowly with your first event until your internal candidate can be properly trained. To train your internal kaizen facilitator it will be necessary for him or her to take part in several kaizen teams held at other companies. There are many public kaizen events taking place all the time. Once again, you may find it easiest to employee a consultant to help you get into the loop. However, professional organizations like APICS may be able to put you in touch with participating companies.

Many companies train one, two, or more of their associates to become full-time kaizen facilitators. They attend several events outside their own company and participate in every event that takes place at their company. After partaking in approximately 12 events they will be ready to facilitate an event on their own. This amount of training is required. The high energy level that takes place during an event together with the variety of tasks being carried out requires an experienced facilitator to maintain group focus.

Once your facilitator is selected and trained, you may proceed. Management and the facilitator, knowing the area to be attacked, should agree on a team captain. This person should be someone who has a stake in the area being addressed during the event. It could be a supervisor of the area, a group leader, or an employee from that area. Whoever it is, they need to have the respect of their co-workers, they need to have an understanding of the overall process being studied, and, most important, they need to have a vested interest in making it work. When the event is over, this person will be expected to enforce the changes that have been made and must be able to solicit the support of the entire department. This person will conduct follow-up meetings to ensure any homework assignments (to be discussed later) are completed.

Now the time is right to select the remainder of the team. A team should contain no more than 12 people plus the facilitator and no fewer than 8. These team members should be selected for several reasons. It is best to have at least a couple members from the area being studied. If you know the location of your next event, this is the time to introduce a couple of people from that area to the process. Get them charged up before hand. If any internal or external suppliers will be impacted by the changes to this area they should be asked to be members. If your suppliers are a part of the solution and have had a hand in developing your process, you can expect a high degree of willingness to provide their service or product in accordance with your requirements. They will have bought in to the changes in advance and will have a complete understanding of the changes you are requesting. You may find it useful to approach their management with the prospect of a free four-day training course for their associate. Also they will be developing a skill they can bring back to their own organization.

In my first event, I had the V.P. of marketing from a service supplier on our team. During the event it became necessary to have his organization provide a service for the changes to proceed. He picked up the phone and had a crew there within a couple of hours. They provided their service to us in record-breaking time. Since we pay them for time and material, it worked out very well for us. If we had to schedule their service under normal non-emergency conditions, we might have waited weeks for the required support activities. His excitement for the process quickly spread to his crew.

Likewise, if your event will impact a customer, internal or external, this is the chance to let them be part of the solution. Their cooperation in weeks to come can be counted on because they feel an ownership of the changes that have been made. They also now have a total understanding as to why the changes were required. What they learn may become a selling tool for them in providing services to other organizations. It is a true win-win situation.

If you have a multiplant company, invite a few members from other plants. Focus on those who may have similar processes in their departments. This can provide cross-fertilization of best practices in both directions. If this process is very technical in nature, make sure you have at least one member with the technical background required. Also encourage members of top management to put on their jeans for four days and roll up their sleeves. They will enjoy the experience, and your associates will see just how important this process is to the organization.

All team members must be committed to four days of no interruption—no pagers, no beepers, no meetings outside the event. Everyone will be expected to work long hours each day. It is not rare for a team charged with enthusiasm to find themselves working until 10:00 p.m.

After selection of your team, and acceptance by your candidates, the plant needs to hear about the event. The vehicle you elect to use is up to you. One idea is a plantwide communications meeting. Here is the perfect forum to announce your plans for a kaizen event. Take this opportunity to begin supercharging your team with some public recognition. Call up your team members and introduce them to the plant associates. Tell them why these people were chosen, and why this area was chosen. If not at a meeting, perhaps a company newsletter, together with a general posting on bulletin boards. Try some banners: "KAIZEN COMING SOON TO A DEPARTMENT NEAR YOU."

Four weeks before your event, the scope of the project should be clear and your objectives or expected outcomes should be done. Objectives for an event should be a stretch, for example, a space reduction of 75 percent, travel distance reduced by 50 percent, 80 percent of all non-value-added tasks eliminated. The reason for stretch objectives is so we don't cut short the potential improvements. If you give an objective to the team of reducing space for their operation by 15 percent, that's what you will get. I mean to say, after reaching their goal the team is likely to say it's time to move on, the objective has been met. If you ask for 75 percent and get 35 percent, the event has been a huge success.

Three weeks before the event, your last-minute changes or additions to the team should be complete. This allows everyone as much time as possible to arrange their professional and personal schedules to allow for the four uninterrupted days the event will require. At this time we should also have a food committee formed to plan for in-house meals and snacks. Your team is going to work hard. They must be cared for accordingly. A space should be made available where their will always be a supply of cold drinks, coffee, and snacks. Likewise this area would be used for delivery of three meals per day. The conference or meeting room they will require for the four days could double for their break area.

As you will see later, we celebrate our victory with much enthusiasm after the event is completed. Because of this, three weeks before the event someone should have the responsibility for procuring token gifts for the team—t-shirts, hats— use your imagination. Some elect to design a kaizen t-shirt. This shirt is only given to persons who have completed an event. There is no other way to obtain one. You might also give a certificate and a token gift like a key chain with "kaizen" engraved on it. The same person will usually also have the task of arranging some entertainment for the celebration. I have had a band come in and play while we have lunch served for the team and invited guests.

All training materials and supplies for the team should also begin coming together by week three. Training materials should be in order. The supplies or "kaizen kit" are refurbished after each event. The kit contains the tools of the trade—six stop watches, writing pads, pens, pencils, tape measures, marking pens, masking tape, calculators, etc. We also make sure there is a supply of hand tools available as well as duct tape, cardboard, flip charts, some pieces of wood, and construction items. These are frequently used for mockups.

Your team leader, management, and other persons with responsibility for preparedness should meet weekly until the event begins. Develop a checklist of the items that we have covered to make sure everything is ready for the event in advance. This list must include any changes that will be made to the production schedule to allow for down time during the event. This will vary depending on the type of area you are working on. Realistically ask yourself if it will be possible to maintain production and at what level during the event.

One thing that I have incorporated is a "pre-kaizen" task list. I have assigned an industrial engineer who is also a kaizen facilitator in training the responsibility for getting some groundwork done in advance of the event. We have found this to be a great head-start for our teams. For example, we go into our event already knowing the "before" data such as square footage consumed by the process, current run times, current travel distances, current average production attainable per shift, etc. By doing this in advance our team has more time to analyze and offer alternatives before implementing their recommendations.

The Event

Day one is mostly spent in the classroom learning the techniques that will be used. The balance of day one is spent in observation of the process as it currently operates. Day two is spent planning and implementing changes to the area. Day three is spent implementing changes and testing the capabilities of the newly modified system. A lot of activity is also begun in the area of management presentation. This can be a late night as changes may be made after testing is complete. Day four is spent with final observations and measurement of success in the early morning. This is followed by finalization of the presentation materials.

Day four comes to a climax with an 11:00 a.m. management presentation followed by entertainment and lunch. Each member is called on one at a time by the team leader. Each member gives a portion of the management presentation. Overheads are used (examples will be shown) that are handwritten, on forms provided. It is not the intention of the presentation to impress everyone with computer graphics skills. As a matter of fact, no computer-generated overheads are used. There is no time for that, nor is that the objective of the event. Improvement to the process is the intent of the event. The presentation is concluded by the team leader, who reviews in summary the original scope and objectives of the event and the delivered results. Any homework assignments are also reviewed publicly at this time.

After your first event, subsequent celebrations will begin with a review of the last event's homework. This will be given by the team leader of that event. Once the presentation portion of the program is concluded, each member is called up by management. Here they are presented with a kaizen shirt, a certificate of participation, and a token gift. Typically management members come to the front of the room. Each one hands out something as they shake hands with each member. Invite a good audience for attendance at the presentation. Include sister plants, suppliers, customers, top management, and associates and supervisors from other departments in the plant.

Once the awards are given out and words of praise have been spoken by management, the fun begins. You might provide live entertainment (a band) to perform while a buffet lunch is served. After lunch a meeting is held with management, the current team leader, the facilitator, and the manager of the next scheduled event location. You will want to know what went well, and what areas of the process could be improved.

The kaizen team then heads back to a central location in the plant where the event took place. All plant associates come to hear the 30-minute presentation and are given the opportunity to tour the area where the event took place. You might try to coordinate this with the afternoon break, allowing you to serve ice cream or some refreshments, and not just take break time away from your associates. This shows everyone how much we honor positive change.

About the Author

J. Michael Lemon, CFPIM, has 28 years of manufacturing experience. He spent 20 years with Pitney Bowes in Stamford, Connecticut, where he held various management positions including, manager P&IC, MRP II project manager, and manager materials and manufacturing systems. Mr. Lemon worked as a manufacturing consultant for Masco Home Furnishings, and with Henredon Furniture Industries as plant manager of their frame plant. He currently holds the position of vice president, materials management for Lexington Home Brands.

Mr. Lemon has hundreds of hours of experience as an instructor and seminar leader in the fields of MRP II and JIT, and has been published numerous times in several different business publications.

Mr. Lemon presented at the APICS International Conferences of 1994, 1995, 1998, and 1999, and at the ACS conferences of 1994, 1995, 1996, and 1997. He served three terms as vice president, education of the Foothills Chapter in North Carolina, and is recognized by APICS to be Certified in Production and Inventory Management at the Fellow level (CFPIM).

Bradley T. Hanpeter is the manager for continuous improvement at Masco Corporation in Taylor, Michigan. He is responsible for developing and implementing lean manufacturing, kaizen, and other continuous improvement initiatives for Masco Corporation, a $6 billion manufacturer of home improvement and building products. Since Masco initiated their continuous improvement program in 1995, Mr. Hanpeter has facilitated more than 100 kaizen breakthrough workshops. These workshops focus on implementing the principals of the Toyota Production System to reduce costs by eliminating non-value-adding activities.

With 18 years of experience, Mr. Hanpeter has worked in a variety of manufacturing management roles including consultant, plant manager, product line manager, product engineering manager, manager of shop operations, and production supervisor. Prior to joining Masco, he was a partner with an international manufacturing consulting firm. Mr. Hanpeter started his career at the General Electric Company.

Mr. Hanpeter has a bachelor of science degree in operations research from Cornell University and a master's degree in business administration from the University of Michigan.

Reprinted from the 1992 APICS International Conference Proceedings.

How to Implement Sales and Operations Planning
Richard C. Ling, CFPIM

The objective of this paper is to describe the process of Sales and Operations Planning and then present an approach to effectively implement the process. The implementation approach has been developed working with a number of manufacturing companies in different industries over the past few years.

What Is Sales and Operations Planning (S&OP)?

"Sales and Operations Planning is a dynamic process in which the company operating plan is updated on a regular monthly or more frequent basis. Here's a capsule description of the process. It starts with the sales and marketing departments comparing actual demand to the sales plan, assessing the marketplace potential and projecting future demand. The updated demand plan is then communicated to the manufacturing, engineering, and finance departments, which offer ways to support it. Any difficulties in supporting the sales plan are worked out, or the sales plans are altered in a process that concludes with a formal meeting chaired by the general manager. The final result is a set of 'marching orders' for all departments that extends through the current fiscal year and as far beyond that as is necessary to effectively plan resources. Most important, an updated operation plan is being set to satisfy the current market, and the consequences of taking various actions are known ahead of time, minimizing costly and disruptive surprises." (Quote from *Orchestrating Success: Improve Control of the Business with Sales and Operations Planning*, Chap. 2, p. 11.)

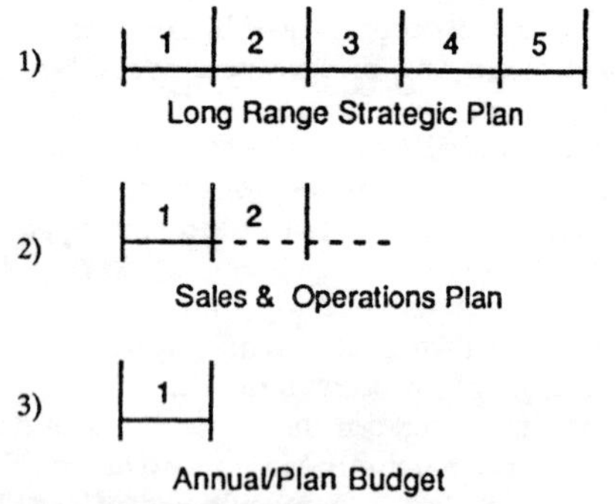

(Fig.1: *Orchestrating Success: Improve the Business with Sales & Operations Planning*, p. 12)

Figure 1. Annual Plan and Budget

Another contribution of Sales and Operations Planning is that it enables a company to fine-tune its long-range strategic plan and annual business plan. To understand how this fine-tuning process works, let's consider the overall business planning process shown in **Figure 1**.

At the top level of the process is the long-range strategic plan, which is reviewed on an annual basis. The middle level of the process shown in Figure 1, the ongoing operating plan, entails developing specific goals and "how tos" through the Sales and Operations Planning process. At the bottom level we encounter the annual business plan, which is used for financial planning and measurement purposes, as well as for communicating with the financial community.

Whereas the long-range strategic and annual business plans are updated on a yearly basis, the ongoing operations plan is continually revised through the Sales and Operations Planning process. This feature, coupled with the fact that the ongoing operating plan should extend well beyond the annual business plan, enables companies to develop business plans that are not only consistent with long-range strategic goals, but realistic in terms of the marketplace.

Let's outline the objectives of sales and operations planning:

1. *Support and measure the business plan.* Sales and Operations Planning helps you determine whether your original financial expectations (budget), current sales plan, and operations plan are in sync with each other. It does this through monthly reviews of the marketplace and updates of the company's operations plan.
2. *Support the customer.* The focus needs to be on the customer. Customer service should be reviewed by product family in order to make appropriate decisions and determine strategy.
3. *Ensure that plans are realistic.* The key players from each department participate in formulating the new plans to make sure that all recommendations can be realistically supported. Since all of the numbers and assumptions are out on the table throughout the process, each department has more time to evaluate its resources and capabilities in the context of the company-wide plan. The result is a solid set of department plans that are based on real numbers and capabilities.
4. *Manage change effectively.* The ability to carry out Sales and Operations Planning is synonymous with being able to manage change, to substitute controlled and appropriate responses for knee-jerk reactions. As a result, companies that do a good job of performing Sales and Operations Planning take an active role in creating their futures instead of passively suffering through them.

The advantages of managing by the brain rather than the knee are well illustrated by the case of an electronics equipment manufacturer that suddenly found itself swimming in a sea of unexpected orders one quarter. For some reason, the general manager convinced himself that the company could add a shift in thirty days. Rather than call a special Sales and Operations Planning session to discuss the situation, this general manager simply decreed that production would be doubled in a month. The sales force confidently began promising orders based on product being available because of the new shift. But the hiring and training just didn't happen in thirty days. As a result, the company had to go to significant overtime in the hopes of solving the problem. And despite the overtime, promised ship dates were missed, customer service declined, and costs were higher and profits lower.

Equally disastrous, as production struggled the company began accumulating raw materials and mismatched components, which merely tied up cash and misused capacity. The net result? Significant opportunities for sales and profits were lost. And it took six months to dig out from under the one-minute, one-man decision and restore reliable service to customers.

5. *Manage finished goods inventory and/or backlog better to support customer service.* Maintaining the right level of finished goods inventory for make-to-stock families is essential for good "off-the-shelf" customer service. Operating at too high an inventory level results in extra costs, while operating at too low a level creates too many back orders. In a similar manner, controlling backlogs for make-to-order products is also essential for good customer service. If actual backlog becomes too large, delivery times stretch out, which eventually will cause customers to go elsewhere. By contrast, insufficient backlog can incur extra operating costs.

The general manager and his staff have the responsibility for establishing targets for what levels of inventory and backlog they believe are necessary to remain competitive. If the general manager and his staff don't establish targets by families, then by default it will be done by people at lower levels as they make individual decisions. Seldom will the sum of these detailed decisions add up to an aggregate plan that would represent what the general manager would have done himself. The linkage of detailed decisions to aggregate is a vital part of controlling the business, ensuring that each is supporting the other.

Maintaining the desired levels of finished goods inventory and backlog is an ongoing challenge for two reasons. First, it may be difficult to gain consensus on what the future targets should be, and second, it will usually be hard to hit the targets economically. Nevertheless, the process of reviewing the targets, discussing the consequences of changing them, and finally approving them is an effective means to meet the challenge.

6. *Control costs.* It is very important all departments are involved in the decision process to make capacity changes that may impact costs and therefore margins.

7. *Measure performance.* Sales and Operations Planning incorporates performance measurements to identify whenever actual performance has deviated significantly from the plan. The two main purposes of this are to separate those activities that are in control from those that aren't, and to quickly bring the out-of-control situation to the surface so that an evaluation can be made and, if necessary, corrective action taken.

Measuring performance against plans is only productive when the plans are valid. This is a very important contribution that Sales and Operations Planning makes to a company. Whenever the targets are challenging but attainable, managers are willing to be held accountable for their performance.

8. *Build teamwork.* A key element of Sales and Operations Planning is that it gives each department an opportunity to participate in the overall planning process. Each executive brings his experience and skills, which add insights to the matter of making changes to current plans. These same talents can respond to proposed changes in terms of consequences and alternatives. This not only ensures that the general manager is receiving the best possible advice before approving the new plans, it also demonstrates that each staff member is an important and valued part of the team. Thus the process not only provides a means of updating the operating plan to bring it into step with changes in the marketplace, it also instills a spirit of teamwork and a shared set of goals in achieving the new company plans. The result of such teamwork, of course, is a better-performing company.

Prerequisites to Sales and Operations Planning

Five prerequisites need to be in place in order to effectively use Sales and Operations Planning to improve a company's performance and become more competitive.

1. Understanding Sales and Operations Planning

For Sales and Operations Planning to be effective, there can be no "black boxes" in the process; all participants must understand how it works and what it is designed to achieve, When people understand that sharing information does not

MANDATORY PARTICIPANTS	POTENTIAL PARTICIPANTS
General Manager	
Sales	
Department Manager	Customer Service Manager
	Distribution Manager
	Service Pans Manager
	Demand Manager
Marketing	
Department Manager	Chief Forecaster
	Product Manager(s)
Manufacturing	
Department Manager	Manufacturing Manager
Materials Manager	Master Scheduler
	Purchasing Manager
	Quality Assurance Manager
Engineering	
Department Manager	Drafting Manager
	Engineering Scheduler
	Manager. Design Engineering
Finance	
Department Manager	Budget Manager
	Cost Accounting Manager
Human Resources	
Department Manager	
Programs/Special Projects	
Appropriate managers	

Figure 2. S&OP Typical Participants

mean giving up control and they see that the exchange actually leads to gaining control, they will be more willing to work in concert with their fellow departments toward the larger objectives of the company.

2. Commitment and People

Once a company embarks on the Sales and Operations Planning process, it is really making a lifetime commitment. Each month, or possibly more frequently, the decision-makers from all departments, along with the general manager, must review and update the company's sales, production, engineering, and financial plans. This "core team" is made up of the top executives from sales, marketing, manufacturing, engineering, finance, and human resources.

Figure 2 suggests the personnel who should participate in the Sales and Operations planning sessions. Note the general manager at the top of the list; it is mandatory that he attend all Sales and Operations planning sessions if the process is to be successful. One the general manager commits fully to the process, the other key people will set aside the time to meet regularly, regardless of their other activities. In business, as in shepherding, the flock will follow the leader's actions.

3. Defining Families

Sales and Operations Planning is carried out at the aggregate level. By "aggregate" we mean product groupings or families rather than individual products or items. Why manage at the aggregate level? Because it's just not practical for top management to juggle every item that the company manufactures. The idea is to get effective input and control from management. This comes about by managing families, not items, and managing rates, not specific work orders.

Managing in the aggregate means grouping products into logical families. This may be straightforward if all parties agree what the families should be. Very often, however, sales and marketing view things in aggregate differently than manufacturing does. Sales and marketing naturally look at their products the way customers look at them—from a standpoint of function and applications. Manufacturing, in contrast, tends to look at products in terms of processes.

When departments have differing views of families, a conversion process will be necessary. This is usually done with a rough cut capacity planning mechanism.

4. Planning Horizon

The term "planning horizon" refers to how far ahead you need to establish your plans. Everyone recognizes that Sales and Operations Planning is long-term, but the word "long" needs to be quantified. The Sales and Operations plan must extend far enough into the future to ensure the availability of all resources. Thus, whichever resource—material, equipment, people—takes the longest determines the length of the planning horizon.

5. Time Fences

All departments must recognize in their Sales and Operations Planning process that changes in the plan are time-dependent; that is, the sooner the change, the more costly or impossible it may become to make changes in the plan. For every product family, there are "time fences"—guidelines that demarcate when changes are feasible. The fences reflect the realities of each business. For each product family, therefore, you need to establish guidelines for determining where changes can be made and where change may incur extra costs. Such time fences can be arrived at by looking at your constraints in terms of capacity and materials.

Sales and Operations Planning as a Process

Sales and Operations Planning is a process not just a meeting. There is a series of steps that are formulated and followed in order to insure that the process is complete. The following is an overview of the necessary steps:

1. *End of month processing.* Data must be available in order to start the monthly review.
   a. Bookings plan/actual
   b. Production plan/actual
   c. Shipments plan/actual
   d. Inventory plan/actual
   e. Backlog plan/actual
   Note: An example is shown later in this paper as Figure 6.
2. *Updated sales plans and forecast.* Marketing and Sales have the responsibility to update future anticipated demand and communicate it to operations. A demand review meeting should complete this phase.
3. *Operations.* Engineering or development manufacturing and procurement need to review the anticipated demand. They will determine in what way they can support the demand and, as quickly as possible, communicate any problems as feedback.

The next steps vary by company depending greatly on size and structure.

4. *Pre-S&OP meeting* (optional). A pre-S&OP meeting is held to work out as much as possible prior to the senior management review. Note: This is a very important step for most companies.
5. *Senior Management S&OP meeting.* This should be a decision-making meeting that is the next to last step in the monthly process.
6. *Final step.* The final step is the distribution of the minutes of the meeting, including a Sales and Operations plan report that is the company's "marching orders."

Implementing Sales and Operations Planning

The implementation of Sales and Operations Planning should be viewed as a project, and every good project should have a project manager. Who should that be? The general — manager—after all, it's his process. While he should delegate data gathering and other clerical duties to his staff, he must assume leadership of the process right from the beginning to understand it thoroughly, to operate it effectively, and to accept responsibility for the results.

The general sequential steps in implementing Sales and Operations Planning are shown in **Figure 3**.

1. *Education.* Everyone who participates in the Sales and Operations Planning process must have sufficient understanding of it to know what's expected of them and how to make the maximum contribution. Sales and Operations Planning education can be accomplished through a combination of outside classes and video courses. Sales and Operations Planning implementation is often done in the context of MRP II implementation, so there are other basic topics that can be covered as well, such as the fundamentals of Manufacturing Resource Planning

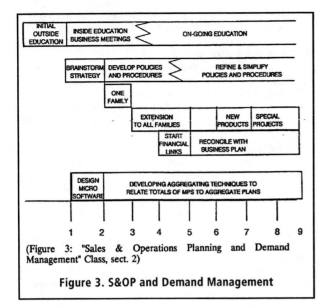

(Figure 3: "Sales & Operations Planning and Demand Management" Class, sect. 2)

Figure 3. S&OP and Demand Management

(MRP II)), Just-in-Time (JIT), and Distribution Resource Planning (DRP).

2. *Brainstorm Strategy.* Following is a list of the subjects that need to be discussed in the brainstorming session:
   - Families
     - Process vs. Product
   - Units of Measure
     - $ vs. Units
   - Planning Horizon
   - Where should you meet the customer?
   - Steps in the Process
   - Time Fences
   - Format of Spreadsheet
   - Systems Resource
   - Departmental Responsibility for Pre-S&OP and S&OP Meetings
   - Create S&OP Policy (see **Figure 4**)

3. *One Family.* It is recommended that in order to start the process quickly, the first real meeting is structured with a review of a single family. This should allow ample time to adequately discuss all aspects of what needs to be discussed, what information is needed and in what format.

   The discussion should include such topics as:
   - Sales Plan assessment
   - Production Plan assessment
   - Inventory and lead time objectives
   - Customer service measures
   - Time fences (capacity and/or material)
   - Documenting Assumptions
   - Develop an agenda for the meeting (see **Figure 5**)

4. *Design Micro Software.* Most companies are developing their mechanics with the help of a PC. This is accomplished by downloading or tracking data from their MRP database and aggregating and displaying it with the PC capability.

   In this manner, it is easier and quicker to implement. Changes that will come as you use the system are easier to accomplish. What-If calculations are much easier to program and run. Some companies actually do this in the Sales and Operations Planning meeting.

   Use **Figure 6** for a model in developing a format for the display of information for each family.

5. *Extension to all families.* This step should be in place by the second or third meeting. Be aware that the first time

Objective

The company is establishing a monthly Sales and Operations Planning process to support the business plan and to improve the ongoing operations of the company.

Process

The process will consist of a series of steps in that each department updates and communicates its plans to other departments in a prescribed sequence in preparation for a Sales and Operations Planning meeting, that will be held to review and approve all plans.

Schedules

The Sales and Operations Planning meeting will be held monthly and a schedule published for the next twelve months in order to ensure attendance.

Personnel

The Sales and Operations Planning Participants will include:
- General Manager
- Vice President of Sales
- Vice President of Marketing
- Vice President of Operations
- Vice President of Engineering
- Vice President of Human Resources
- Vice President of Finances
- Director of Materials

  Other people will be called to participate from time to time.

Families

The Sales and Operations Planning Team will develop and agree on the most appropriate aggregate levels in order to communicate most effectively. The plans must support the customer (marketing) requirements and be convertible to financial and capacity requirements so that all departments can support the plans.

Horizon

The planning horizon must be long enough to ensure the required resources can be provided when needed and in an economical manner.

Time Fences

The Sales and Operations Planning Team will establish time fences to manage change.

Review

The Sales and Operations Planning Team will constantly review and critique the Sales and Operations Planning process in order to keep it up to date with the needs of the business.

Signature

This policy is signed and agreed to by:
(All managers must sign)

Figure 4. Sales and Operations Planning Policy

Typical Agenda

1. Special Issues
2. Performance Reviews
3. Review Assumptions and Vulnerabilities
4. Family by Family Review
5. New Product
6. Special Projects
7. Review of Minutes
8. Critique of Meeting

Figure 5. S&OP and Demand Management Class

this is attempted, you will have a fairly lengthy meeting. Over time, you will learn how to make it more efficient.

6. *Financial links.* As soon as it is practical, the links to the business plans should be made. Only when this occurs, will the company be able to achieve the objective of having one set of numbers for the business.

Operating Sales and Operations Planning

The *General Manager* has the key role in making Sales and Operations Planning work in your company. The following is a checklist that he might use as an aid to critique his role in the process.

- Insist on everyone's participation
- Make decisions
- Insist that homework is done
- Encourage realistic improvement
- Resolve conflicts that will occur
- Act as a consensus maker
- Look at S&OP as a management development process

Oliver Wight ABCD Checklist

The Oliver Wight Companies have developed an ABCD Checklist for manufacturing excellence. The ABCD Checklist has an overview question related to Sales and Operations Planning with 18 detail questions that are extremely helpful in determining whether the S&OP process is being conducted properly. After S&OP has been operating for 3 or 4 months, we recommend that it be utilized to critique the process.

About the Author

Richard C. Ling, President of Richard C. Ling, Inc., provides education and consulting services to manufacturing companies in a variety of industries within the United States and internationally, primarily, the United Kingdom, Australia and Japan.

After earning his Economics degree from the University of Rochester, Dick joined IBM in a System Engineering capacity where he was a pioneer in developing MRP systems in the early 1960s.

He joined Arista Information Systems, leading the company's efforts to develop both consulting and effective software systems to support manufacturing operations. While at Arista, Dick earned recognition for his design and implementation of computer systems for Manufacturing Resource Planning, that included the first Master Schedule Module.

As a principal of Oliver Wight Education Associates, he conducts regular classes both in Top Management and Sales and in Operations Planning and Demand Management. He also helped to develop and in an instructor to these classes held in the United Kingdom, Australia and Japan.

Dick is a member of the American Production and Inventory Control Society (APICS) and is a frequent speaker at APICS International conferences and chapter meetings. He is a certified Fellow of APICS and a past president of the Piedmont Triad Chapter.

Dick, with Walter Goddard, is the author of *Orchestrating Success: Improve Control of the Business with Sales and Operations Planning.*

MONTH	J	F	M	A	M	J	J	A	S	O	N	D	Yearly Total	J	F	M
Days in Month	20	20	20	20	20	20	20	20	20	20	20	20	240	20	20	20
SALES PLAN																
Last Year's Actuals	154	156	175	172	191	198	190	175	174	162	155	136	2038	—	—	—
Annual Business Plan	160	160	180	180	200	200	200	180	180	160	160	140	2100	—	—	—
Current			180	180	200	200	200	180	180	160	160	140	2110	160	160	—
Proposed	164	166	187	190	205	205	205	185	185	160	160	150	2162	170	170	190
Deviation	+4	+6	+7													
Cumulative Deviation	+4	+10	+17													
PRODUCTION PLAN																
Annual Business Plan	170	170	170	170	200	200	200	200	160	160	160	160	2120			
Current			170	180	200	200	200	200	160	160	160	160	2119	170	170	—
Proposed	164	165	168	180	200	210	210	200	200	160	160	160	2177	180	180	180
Deviation	-6	-5	-2													
Cumulative Deviation	-6	-11	-13													
INVENTORY																
Annual Business Plan (161)	171	181	171	161	161	161	161	161	181	161	161	161	181	—		
Current			155	155	155	155	155	175	155	155	155	175	—	185	195	—
Proposed	163	165	155	150	147	142	137	152	167	167	167	177	—	187	197	187
Deviation	-8	-16	-16													
Days Cover	20	18.3	16.3	14.6	14.3	13.8	14.8	16.4	20.8	20.8	23.8	22.1	—	20.8	22	19.7
BACKLOG																
Annual Business Plan	10	10	10	10	10	10	10	10	10	10	10	10				
Current			15	15	15	15	15	15	15	15	15	15		15	15	
Proposed	12	15	24	29	29	31	21	11	11	11	11	11		11	11	11
Deviation	+2	+5	+14		+1											
SHIPMENTS																
Annual Business Plan	160	160	180	180	200	200	200	180	180	160	160	140	2100			
Current			180	180	200	200	200	180	180	160	160	140	2105	160	160	
Proposed	162	163	178	185	203	215	215	185	185	160	160	150	2161	170	170	190
Deviation	+2	+3	-2													
Cumulative Deviation	+2	+5	+3													

Figure 6.

Overview Question

4. Sales and Operations Planning
   Sales and Operations planning is the management process that maintains the current operating plan in support of the business plan. The process consists of a formal meeting each month run by the general manager and covers a planning horizon adequate to plan resources effectively.

Detail Questions

1. There is a concise written Sales and Operations planning policy that covers the purpose, process and participants in the process. _____.

2. Sales and Operations planning is truly a process and not just a meeting. There is a sequence of steps that are laid out and followed. _____

3. The meeting dates are set well ahead to avoid schedule conflicts. In case of an emergency, the department manager is represented by someone who is empowered to speak for the department. _____

4. A formal agenda is circulated prior to the meeting.

5. The plans are reviewed by product family units of measure that communicate most effectively. _____

6. The new product development schedule is reviewed at the Sales and Operations planning meeting. _____

7. All participants attend the Sales and Operations planning meeting prepared. There are preliminary meetings by each department in preparation for the Sales and Operations planning meeting. _____

8. The presentation of information includes a review of both past performances and future plans for: sales, production, inventory, backlog, shipments and new product activity. _____

9. Inventory and delivery lead time (backlog) strategies are reviewed each month as part of the process. _____

10. There is a process of reviewing and documenting assumptions about business and the marketplace.
    _____
    This is to enhance the understanding of the business and represents the basis for future projections.
    _____

11. Sales and Operations planning is an action process. Conflicts are resolved and decisions are made and communicated. _____

12. Any changes—large or unanticipated—are communicated to other departments before the meeting. —
    _____

13. Minutes of the meeting are circulated immediately after the meeting. _____

14. The mechanism is in place to insure that aggregate sales plans agree with detailed sales plans by item and by market segment or territory. There is a consensus from sales, marketing and operating management. _____

15. Time fences have been established as guidelines for managing changes. In the near-term, there is an effort to minimize the changes in order to gain the benefits of stability. In the mid-term range, changes up or down are expected but are reviewed to insure they can be executed. In long-term, less precision is expected but direction is established. _____

16. Tolerances are established to determine acceptable performance for: sales, engineering, finance and production. They are reviewed and updated. Accountability is clearly established. _____

17. The production plan is the driver of the master schedule and is supported by a procedure that defines a summarization to insure that they are in agreement. _____

18. There is an ongoing critique of the process.

Scoring: 4 = Excellent, 3 = Very Good, 2 = Fair, 1 = Poor, 0 = Not Doing

Class A in Sales and Operations Planning is a prerequisite if you want to be a Class A Company.

Figure 7. The Oliver Wight Companies ABCD Checklist—Class "A" Program

Reprinted from the Production and Inventory Management Journal, *First Quarter, 1993.*

How to Compete in Your Industry
Archie Lockamy III, Ph.D., CPIM

International competition has caused manufacturing companies to rethink how to compete in the marketplace. Financial results can no longer dominate management decision making [3]. To compete effectively, manufacturing firms must define strategic objectives based on current and future market requirements, develop performance-measurement systems consistent with these requirements, and create mechanisms for ensuring consistent actions on shared objectives between organizational levels and across functional areas [7].

Strategic Objectives

Authors such as Schonberger [10], Ohmae [9], Kaplan [6], Goldratt and Fox [4], and Cox [1] have collectively identified the following strategic objectives as critical to international competition: lower cost, better quality, shorter lead times, on-time delivery, increased process/ product innovation, increased process/product flexibility, and more responsive field service. Firms must develop strategies which provide the link between the objectives the organization wants to achieve and the various functional area policies and operating plans it uses to guide day-to-day activities. Performance-measurement systems offer a means for communicating objectives and achievements throughout the organization and for ensuring that the firm is using its resources in the most effective manner. As competitive pressures increase within a manufacturing industry, it becomes increasingly important that all organizational levels: (1) use measures for assessing performance on the firm's strategic objectives which are consistent and (2) develop performance measurement systems which contain mechanisms for exchanging information on these objectives between organizational levels and across functional areas.

Vollmann [11] suggests that strategy is the key element in determining the appropriate measures for an effective performance-measurement system. He contends that organizations must measure things which are congruent with the present set of perceived strategic objectives in order to provide the firm's focus. Therefore, companies which compete internationally must develop relationships among strategy, performance-measurement systems, and the supporting activities of the organization which are consistent.

Performance-Measurement Systems

In order for decisions to be supportive of one another between organizational levels and across functional areas, performance results must be communicated and evaluated at all levels of the firm. Performance-measurement systems provide a mechanism for assessing progress toward functional and company objectives. Effective performance-measurement systems must contain performance criteria, measures, and standards [2] for each strategic objective. These systems should also result in the firm focusing on a narrow range of pursuits, developing a consistent pattern of decision making, and embracing strategic objectives acknowledged by the entire company. McNair et al. [8] state that the ultimate goal of a performance-measurement system is to integrate organizations across various managerial levels and functions.

Performance-Measurement System Linkages

Hayes and Wheelwright [5] suggest that in order for true worker-manager participation to occur, natural interactions must occur among production workers, engineers, and managers. The authors note that such interactions result in relationships which are productive to both parties. This concept also holds for inter and intra-organizational relationships. Mechanisms are required which aid in focusing various levels and functions of the firm on its strategic objectives. Performance-measurement system linkages between organizational levels and across functional areas are needed to promote productive relationships which facilitate "organizational focus." The term organizational focus is used to depict a state whereby the actions and behaviors of the firm concentrate on achieving stated objectives, the decisions made within the firm follow a consistent pattern throughout the company, and a pervasiveness exists in the company for supporting activities necessary for the successful accomplishment of objectives.

A Case Example: The Trane Corporation

The Trane Corporation is a worldwide manufacturer of air-conditioning products, with headquarters in Lacrosse, Wisconsin. The corporation is the largest commercial air-conditioning manufacturer in the United States, and is recognized as an industry leader. Trane is divided into ten autonomous strategic business units (SBUs). The Self-Contained Systems SBU is part of the Commercial Systems Group and is located in Macon, Georgia. The firm's customer base is 90% make-to-order and 10% engineer-to-order. Although Self-Contained Systems' products are produced in low volumes (five units per day) and can be ordered in 40,000 different configurations, the manufacturing process is repetitive. The SBU employs elements of material requirements planning (MRP), Just-in-Time (JIT), and theory of constraints (TOC) to plan, monitor, and control production processes and the overall business.

Function	Performance Criteria	Performance Measure	Performance Standard
Operations	Cycle counting	% accuracy	100% accuracy
	Spoilage/scrap	Daily spoilage and scrap dollars by work team	Improving trend
	Small tools/gauges	Daily small tool and gauge account dollars by work team	Improving trend
	Housekeeping (future)	Housekeeping grading scale	Highest grade
Supplier Dev./Mat'ls	Material outages	Total daily number and % due to vendor late delivery, vendor quality, BOM/inventory accuracy and material planning	No outages
	MRP exception messages	Daily ranking of no. of MRP messages by planner	No messages
	Defective material	No. of days defective materials are held in return or review area.	Improving trend
	Service orders	Daily no. of service orders received	Improving trend (less service orders)
	Service order parts	Daily no. of service order parts shipped	Improving trend
	Service order processing time	No. of days to process a service order	Improving trend
Marketing	Customer hours	No. of hours spent with customers by marketing engineers	4 customer locations per month spending the no. of hours necessary
	Order pace	Daily no. of incoming orders	Order forecast
	Price	Daily price of booked orders	Budgeted price
P/D Eng.	Sales order specials	No. of days to process	Improving trend
	Warranty claims	No. of days to process	5 days
Accounting	Expense vouchers	No. of days to process	Improving trend
	Invoice discounts	Frequency of using available cash discounts	100% usage
	Expense reports	No. of days to process	Improving trend
	Direct base billing outstanding	Daily dollar value of receivables	Improving trend
Human resources	Performance appraisal timeliness	% on-time performance of appraisals by management team	100% on-time

Table 1. Self-Contained Systems Functional Area Performance-Measurement Systems

Performance Criteria	Performance Measures	Performance Standards
Manufacturing performance	Units per day	5.6 Units per day
	Man hrs. paid per unit	155 hrs. per unit
	Man hrs. paid per unit per production worker (productivity ratio)	1.24
	Floor cycle	3 days
Inventory management	Turns	Finished: 20 per year RIP: 10 per year Total: 10 per year
	Inventory accuracy	98%
	% material outage days due to late delivery, vendor quality or other reasons	No outages
	% permanent homes for point of use inventory on plant floor (i.e., permanent locations)	100%
	Machine downtime hours due to material outages	0 hours downtime

Table 2. Self-Contained Systems Total Business Performance-Measurement System

TABLE 2: *Continued*

Performance Criteria	Performance Measures	Performance Standards
Shipping performance	% on-time delivery	98%
	Average days late	0 days
	Weekly promise cycle versus customer request date	Promise cycle = customer request date
	Master production schedule (MPS) changes	Weeks 1–2: <2%
		Weeks 2–6: <5%
	Ship cycle	7 weeks
MPS performance	Weekly MPS deviations	±7%
	Monthly MPS deviations	±5%
P/D eng. performance	No. of ECN completed monthly	Improving trend (increase monthly no. completed)
	Average ECN backlog	<25
	ECN throughput rate	30 days per ECN
	% new products/options introduced in last 2 years	5% of total sales
Marketing performance	*Closure rate on major jobs (>$100K):	Improving trend
	Total jobs won	Improving trend
	Projects dropped	
	Projects lost:	
	Price	Improving trend
	Ship cycle	Improving trend
	Features	Improving trend
	% international units sold	5% of total sales
	% market share	50%
Business performance	Operating income dollars before interest and taxes	Financial plan
	Cash flow before interest and taxes	Financial plan
	Order dollars (actual bookings)	Financial plan
	Sales dollars (actual billings)	Financial plan
	Operating expenses	Financial plan
	Return on sales	Financial plan
	Return on net assets	Financial plan
	Sales dollars per person	Non-production: $517K
		Production: $284K
	Scrap/spoilage	0.8% of total sales
	Service expense	1.8% of total sales
Accounting performance	Sales expense disposition	20 days
Vendor performance	% on-time delivery	95%
	% defect free	98%
	Lead time:	
	% less than 8 wks.	85%
	% less than 3 wks.	35%
Customer contact	Customer days:	
	Average days per month	5
	Customer in Macon/SBU personnel in field	30 days per month for the combination
Personnel/safety performance	Absenteesim rate	<2.0% annually
	Lost time accidents	<2.5 days annually

* Expressed in total units, total dollars, and as a percentage of sales.

Strategic Objectives

Quality and cost objectives are acknowledged between organizational levels and across functional areas within Self-Contained Systems. The term "quality" is used in the broadest sense at the firm. For example, the marketing department views quality as meeting customer requirements relative to delivery, product reliability, field support, and overall expectations. Although quality is recognized as strategically important to the firm's success, there is no separate quality-assurance function. Activities which promote quality are managed within the responsible organizations. Cost objectives at Self-Contained Systems are targeted on material cost control, since material represents approximately 77% of total manufacturing cost.

Performance-Measurement Systems

The performance-measurement systems used at Self-Contained Systems for monitoring quality and cost objectives are visual, easy to understand, focused on daily trends, and linked between organizational levels and across functional areas. Self-Contained Systems utilizes both functional area and total business performance-measurement

ESOP–Details
T–OE–NA
TOC–Managing priorities
Planning BOM strategies
MPS policy
Teamwork
Trane overview
Participative management/people empowerment
Supplier development philosophy
Visual floor management
Interview skills
Counseling/terminations
Interview tell sessions
Employee orientation tell sessions
Material point certification/inventory quality
Labor economics
SCS markets/customers/strategy
Product/BOM change process
Operations report/MBO process
T–OE–NA ECN justification process
SOP process
MRP/JIT/TQC—WCM
Financial statements
QIP
Rings of defense
Basic refrigeration
Shop math/reading prints
Basic SCS product training
ICS for field offices
Acoustics for field offices
Modular bill concept

Table 3. Macon Way Education Modules for Self-Contained Systems SBU

systems. Functional systems are used to communicate departmental performance to other business areas, support resource-allocation decisions, and monitor internal customer-oriented relationships between functional areas. The total business unit performance-measurement system focuses on key performance criteria, measures and standards used to monitor the SBU's progress towards excellence. The measures are shared across functional boundaries, and multiple functions are responsible for the achievement of established performance standards. An illustration of the functional and total business performance-measurement systems used by Self-Contained Systems is presented in **Tables 1 and 2**, respectively.

Performance-Measurement System Linkages

A key feature of how performance-measurement system linkages are accomplished at Self-Contained Systems is the visual display of measures at the work place by each functional area. The measures are simple and assessable to all employees. The display of performance measures allows for "management by sight" and helps other departments to develop ways of supporting functional along with total business-unit objectives. The development of functional charters which support business-unit strategy and tactics is also critical to achieving linkages between functional and business unit systems. Department managers develop functional charters outlining functional strategies for supporting overall business objectives, success criteria relative to the objectives, and performance measures used to monitor success criteria. Each charter is presented to the management team (which consists of the general manager and the functional department managers) for review and suggested improvements. The charter-development process ensures linkages across functional performance-measurement systems. Educational modules developed and taught to all employees by the management team help to improve overall organizational understanding of the business and indirectly assist in performance-measurement system linkages, A listing of the educational modules is presented in **Table 3**. Finally, formal inter-functional interactions via periodic meetings dealing with specific performance issues along with periodic performance reports provide performance-measurement system linkages on quality and cost objectives between levels and across functions.

The mechanisms described to accomplish performance-measurement system linkages by Self-Contained Systems is part of the firm's "global-optimization" concept, illustrated in **Figure 1**. The intent is to develop an organizational culture conducive to a thinking work force focused on each functional area contributing to the global objectives of the firm.

Conclusions

Agreement between organizational levels on the firm's strategic objectives is a prerequisite for manufacturing companies to successfully compete internationally. A multifunctional assessment approach is the most effective means of ensuring progress towards achieving established performance standards. To maintain effectiveness, the performance-measurement system criteria, measures, and standards established on current strategic objectives must be dynamic and change with the internal and external environmental conditions of the business. Finally, firms must develop organizational cultures conducive to the development of interorganizational and multifunctional consistency on the strategic objectives.

References

1. Cox, James F. "How To Schedule To Improve Manufacturing Performance." In *South African Production and Inventory Control Society Proceedings*, 1-7. Durban, South Africa: APICS, 1989.

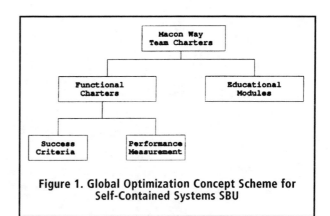

Figure 1. Global Optimization Concept Scheme for Self-Contained Systems SBU

2. Crawford, Karlene M., James F. Cox, and John H. Blackstone. *Performance Measurement Systems and the ITT Philosophy.* Falls Church, VA: APICS, 1988.

3. Eccles, Robert G. "The Performance Measurement Manifesto, *Harvard Business Review* (January-February 1991): 131-137.

4. Goldratt, Eliyahu, and Robert E. Fox. *The Race,* Croton-on-Hudson, NY: North River Press, 1986.

5. Hayes, Robert II. and Steven C. Wheelwright. *Restoring Our Competitive Edge: Competing Through Manufacturing.* New York: John Wiley, 1984.

6. Kaplan, Robert S. "Measuring Manufacturing Performance: A New Challenge for Managerial Accounting Research." *The Accounting Review* (October 1983): 686-703.

7. Lockamy III, Archie and James F. Cox. *Critical Linkage: Aligning Performance Measurement Systems for Competitive Advantage.* Homewood, IL: Business One Irwin/ APICS, forthcoming, 1993.

8. McNair, Carol J., William Mosconi, and Thomas F. Norris. *Beyond the Bottom Line: Measuring World Class Performance.* Homewood, IL: Dow Jones-Irwin, 1989.

9. Ohmae, Kenichi. *The Mind of the Strategist: Business Planning for Competitive Advantage.* New York: Penguin Books, 1983.

10. Schonberger, Richard J. *World Class Manufacturing: The Lessons of Simplicity Applied.* New York: The Free Press, 1986.

11. Vollmann, Thomas E. "Performance Measurement: A Key to Competitive Survival in the 1990's." In *Proceedings of the 1989 Academic-Practitioner Liaison Operations Management Workshop,* 43-53. Falls Church, VA: APICS, 1989.

About the Author

Archie Lockamy III, Ph.D., CPIM, is an associate professor of operations management at Florida A&M University. He received a BCHE in chemical engineering from Georgia Tech, an MBA from Atlanta University, and a Ph.D. in operations management from the University of Georgia. His research interests are manufacturing strategy, performance measurement, total quality management, Just-in-Time, and theory of constraints. Prior to his academic career, Dr. Lockamy held various engineering and managerial positions with DuPont, Procter and Gamble, and TRW.

Reprinted from the Production and Inventory Management Journal, *Second Quarter, 1995.*

Quality Function Deployment: A Case Study

Archie Lockamy III, Ph.D., CFPIM, and Anil Khurana, Ph.D.

Quality function deployment (QFD) originated in Mitsubishi's Kobe shipyard in 1972, possibly as an outcome of Derning's teachings [7]. The original Japanese name was Hin Shitsu Ki No Ten Kai, translated as:

Hin Shitsu—quality or features/attributes.

Ki No—function or mechanization.

Ten Kai—deployment, diffusion, or development/evolution.

QFD is an integrative, four-phase process which links together customer needs, product and parts design requirements, process planning, and manufacturing specifications during product development. Various tools and mechanisms are used to operationalize the QFD concept. For example, design for manufacturing and assembly (DFMA) is often used as a part of the QFD process. QFD can also help identify consistent performance measures for the different stages in the product design-process design-manufacturing-customer chain. A flow diagram of the QFD process is provided in **Figure 1**.

QFD Benefits

The benefits of QFD are:

* Better customer satisfaction resulting from improved quality of design
* Shorter lead times due to fewer and earlier engineering changes
* Better linkages between various design and manufacturing stages
* A reduction in the number of product components
* An improved work atmosphere through the horizontal integration of functions [8].

Also, QFD provides a structure for benchmarking competitors' designs. Japanese auto makers attribute tangible benefits, such as low product cost, high quality, and short development lead times, to QFD [1, 2]. Engineering changes are fewer and take place earlier, resulting in reduced product lead times [3, 5].

Purpose of Study

The purpose of this study was to gain insights into the use of the QFD process through its examination in a live organization. By examining the QFD process in practice, valuable lessons can be learned which may help facilitate future QFD adoptions by other organizations. Given the exploratory nature of this study, it may also be used as a basis for future empirical QFD research.

Research Methodology

Since the central purpose of this research was to study the QFD process, a qualitative research methodology was adopted. We conducted a detailed case study of the QFD process applied to two different vehicle programs within Chrysler Motors Corporation.

The Chrysler study included ten semi-structured interviews with program managers, design and manufacturing engineers, QFD team leaders, QFD specialists and facilitators, and DFMA specialists. Each of these interviews lasted one to three hours. In addition, we had extensive discussions with the QFD planning group at Chrysler. Of great benefit was the close interaction we had with active QFD teams. Chrysler engineers motivated us to "live" the QFD process in order to get a better feel for the working philosophy. We participated in the weekly meetings of one of the QFD Phase 1 teams. In addition, we attended meetings of a QFD Phase 3 team comprised of program management, design, advanced engineering, logistics, and plant management representatives.

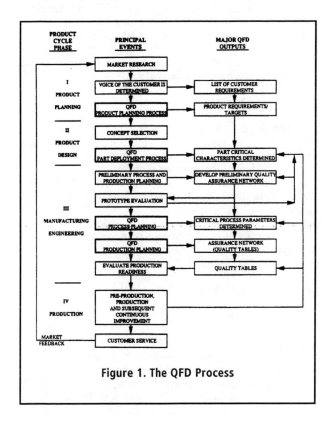

Figure 1. The QFD Process

Another source of information for the case study was company data. Documents pertaining to product policy, supplier meetings, and market feedback were reviewed. Chrysler also shared company manuals, QFD charts, and information on past QFD teams. We also benefitted from attending Chrysler-sponsored QFD training sessions.

Case Study: Chrysler Motors Corporation

QFD was formally launched at Chrysler in September 1986, though the first application started in June 1986. Initially, only a few of the cross-functional design teams embraced the QFD concept. Later, some of the product managers recognized the potential of QFD and implemented it for their vehicle programs. After the reorganization of Chrysler's product design function into design platforms several years ago, QFD received more support from senior managers.

The American Supplier Institute (ASI) provided QFD training for Chrysler during the first few years. This role has been taken over by Chrysler's quality planning group. During the early years of QFD adoption, the company also sought the help of well-known Japanese quality, design, and QFD experts such as Akashi Fukuhara (assistant director, Central Japan Quality Control Association).

Adoption of QFD

The first-time implementation of QFD procedures within a Chrysler vehicle program is viewed as a four-stage process: spreading awareness; developing successful case studies and examples to motivate subsequent teams; companywide training and education on QFD techniques and philosophy; and adoption of QFD as a business philosophy.

Although our research confirmed the use of a fourstage process by Chrysler for QFD adoption, our interviews with design engineers in one vehicle platform revealed that QFD was not fully accepted as the preferred design methodology. Since QFD was not considered an integral part of the overall design process by this vehicle platform, the QFD process was perceived as requiring additional time and effort. Such opinions led to organizational and perceptual barriers regarding the successful implementation of QFD.

The QED Process

At Chrysler, the QFD process began at concept generation. At the business planning stage, the concept generation is implemented by initially starting with a program management-level team that sets overall guidelines and allocates responsibility to different design groups for different systems. These design groups then set up QFD teams which begin by determining system-level needs. Once these requirements are established, the team breaks up into smaller groups that focus on the various components comprising the system. The system-level QFD team, however, still maintains overall responsibility for the system, At the same time, progress is made on the sequential phases of the QFD process depicted in Figure 1.

QFD Software

In order to keep track of the QFD teams' activities, responsibilities, and progress, some QFD teams at Chrysler used a commercially available QFD software package. The software has the capability of constructing and analyzing the "house of quality" and other QFD matrices. The use of such software was not widespread in the product groups we visited. Often, it was the responsibility of the QFD facilitators/coordinators to maintain QFD charts and other information.

Making Design Trade-offs

What happens when customer requirements lead to conflicting design requirements? Although such conflicts may occur during any of the four QFD phases, they are most likely detected during the product planning phase as negative correlations in the roof of the "house of quality." Engineers at later design stages must be made aware of such conflicts-managing information transfer and communication is the key to resolving such conflicts.

Two kinds of solutions to such trade-offs normally occur. The first uses the approach suggested by the Pugh concept selection method. In this approach, alternatives are generated, and the best alternatives are chosen based on previously set cost, quality, weight, and investment constraints and objectives. Failure mode and effects analysis (FMEA) is used to challenge the best design alternatives to expose their weaknesses and to find potential problems. However, the best alternatives may still not be very attractive. The second approach may be useful in such cases. The Taguchi design of experiments can be used to "optimize" the design by isolating controllable variables. By determining the effect of these variables on the design requirements, it is possible to determine optimum levels for controllable parameters. By understanding the behavior of certain design outcomes as a function of these controllable parameters, mathematical optimization (such as linear/nonlinear programming) can be used to determine optimal parameter settings and design outcomes. Chrysler employed both approaches in making design trade-offs,

Since QFD brings together a multifunctional team and helps challenge traditional design objectives and targets, the researchers expected an increase in design innovations resulting from the need to make such design trade-offs. A few examples did exist. For example, the cruise-control device on the new LH mid-size cars is an improved version resulting from conflicting design objectives, However, discussions with several QFD design teams revealed that such innovations have not yet become common. We hypothesized that the lack of increasing levels of design innovation was due to the use of QFD primarily as a design tool. This hypothesis was confirmed through discussions with several design engineers and managers.

Getting Data for QFD

Due to various resource constraints, Chrysler management was sometimes unable to authorize firsthand customer research for determining customer requirements. In such cases, teams were encouraged to document what they knew based on their experience. Thus, the teams would only research product areas where they did not know the customers' requirements, or felt that there was a risk of misinterpreting customers' needs. Often, team members simulated customers by actually evaluating competing vehicles, and reviewing customer ratings. The teams also relied on secondary data derived from private reports or warranty information,

Strategic Role of QFD

Our research revealed strategic benefits for Chrysler in the launch of their LH platform for mid-size cars (e.g., the 1993 Dodge Vision). The total product design cycle took approximately 36 months, versus historical cycles ranging from 62 to 54 months. LH prototypes were ready 95 weeks before the scheduled start of production, compared to the traditional 60 weeks. The program required only 740 people, compared to historical involvement levels of 1,600 people. Also, by focusing on customer requirements instead of only cost, Chrysler made significant design changes that are gaining acceptance in the marketplace [4].

Performance Evaluation Systems for QFD

Our interviews with Chrysler managers revealed that records relating to QFD and project performance were rarely kept. One reason for this void was the lack of an established evaluation system suited to QFD. Another reason was the evaluation of design engineers was not always consistent with QFD objectives. A senior program executive mentioned that establishing merit and reward systems consistent with QFD and other team-based programs has been a challenge. Creating a performance measurement system that is consistent with organizational and program objectives is clearly difficult. However, the success of any program depends on measuring performance and using this to provide constructive feedback.

Conclusions

Upon examining the case study data, we offer the following "lessons learned" concerning the use of the QFD process.

Lesson 1: QFD Is More than a Product Design Tool

Tomatzky et al. [9] describes the adoption of innovations or new technologies as a four-stage process composed of the following elements: identification, transfer, amplification, and acceptance. The identification stage focuses on educating the organization on the benefits of the innovation. The transfer stage consists of training a selected group in the use of the innovation, and demonstrating its successful application via pilot projects. After successfully demonstrating how the innovation can provide benefits, total adoption begins in the amplification stage through: (1) company-wide training and education on the use of the innovation and (2) companywide information sharing on how the innovation has benefitted the firm. However, total adoption does not occur until the innovation is directly linked to the firm's philosophies and strategies during the acceptance stage,

QFD can be viewed as a process innovation for developing products. The adoption of QFD, therefore, requires a process analogous to the one provided by Tomatzky et al. [9], Although Chrysler had a similar implementation process, QFD was still viewed by some design teams as a "tool" unrelated to the firm's business strategy or design philosophy. To avoid this situation, QFD-related performance measures are needed which link design team actions to the firm's strategy. These measures should provide the basis for performance evaluations and rewards. A QFD performance measurement system is needed to monitor and control the product development process.

Lesson 2: QFD Can Provide Firms with a Competitive Advantage

Rosenthal [6] notes that the benefits of QFD outlined previously can provide firms with a competitive advantage in the marketplace. Chrysler's results of using QFD in the development of its LH platform for midsize cars illustrate the potential strategic impact of the QFD process.

Lesson 3: The Four Phases of the QFD Product Development Cycle Are Dynamic and Must Be Adapted to the Organization's Culture and Needs

In our study, we found that the design teams used the four-step approach illustrated in Figure 1 as a framework, but often improvised within the theoretical approach. Thus, a more fluid approach to using the QFD process may be more suitable for some organizations.

The QFD process provides a means for firms to design products which result in "customer delight." Further research in actual organizations adopting QFD is needed to understand how to most effectively operationalize the QFD process. Theoretical foundations for QFD have already been established in the literature and must now be validated to assist practitioners in its proper application.

Acknowledgment

The authors would like to thank Chrysler Motors Corporation for supporting this research effort. Special thanks are given to Robert J. Dika, Glenn W. Czupinski, Chris W. Kuroswki, and Alan C. Carlson.

References

1. Clark, K. B., and T. Fujimoto. *Product Development Performance—Strategy, Organization, and Management in the World Auto Industry.* Boston, MA: Harvard Business School Press, 1991,
2. Ealey, L. "QFD—Bad Name for a Great System." *Automotive Industries* 167, no. 21 (July 1987).
3. Hauser, J. R., and D. Clausing, "The House of Quality." *Harvard Business Review* (May-June 1988): 63-73.
4. "Long Road Ahead: American Auto Makers Need Major Overhaul To Match the Japanese." *Wall Street Journal* (January 17, 1992): 1.
5. McElroy, J. "The House of Quality—For Whom Are We Building Cars?" *Chilton's Automotive Industries* (June 1987): 68-70.
6. Rosenthal, S. *Effective Product Design and Development.* Homewood, IL: Business One Irwin, 1992.
7. Sherkenbach, W. W. *The Deming Route to Quality and Productivity: Roadmaps and Roadblocks.* Washington, D.C.: CEE Press Books, 1988.
8. Sullivan, L. P. "Quality Function Deployment." *Quality Progress* (June 1986): 39-50.
9. Tomatzky, L. C., J. D. Eveland, M. G. Boylan, W. A. Hetzner, E. C. Johnson, D. Roitman, and J. Schneider, *The Process of Technological Innovation: Reviewing the Literature.* Productivity Improvement Research Section, Division of Industrial Science and Technological Innovation, National Science Foundation (May 1983).

About the Authors

Archie Lockamy III, Ph.D., CFPIM is an associate professor of operations management at the Florida Agricultural and Mechanical University. Dr. Lockamy received his BCHE from the Georgia Institute of Technology, an MBA from the Atlanta University Graduate School of Business, and a PhD in operations management from the University of Georgia. His research interests include manufacturing strategy, performance measurement, total quality management, Just-in-Time, and theory of constraints. Dr. Lockamy has published articles in the International Journal of Production Research and this journal and coauthored the book *Reengineering Performance Measurement*. He also serves on the APICS Systems and Technologies Committee. Prior to his academic career, Dr. Lockamy held various engineering and managerial positions with DuPont, Procter and Gamble, and TRW. He is certified as an Academic Jonah by The Avraham Y. Goldratt Institute.

Anil Khurana, Ph.D., is an assistant professor of operations management at the Boston University School of Management. Dr. Khurana received a BA and an MA from Panjab University (India) and his MS, MBA, and PhD from the University of Michigan, His research interests include product development, global operations, manufacturing strategy, and quality management. Dr. Khurana has lectured to academics and practitioners in the United States, Japan, and India.

Reprinted from the Production and Inventory Management Journal, *First Quarter, 1996.*

The Electronic Change Request: Applying TQM to the Creative Design Process

William J. Martini

Total quality management (TQM) has been applied to a wide range of processes; however, the design engineering process has had difficulty in applying TQM techniques. Design process quality has been difficult to measure due to its creative aspects and the subjective nature of variations in product size, technology, and complexity. This subjectivity leads managers to use their previous process for their next design, resulting in no process quality measurements or corrective feedback. For this reason, the need for an objective approach which measures the quality of the design process appears evident. Objective measurements, however, need to be flexible, easy to use, and allow designers to maintain their creativity.

The electronic change request (ECR) approach that Westinghouse has developed detects errors, determines their cost, isolates their causes, and recommends a technique for error prevention. When causes of errors are located, resources can be directed towards their reduction. This approach provides continuous correction of the process, and it presents a proven practical statistical framework for measuring and improving design engineering process quality.

Design process quality is defined as the absence of errors in the initial "paper" design. To allow comparisons between various designs, the number of errors must be normalized based on design complexity. The quality of a design process can be measured by the type and number of errors made on the design. Errors are introduced in the design for various reasons: design requirements may be misunderstood; suppliers may provide faulty components due to their own design errors; design personnel may make previously undetected mistakes; or computer-aided design (CAD) tools may introduce errors due to inaccurate models. The net effect of these errors in the design process is added cost and time to market.

The approach presented here is a simple and effective means of measuring the quality of the design process. These measures of design process quality can then be used from a TQM view to provide cost-effective feedback into the process along with continuous improvement to quality. It is important to note that because the feedback would address the errors from a quantitative measurement standpoint (and not a subjective, qualitative standpoint), the feedback into the design process is unbiased. A TQM framework for the design engineering process will be introduced along with a practical example from Westinghouse's digital design department.

Approach

A process quality measurement framework was developed by the Aerospace Processing Engineering Solution (APES)

quality circle (QC). The vehicle to implement this framework was the electronic change request. The particular design process which is targeted in this study is the design of digital printed circuit boards at Westinghouse Electric. The techniques developed provide a valid structure for measuring design quality in any design engineering discipline or other creative disciplines.

There are numerous examples of firms that are actively pursuing design quality goals in various disciplines. Motorola provides manufacturing with real-time defect data to identify, correct, and improve processes. Texas Instruments emphasizes producibility considerations in order to respond to electronic changes (ECs) earlier in the design process. Northrop Aircraft Division utilizes concurrent engineering and a detailed database of relevant statistics to achieve quality [7]. The ECR is the quantitative method employed by Westinghouse Digital Design; however, the parameters of the ECR could be adapted to meet the requirements of other firms.

Definitions

The design process consists of translating a set of requirements for functions into an operational product. The number of errors made during the design process determines the "design process quality." Taguchi writes that "quality is a virtue of design" and that "mediocre designs will always result in mediocre products [10]." Emphasis placed on providing customers with high quality products simultaneously addresses obtaining a high quality design process.

A design error is an instance of redesign attributed to or precipitated by test failure, incompatible components, incorrect material strength specified, etc. An error will result in a change to the baseline design. Each design error can usually be traced back to a change request or revision notice to the assembly drawing.

To compare the quality of designs which may vary greatly in size, technology, and complexity, the normalized measurement of the error becomes the design quality "figure of merit." The figure of merit allows a comparison between the various design processes. For each error, three key related statistical values need to be measured—the cost, cause, and prevention of each error. The cost of each error is a function of the magnitude of rework required to correct the error, and the stage in which it is found in the design or verification process. Errors discovered later in the process or when the products have been shipped to the field have a much higher cost than those found in the early stages of design. This relationship is shown in **Table 1**.

The rework required to correct an error can be estimated by the extent of the change and how many units are in the field. Also, each error can be attributed to a primary cause

Stages In A Design Process	Cost To Modify
Conceptual design	Low
Preliminary design	Low
Detailed design	Med Low
Simulation	Med Low
Prototype development	Medium
First production unit	High
Customer field use	Very High

Table 1. Cost of Errors

and prevention. A common set of causes of errors must be identified in addition to ways of preventing them. These common sets of causes vary among the creative design disciplines.

Individuals actively involved in the design process should develop a list of common causes, and preventions. The following is a list of common causes across design organizations:

Customer Requirements Change—For complex high technology designs, the customer will request changes in the design. This is common on military programs. Architectural firms may have their requirements changed based on customer preferences. Although the design team did not make the change, a customer requirements change is considered an error in the design process since the baseline design was modified.

Requirements Change—The internal product or systems engineers may change the design from the original specifications. As the design develops, the product engineers make trade-offs which may modify the original prototype.

Supplier Communication—A design error may result from miscommunication with a supplier on the particular specification of a device.

Manufacturing Defect—A design change may be required to make the device more manufacturable.

Testability, Maintainability, or Reliability Request—A design change may be needed for testability, maintainability, or reliability requirements.

Other—This category requires comments to indicate what these errors would be.

Specific creative disciplines will want to expand or tailor these causes to meet their specific needs. Similarly, a set of preventions for the causes of errors can be selected as being representative of the engineering design process. It is also recognized that any given error may have been prevented in a number of ways and it is possible, therefore, to have multiple preventions for a design. However, only the most cost-effective prevention is collected. Common preventions are listed below.

Supplier Requirements Reviews—The error could have been prevented by giving the supplier a better set of requirements, or reviewing the supplier specification more carefully.

Design Rule Checking—The error was a violation of the project design rules, and could have been prevented by checking the design against the design rules for the program.

More Complete Requirements Available—The error could have been prevented if more complete requirements were available when the design was initiated.

Schedule Relief/Additional Manpower—The error would have been prevented given more time or manpower to review the design for accuracy and/or completeness.

System Architecture Understanding—The error would have been prevented had the designer better understood how his/her design fit into the system architecture.

Computer-Aided Design (CAD) Maintenance—The error was due to a bug in CAD hardware or software systems, which could have been prevented by better CAD maintenance.

Data Collection

Given the above definitions of design process quality, errors, reworks, and the categories of causes and preventions of errors, data can be collected from recently performed designs. Initial data can be gathered by reviewing the design or engineering change request forms. The information on the change request may not provide sufficient detail, so follow-up surveys or interviews with the designers can be performed to determine the cause, prevention, and location of the error. This process will establish an initial database. The database will be organized as follows. Each program will be identified by its name, and each similar subassembly will be characterized by a set of design errors. Each design error will be described by its cause, prevention, and cost.

Design Error (i) = {Cause (j), Prevention (k), Cost(l)} where,
Design Error (i) equals the number of errors

Cause (j) identifies which of the cause categories is selected as the primary cause of error

Prevention (k) identifies which of the prevention categories is selected as the best prevention

Cost (l) is a function of the amount of rework, and location of the error in the design process.

Generation of Statistics

After the data is collected and entered into a database, a number of valuable statistics can be used to evaluate the design process quality. These statistics are determined for each subassembly, averaged across each product and all products at that specific design center. This allows for a comparative analysis on the design process between subassemblies and programs in addition to a comparison with the design center average. If one design was simulated and prototyped while another was only prototyped, an objective comparison of quality can be made to determine which design process was the most successful. The APES quality circle identified key statistics that would be useful in measuring design process quality.

Subassembly Level Statistics:

Design Quality = # of Errors/Normalization Factor

Normalized Cost = # of Reworks/Normalization Factor

Error Cause (j) = # and % of Errors caused by Cause (j)/Total Errors on Subassembly

Error Prevention (k) = # and % of Errors prevented by Prevention (k)/Total Errors for Subassembly.

Program Statistics—Calculate the mean and standard deviation of all the statistics defined above for all the designs on the program.

Overall Statistics—Calculate the mean and standard deviation of all the statistics defined above for all the designs in the database (e.g., composite of all program statistics).

Main Causes	% of Total Errors
Requirements error/change	18%
Interface misunderstood	16%
Component error	16%
Logic error	15%
Supplier	12%
CAD error	10%
Electrical noise	3%

Table 2. Digital Design Errors

Prevention	% of Errors Prevented
Additional simulation	40%
More complete requirements	11%
Better system knowledge	10%
Vendor reviews	9%
CAD maintenance	9%

Table 3. Prevention of Errors

Because the data resides in a database, other information can be generated by further grouping or sorting of the data. Examples of other sorting are trending, histograms showing the frequency of boards or programs having statistics in predefined ranges, percentages of causes, preventions, and errors. This information can be used for an in-depth analysis of design process quality.

Automated Quality Systems

During the initial data collection phase, surveying and interviewing is used to populate the database based upon past designs. However, a simple, efficient mechanism for collecting future data is necessary. The change request and the design process information can be captured electronically and placed in an electronic database. This electronic change request can reside on a CAD workstation or personal computer where the engineer performs his/her work. By entering the information at the time of the error, the information will be accurate, up to date, and allow statistics to be calculated immediately after the data is entered.

The U.S. Navy's best manufacturing practices program (BMP) has surveyed what some U.S. firms have accomplished in this area of management information tracking, such as number and cost of engineering changes. The BMP survey shows that most of the firms support a shared database to store engineering and manufacturing data [7]. In addition, BMP emphasizes that the firms not only track manufacturing information, but also provide timely feedback to designers.

Electronic Change Request

There are several needs for an automated quality evaluation tool in the design environment:

Specific processes need to be evaluated and compared to determine what is the best approach for a design process.

The causes of an error need to be correlated to the effect.

The subjectivity of quality needs to be eliminated.

The problems of the process need to be captured while that information is still prominent in the designer's mind.

Large amounts of data need to be collected and centralized to give more accurate results when evaluating the process.

The ECR is an automated tool developed by Digital Systems that meets these needs. The ECR approach can be used across design disciplines to measure process quality. The data collection portion of the system succeeds by providing the user with an immediate benefit. In addition to receiving a typed output of the change, the user can search and examine all change requests for a particular design as

a result of the organizing and archiving aspects of the automated ECR. The key benefit for the user is the ability to examine the summarized real-time statistical reports on design process quality.

The ECR's most important benefit for managers is to allow comparison of design methodologies across projects. For instance, if one product is designed in parallel with multiple designers whereas another product is designed with a single designer serially, an objective comparison of these programs will result in future design methodologies being based on tangible evidence from the past.

The Westinghouse Example

In 1990, the APES quality circle set out to develop a methodology to measure design process quality. For one year, this team of eight design engineers met on a weekly basis to create and design the electronic change request. Once the ECR framework was developed, a software engineer joined the team to develop a user-friendly program, the automated ECR. The first Westinghouse design organization to implement the ECR was Digital Systems.

The Digital Systems department is responsible for receiving inputs from systems engineering, software engineering, manufacturing, testing, reliability, etc.; designing the digital assembly; and testing the prototype. Upon completing the prototype verification, the design organization will continue to support the manufacturing and test departments as the design is transitioned into production.

Previously, the Digital Systems department had no objective metrics which measured the design engineering process. A definition of the department's status at the beginning of the study was required as a baseline, and then targets could be set on how to improve.

To establish the baseline, the APES quality circle looked at the major systems or products which had recently been designed by Digital Systems. Each QC member was assigned a product line to research. The change request or revision notice documents were examined for each product line. The QC members interviewed the engineers who recently worked on the programs and questioned them on each change request. The three key questions were: In what phase of the program did the error occur? What was the cause of each error? and How could the error be prevented? Together the QC member and the program engineer would decide in which of the preestablished categories the cause of the error should be classified. The statistics showed that the main causes of digital design errors were in the areas as shown in **Table 2**. Note that several of the causes correspond to those previously defined as common causes while others are specific to the digital design process.

This information changed the perception of where the errors were for Digital Systems. Previously, it was the general

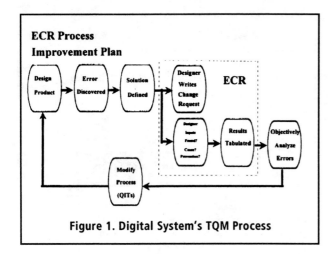

Figure 1. Digital System's TQM Process

Main Causes	1990 % of Errors	1993 % of Errors
Requirements error/change	18%	18%
Interface misunderstood	16%	10%
Component error	16%	6%
Logic error	15%	27%
Supplier	12%	7%
CAD error	10%	8%

Table 4. Causes of Errors

consensus that many of the errors were due to electrical noise problems; however, this accounted for only 3% of the total errors. Without this insight, Digital Systems would have continued to focus its resources on electrical problems instead of the major causes.

The APES QC also compiled baseline data on the prevention of errors. Overwhelmingly, the designers thought that additional simulation would have prevented most errors. The findings are shown in **Table 3**.

A third key quality statistic generated by the QC was a figure of merit. The figure of merit (FOM) was the number of errors divided by the normalization factor. A normalization factor was needed to compare designs of various size, technology, and complexity. Printed circuit boards vary in their physical dimensions which results in more or less components being placed on the board. Technology and complexity of the boards vary since one board may have a complicated microprocessor system on it while another may have basic resistors and capacitors. A normalization factor allows for a comparison across these variables. For electrical designs, it was determined that the number of solder joints on the printed circuit board would be used as the normalization factor. FOM (errors) = # of errors/number of solder joints.

In 1990, the FOM (errors) was .019. This means that for every 1,000 solder joints on a board there would have been 19 errors. Digital Systems' target was to continuously reduce the FOM while striving to attain zero. This would result in zero errors on the initial design.

The department interviewed its customers (mostly Westinghouse internal) on how Digital Systems could improve its performance. The customers' responses concurred with the data collected by the APES quality circle.

The department formed quality improvement teams (QITs) to focus on the major causes discovered by the APES QC along with improving simulation techniques. Logic errors, requirements, documentation, simulation, and vendor interface QITs were formed. These QITs made recommendations on how to improve the process. **Figure 1** illustrates the straightforward Digital Systems' TQM process.

The QIT's process modifications had a significant effect on the number of errors, reducing them by nearly 33% from 1990 to 1993.

1990 Figure of merit for errors = 19 per 1,000 board pins
1993 Figure of merit for errors = 13 per 1,000 board pins

Not only has the number of errors been reduced, but the mix of error types has shifted tremendously as shown in **Table 4**. Despite the significant progress, further work

is still required, as logic errors have grown as a percentage of causes and errors. To combat this, Westinghouse has instituted a logic design course and logic design reviews.

Conclusion

Total quality management, continuous quality improvement, and quality imperatives are goals many firms are striving to attain. A recent article on ISO 9000 indicated that "studies confirm that companies can expect improvement programs to achieve profits of up to five times their cost [9]." Fleischer and Liker note that "not only is design recognized as a crucial cost driver, but it is also recognized as a major determinant of quality, because quality is designed into the product at least as much as it is built in during manufacture [5]."

In this article, the question of design process quality has been addressed by providing a simple, practical, and effective approach for measurement of quality. Based on well-defined statistics, it identifies errors in the process, locates their causes (based on frequency of causes or errors), and identifies their prevention (based on frequency of recommended prevention of errors). It measures the price of design quality by the reworks required to correct design errors. As a result, it is an effective tool that allows management to compare different design processes. The Westinghouse Digital Systems department has utilized this methodology to improve its design process quality over 30%. The ECR allows the design process to be continuously improved, driving the design process quality to a maximum.

Acknowledgments

The author wishes to thank the Westinghouse Electronic System's Aerospace Processing quality circle and Karl Avellar, Digital Systems' engineering manager.

References

1. Burch, J. "To Predict Business Contribution, Look at Systems Design Quality." *Information Strategy: The Executive's Journal* (Spring 1992): 17-22.

2. Day, J. "A Cost Model for Parameter Design." *International Journal of Quality & Reliability Management* 10 (1993): 50-55.

3. Dixon, J. R. "New Goals for Engineering Education." *Mechanical Engineering* (March 1991): 56-62.

4. Granata, P. "Design in the 90's: What Dealers Need To Know." *Vital Speeches of the Day* (September 15, 1990): 734-736.

5. Liker, J. K., and M. Fleischer. "The Hidden Professionals: Product Designers and Their Impact on Design Quality." *IEEE Transactions on Engineering Management* 39 (1992): 254-264.

6. Nichols, D. "Bottom-Up Strategies: Asking the Employees for Advice." *Management Review* (December 1989): 44-49.

7. Noaker, P. M. "How The Best Make It." *Manufacturing Engineering* (November 1989): 52-54.

8. O'Lone, R. G. "777 Revolutionizes Boeing Aircraft Development Process." *Aviation Week & Space Technology* (June 3, 1991): 34-36.

9. Sprow, E. E. "Quality Advisor—ISO 9000 Is Setting High Standards." *Manufacturing Engineering* (July 1993): 12-14.

10. Taguchi, G., and D. Clausing. "Robust Quality." *Harvard Business Review* (January-February 1990): 65-75.

About the Author

William J. Martini received a BSEE from Rose-Hulman Institute of Technology and an MBA from Loyola College of Maryland. He is currently studying in The George Washington University doctoral program and is a design engineering supervisor for Westinghouse Electric. Mr. Martini was the leader of the APES QC during the ECR development.

Reprinted from the Production and Inventory Management Journal, *Second Quarter, 1992.*

Optimize Your Product Variety
Hal Mather

Everyone is clamoring for new products. Consumers, industrial managers, and sales and marketing people all demand new products to improve their lifestyles or to gain an edge over the competition. Many companies even set targets for the percent of sales they want in any one year from new products.

But unlimited product variety is not the way to be successful; there has to be an optimum. We can all agree that one product is probably not enough, infinity too many. The question is, where is the best position (best referring to the goal of the business)? If the objective is return on assets, then a given product portfolio is the optimum. If market share is the objective, then another range of products is optimum.

How do you know you are at the optimum? How do you ensure you stay there? Both these questions must be answered by senior managers of a company, but rarely are, with the result that companies operate portfolios that are decidedly non-optimum. The waste of resources this creates is enormous. Scarce design talent is siphoned off to work on products that don't support the company's objective, sales and marketing people work to sell these products that shouldn't be in the portfolio, and manufacturing has to plan, control, and build these unnecessary products.

Often, new product introductions are not the problem, product deletions are. Companies don't prune the deadwood from their lines as quickly as they should, diverting resources away from tomorrow's winners.

Manage Variety Better with Better Cost Allocations

Many authors have written about the problem of cost allocations[1,3,4]. These authors describe how to allocate costs better but do not define the variety of decisions a manager can make. These decision choices must be clear to avoid simplistic acceptance of the cost numbers as the basis for decisions. Better cost allocation is a clarification process, not a decision process. Hence this article will be presented in two main segments: understanding the costs of variety better, and the choices this better understanding will help you make.

What's Wrong with Classical Cost Allocations?

Typically, cost-allocation systems accurately relate 50% or less of business costs to a product. The balance of business costs, classified in my terminology as support costs (accounting, sales, engineering, factory overhead, and general and administrative), are allocated arbitrarily. Factory overheads are linked to production volume through labor,

machine hours, or material burden rates. The other support costs are defined as period costs and are deducted from gross margin.

In neither case are costs correctly allocated to how they are incurred. Burden rates transfer the high support costs needed for some products to others with low support needs. Gross margin deductions for the other support costs infer it costs as much to sell and process $1 million in one sales order as $1 million in several orders. A similar inference is made for accounting, engineering, and G&A costs. None of this is true.

A few companies recognize this problem at the product-family level where incurred costs are accurately allocated to each family group. Within the family, though, the same problem of misallocation of costs occurs. What every company needs to know is the actual, fully delivered cost of every product in their line. This includes all costs, whether direct, indirect, or support. The company must also know the asset needs of a product. This is the only way to know if a product is pulling its weight in support of the company's ROA goal. ROA (return on assets) *may* not be your short term goal; market share or growth may be. But long term, ROA has to be the goal for every business. It's the only yardstick of success in the long run.

Cost Allocation Revisited

The curves in **Figure 1** explain the cost-allocation problem. At the bottom is the word *Variety*, deliberately not

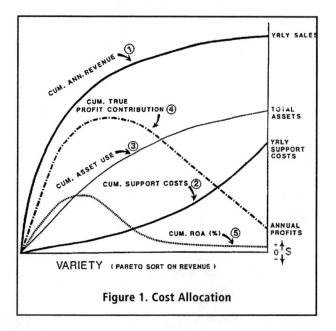

Figure 1. Cost Allocation

defined clearly. For one business, it could be the variety of finished goods or stock-keeping units (SKUs). For another it could be the variety of components, raw materials, and subassemblies in the end products. For still others it could be the variety of customers, vendors, processes required to make the product, customer order size, and so on. I have used the variety of end products a company offers as an example. Change this to your correct variety if my selection is incorrect for you. For most companies, all of these varieties are correct. The vertical axis is money.

The first curve is a Pareto (ABC analysis, 80/20 rule) display of the cumulative annual sales revenue. Hence, the first end-product item listed on the left of the variety line is that item with most annual sales revenue. The next item has the second most revenue, and so on. The typical 80/20 cumulative distribution is shown.

The second curve is labeled *cumulative support costs.* (Support costs are total revenues less profit, less direct materials sent to the customer and retained by him, less unburdened direct labor also sent to the customer as value added.) This is how these support costs are truly incurred; ask the managers of each support area. The shape of this curve is supported by references 1, 3, and 4.

The third curve is labeled cumulative asset use. In this case, the four major assets of buildings, machinery, inventories, and receivables are considered. It is obvious that the inventories to support low volume, high variety items are proportionately larger than those for high volume, low variety items. More changeovers on machines for low volume, high variety items indicate the same pattern is true of the machinery. Warehouse and plant space to contain the inventories and machinery, therefore, can be allocated to products the same way as inventories and machinery. Receivables probably follow the revenue curve. Add these four elements together to get curve 3.

In both the support and asset curves, I have assumed a start at zero. To the purist this is not true, of course. But we could rent out part of the buildings if they were empty; bring in sub-contract work to use idle machinery; or even sell unused machines. Theoretically, the salaries of all support people could be shared by other companies' products. So a zero start for these curves is theoretically correct.

The fourth curve, cumulative profit contribution, ends at the annual reported profits. These profits are obviously the accumulation of profits earned by each individual product. Profits are calculated for each product from the product's annual sales, less its direct materials and unburdened direct labor sent to a customer (assumed to be a curve with a shape similar to the annual revenue curve), less its support costs. Accumulating these profits across the variety spectrum gives curve 4.

The fifth curve is the profit curve divided by the asset curve for a cumulative return on assets contributed by product. The curve ends at your annual reported ROA.

What Do the Curves Say?

First, traditional cost-allocation methods will not parallel this figure. They will transfer the support costs of the high variety, low volume items to the low variety, high volume items using burden or allocation rates. This paints a very different picture of what is profitable and what is not.

A few cases exist where the low volume, high variety products subsidize the high volume, low variety products; where the selling prices of the high variety items cover their incremental support costs. This is a rare situation however.

Don't confuse high contribution margins with high profits. The items on the right-hand side of the chart probably have the highest margins. But margins must pay for the support costs these products consume. If you agree with the shape of curve 2, it is apparent that its slope on the right is steeper than the revenue line. Hence, these high contribution products must be losing money.

To be clear on the degree of subsidy the curves show, look at the right half of the variety line. Many companies find the following relationship:

Fifty percent of product variety generates 5% of annual sales revenue, needing 50% or more of the support costs and consuming or generating up to 40% of the total assets.

How Can You Draw the Curves for Your Business?

The first question is, "Do you need to?" If you agree the curves are conceptually correct, do you need to position them precisely to make decisions? In the majority of cases the answer is no. You can skip over this exercise and get right to the decision-making segment.

If you decide you would like to get a quantitative picture of your product-variety problem, you have three choices. You won't get the information you need from your traditional cost-accounting system except, perhaps, for the Pareto curve of annual revenues. So you will need to engineer the numbers.

First choice, break up your product range into several groups. Let each department manager make a judgment call as to how his budget is spent on each group. Do the same for the asset distribution.

Second choice, conduct a survey. Have everyone in all support departments record time spent on various product groups, categorized to suit the variety line. You can then break up the various departmental budgets based on prorating the time recorded, and then summarize them by product group.

Third choice, use activity based costing (ABC)[2], a relatively new way of charging costs to products. Its basis is that all incurred costs should be directly charged for products, not allocated by some arbitrary system.

Cost drivers are developed for every business function. These cost drivers are then consumed by the products that use them. Hence, total incurred costs by product can be calculated. In simplistic terms, overhead costs are a function of transactions. A transaction is every time material or data is moved, entered, recorded, stored, procured, inspected, etc. Today's computerized systems can summarize transactions by type by product. Thus, incurred costs can be traced to the product causing them.

As a simple example, take two products with exactly the same material and labor standard costs; however, one product has twice as many different purchased components as the other. The overhead allocation system will give both products the same overhead rate. The activity-based costing system will direct charge the product with more purchased components for additional costs of purchasing, receiving, inspecting, storing, moving, accounts payable, etc. Hence, better incurred costs can be calculated using this method.

These engineered costs should be calculated on a regular basis, perhaps quarterly, semi-annually, or annually, depending on the volatility of your product line.

What Choices Do the Curves Suggest?

Assume your curves look like Figure 1. These are your choices.

Do nothing. Accept the fact you need some losers to get winners. This crossover sales need is a real possibility.

At least the curves tell you to what extent you are subsidizing some sales.

But this crossover sales link between products is not as common as most sales and marketing people make you think. To check that the subsidy is valid for your business, force an analysis of which companies and to what degree they buy both profitable and non-profitable products. Let this guide your decision.

Some of today's losers will be tomorrow's winners, so they can be subsidized for a while. New products are certain to be on the right side of the variety line until they gain acceptance in the marketplace. Thus, doing nothing, even though these products are losing money, is valid for a period of time.

But doing nothing is very dangerous. A niche player will love this decision; he will attack your high volume, low variety, very profitable products. Without your need to subsidize the unprofitable products, he can underprice you and still get a very good return on investment.

Truncate the line. Take an aggressive look at the true profitability of each item and severely prune the losers. This is what turnaround artists do with losing companies. Along with this pruning, you must also slash support costs and downsize the business to accommodate the cuts. Don't prune tomorrow's winners unless you are only interested in short-term results.

Price to reflect true costs. Now that you know the real profitability by item, you can rearrange the pricing. Three results of this action are possible.

1. Acceptance. Customers accept the change and continue to buy at past rates. Profits increase from the reduced subsidization.
2. Rejection of price increases. Customers don't buy the product on the right-hand side of the variety line but continue to buy those on the left side. In this case, the marketplace is truncating the line for you. Don't forget to slash the support costs and downsize the business in concert with the product sales change.
3. Complete rejection. Customers won't buy the losers or the winners. Crossover sales are the key to getting business.

The danger of the latter event occurring is what prevents many companies from becoming more aggressive with their pricing strategies. But trying it out on a limited product line or slowly rearranging the pricing over several years will allow you to back off if you sense that complete rejection may occur.

Redesign—variety without variety. Keep the same application variety in the marketplace without the variety of products. One company making medical electronics used to have domestic and European voltage models, but never had the right ones in stock. A redesign allowed the products to be universal voltage. Although this increased the standard costs, total costs were reduced and the company became more profitable. Since the variety of products was halved, they immediately pared the support costs.

This decision yields the best of all worlds, a limited variety of products with small variety costs but sales to the full spectrum of needs. Standardizing raw materials, components, and ingredients in products will give similar benefits. The curves are as valid for this type of variety as they are for end products. This standardization should be done even if the standard costs increase, since the reduction in support costs will more than offset small standard-cost increases.

Restructure the business. Many companies mix wide disparities of product volumes in the same plant. But the support needs of a high volume, low variety business are quite different from a low volume, high variety one. By splitting these two businesses and uniquely structuring the support systems for each business, you will see which products make money and which do not. Make structural decisions to gain profits from both segments.

Minimize support costs and needed assets. Much of the Just-in-Time (JIT) movement results in eliminating support costs, especially in the factory. Asset use is also improved with quality programs, changeover reductions, lower inventories, and the like.

Buy and resell. By becoming a wholesaler for the products on the right-hand side of the curve, you become a full-line provider of products without the costs of being a full-line producer. Of course, the margins of resale must be enough to cover the accounting, sales, engineering, and G&A costs in order to make sense.

Why Go to This Much Trouble?

Many wrong decisions are made today because of incorrect product costs. Some companies are increasing capacity to handle their growing business. But, in many cases, this increased capacity of machines, factory expansions, overtime premium, or sub-contracting allows more losing products to be made. This is nonsensical. Other companies are expanding their product lines in the mistaken belief they are absorbing overheads and becoming more profitable. Their costing systems refuse to reveal they are not absorbing overheads, but creating overheads faster than revenues.

The major problem is that companies with curves like Figure 1 are very vulnerable to niche competition, especially overseas competitors, who will attack the company's product range on the left side of the curves with significantly lower prices, leaving it with the other products to round out the complete line.

Summary

Product portfolios have a significant impact on a company's profitability. Few companies manage them well, usually resulting in too many products for optimum business results.

Understanding how the total cost structure of a business is affected by product variety helps to clarify the situation. The choices to manage variety better are few. Done correctly, the focus must be on tomorrow's winners, with aggressive pruning of the losers. Learning the true incurred costs of products will allow designers to design products with lower total costs.

The end objective is better business results. You can only do this by optimizing your product variety.

References

1. Cooper, Robin and Kaplan, Robert S., "How Cost Accounting Systematically Distorts Product Costs, "*Proceedings of the 1986 Annual Conference of the Association for Manufacturing Excellence.*
2. —, "Measure Costs Right: Make the Right Decisions," *Harvard Business Review,* September-October 1988.
3. Dudick, Thomas S., "Why SG&A Doesn't Always Work," *Harvard Business Review,* January-February 1987.
4. Miller, Jeffrey G. and Vollman, Thomas E., "The Hidden Factory," *Harvard Business Review,* September-October 1985.

About the Author

Hal Mather is President of Hal Mather, Inc., Atlanta, GA, an international management consulting and education company. Since 1973 he has been helping all types of industrial concerns to become more competitive and improve their business results. Recent assignments have taken him throughout North America, Europe, the Far East, Australasia, South Africa, Mexico, and Brazil. Mr. Mather has published articles in the *Harvard Business Review* and *Chief Executive*, and has been quoted in *Fortune* and *Industry Week*. He won the Romeyn Everdell award for his article in this journal in 1987. His books include *Bills of Materials, How to Really Manage Inventories,* and *Competitive Manufacturing*. He has been certified at the Fellow level by APICS, is a Fellow of the Institution of Mechanical Engineers (U.K.), a senior member of the Computer and Automated Systems Association of the Society of Manufacturing Engineers, and the Association for Manufacturing Excellence. He is listed in *Who's Who in the South* and *Who's Who in Finance and Industry*.

Reprinted from the 1996 APICS International Conference Proceedings.

Making Supply Chains Agile for Niche Products

Michael F. McGrath

Background

Modern supply chains are not simple chains of supplier to customer but rather complex webs in which information and material need to flow. **Figure 1** shows a modern supply chain.

Johnson Controls supplies automotive seats to the big three US auto manufacturers. The tiers below Johnson Controls include suppliers—some large, some small—of hardware for the seat mechanisms and of soft goods for upholstery. At the top tier, there is a just-in-time interface between Johnson Controls and Chrysler. Approximately one hour of inventory exists as a buffer between the two companies and it is held on a truck at the Chrysler loading dock. Seats come out of the truck and go into a car on the assembly line. Quality is always perfect, and the line never shuts down for want of a seat. This truly is a world class operation.

At the tiers below Johnson Controls, things are more chaotic. Information does not flow quickly or easily, and it can take weeks for suppliers down the chain to get word of a change in Chrysler's production plans. Most of the shipments of fabric from Milliken are handled as emergency air freight, not to reduce inventory costs but simply because it is the last available workaround to respond to a change. Chrysler and other large customers see the opportunity for big savings by improving the efficiency supply chains like this one. DoD has a similar interest in improving supply chains for defense manufacturing.

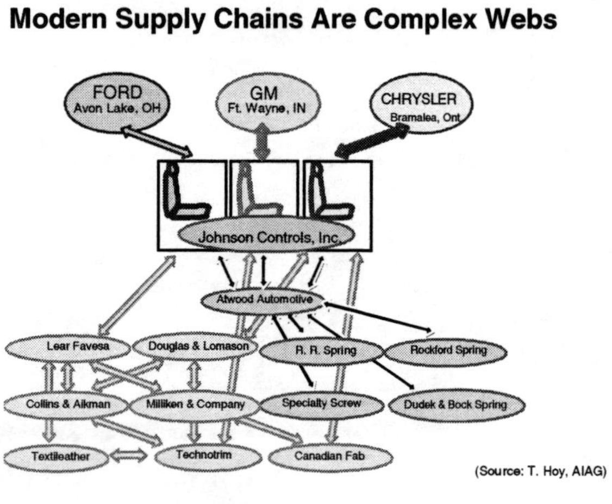

This paper will discuss trends in modern manufacturing, and the implications for Defense Manufacturing. The paper will also discuss the importance of Supply Chain Management and share some evolving insights from DoD-sponsored studies of Lean and Agile manufacturing practices. Finally, this paper will discuss the need for new tools and new analyses to help decision makers plan and operate the supply chains of the future.

Trends in Modern Manufacturing

Two influential books in the 1990s have prompted a new understanding of how manufacturing is evolving from the mass production thinking that has dominated most of the 20th century. First, MIT's study of the global automotive industry was documented in *The Machine that Changed the World*. This study coined the term "lean production" to describe the way Japanese auto companies had found ways to eliminate waste in every process. The result was an ability to make higher quality products at a lower price than US and European competitors, and to break even on 30,000 cars rather than 200,000. The US auto industry has since invested heavily in becoming lean. The US Air Force is now teamed with aircraft manufacturers in the "Lean Aircraft Initiative" to explore opportunities for lean production of military aircraft.

Second, an industry study facilitated by Lehigh University produced the *21st Century Manufacturing Enterprise Strategy*, which coined the term Agile Manufacturing. Agility is an enterprise management concept that embraces the ideas of lean production, but further emphasizes "reconfigurable everything" as a way to thrive in an environment of continuous unpredictable change. DoD and the National Science Foundation have sponsored continued development of Agile Manufacturing concepts at several leading universities, teamed with industry. Together, lean and agile studies have provided a growing understanding of the importance of, and the strategies for, eliminating waste, pursuing niche markets, building new business relationships, and thriving on change.

There has been change on a massive scale in aerospace and defense in the past 5 years. Global competition has grown fierce not just in automotive and consumer electronics, but in all sectors. Just ask Boeing about the commercial aircraft business. Companies have to be world class competitors to survive.

Mergers and acquisitions have been a big factor in the defense industry. Giant defense firms have been swallowed up in this process. For example, the recent acquisition of the Loral conglomerate by the Lockheed Martin conglomerate creates a single company that accounts for 40% of defense R&D and Procurement. The first thing

Modern Supply Chains Are Complex Webs

(Source: T. Hoy, AIAG)

Figure 1.

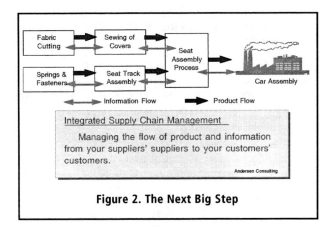

Figure 2. The Next Big Step

these companies do is begin reengineering, downsizing and outsourcing. Leading commercial companies are now at the point where quality is a given, and competitive edge comes from being first to market with products and services that delight the customer. As companies strive to improve their competitiveness, they have a plethora of tools, techniques and technologies to draw upon. New 3 and 4 letter acronyms appear every month. For the most part, large companies have focused first on using these tools to get their own house in order. The next big step for these companies is to extend improvements across the whole supply chain. A simple definition of Integrated Supply Chain Management, borrowed from Andersen Consulting is illustrated in **Figure 2**. This figure captures the new vision of Integrated supply chain management.

The management tools and concepts for eliminating waste and non-value-added activities can be as successful in the supply chain as they have been at the OEM level in reducing cost, improving quality and shortening cycle times. DoD has paid close attention to these commercial success stories. DoD needs to achieve similar results in its defense acquisition programs. With a modernization budget that is 60% lower than its cold war peak, we can no longer afford a separate defense industrial base, with its own peculiar way of doing business. Rather, we need to move toward an integrated industrial base that uses commercially successful approaches. DoD is aligning with commercial trends by focusing on certain areas for implementing changes such as MILSPEC reform, electronic commerce, integrated product/process development (IPPD), life cycle cost reduction and "single-process" industry facilities. All of these improvements are reflected in our new acquisition policy documents (5000.1/.2), and are being implemented in acquisition programs.

The Defense Manufacturing Council (DMC) is the senior level group in the Pentagon whose charter is to accelerate implementation. The DMC has focused initially on the interface between DoD and defense prime contractors. For these initiatives to have their full intended effect, however, implementation must extend to the supply chains below the prime contractor level. Most primes will continue to operate separate defense divisions. Missiles and microwave ovens won't be coming off the same production line. It is at the lower tiers that the target of an integrated industrial base—which responds to both commercial and defense needs—becomes a decisive factor in achieving affordable defense.

The story goes that when Willie Sutton was asked why he robbed banks, he replied "Because that's where the money is!" DoD is interested in supply chains for the same reason.

While cost data for tactical missile production was specified, other defense products show a similar pattern. About half of the product cost is in material, i.e., purchased components from suppliers. (The percentage is as high as 80% for some other defense products). The rest of the costs are accrued at the prime contractor level. For missiles, only 15% of the cost is labor at the prime contractor level, and the balance is overhead and facility cost. It should be noted, however, that first tier suppliers have a similar breakdown of labor, material and overhead, according to an LMI study. Of the 50% of supplier cost, about a third is overhead. Counting both prime and subtier contractors, overhead costs account for more than half of the total product cost. The message is that supplier interface costs and overheads throughout the supply chain need to be major targets in the defense manufacturing strategy.

Another reason for defense interest in supply chains is the need for rapid response manufacturing. The average lead time for competitively procured aircraft spare parts is about 14 months. Five or six of those months are taken up by DoD contracting procedures which are the target of acquisition reforms. The remaining nine months are taken up within the contractor supply chain, and are an inviting target for improvement. Rapid response manufacturing is important both for military need—as was met by US industry's admirable response to Desert Storm—and for economic reasons. Time is money. DoD today carries about $60B in spare parts inventories.

Much of that investment is to fill the long pipeline associated with today's supply chain management, and to provide safety stock to cover uncertainty in demand forecasts over a 14-month horizon. Flexible manufacturing systems, driven by digital product data, offer the possibility of manufacturing parts in small batches "on demand," or certainly within 30 days. Imagine the savings potential if we can reduce production lead time from nine months to one.

A third reason is that supply chains management is essential to military operations. Supply chains extend from the front lines all the way back to the factory. They are notoriously complicated to plan and control in a crisis.

Rethinking Supply Chain Management

The fields of Management Science and Operations Research have had a long interest in supply chain problems, and have found this to be a fertile field for applying the tools of the trade.

The traditional analyses have addressed supply chain design—i.e., make/buy decisions, supplier selection, and location decisions—primarily with cost benefit studies and multi-attribute utility models. These analyses need to be expanded to address modern manufacturing concerns regarding long term implications for core competencies and future competitiveness, and the new interest in robustness in the face of change. At the operational level, stochastic modeling and mathematical programming have been used to find optimal or near optimal solutions for scheduling, inventory, and distribution functions. Some of these analyses have taken multi-echelon supply chains into account, but more work is needed to expand these analyses to integrated decision support systems and transaction processing capabilities for complex supplier webs.

DoD is sponsoring research in supply chain management as a part of the lean aircraft initiative (LAI) and the Agile Manufacturing program. The LAI involves 16 major airframe, engine and electronics companies. There were more three years ago when the program started, but they keep buying one another up. The program also involves universities, organized labor, and government organizations. There are five research thrusts, including one on Supplier Systems and Relationships. A key output from this program is the Lean Enterprise Model, which organizes case study information and heuristics to guide managers in implementing lean enterprise practices.

The Agile Manufacturing program grew out of the 1991 study mentioned earlier. It includes over 20 development and demonstration projects conducted by industry and academia. Most of these projects are focused on technology and business practices to support next generation supply chains. Outputs range from decision support systems and information infrastructure capabilities, to legal toolkits to assist in virtual enterprise formation.

DoD's Lean Aircraft Initiative has documented current trends in supply chain management areas (i.e., focus, make-buy, design, quality and business relationships) in the best commercial firms. The focus, which used to be strictly on parts procurement, has broadened to consider the long term effects of supplier partnerships on the overall competitiveness of the firm. Make-buy decisions now take into account not only least cost criteria, but also the strategic impact of outsourcing technology in areas where the prime needs to maintain core competence. Suppliers used to be predominantly thought of as build-to-print shops, but now are being given an increasing share of responsibility as part of the design team. The 1980s revolution in quality has extended to supply chains. Primes are eliminating incoming inspections, and relying on supplier processes that build in quality. Finally, business practices are shifting from adversarial short term contracts to long term partnerships with shared risks and rewards.

Agile Manufacturing studies have shown that the relationship between the prime contractor and the supplier needs to consider three dimensions: the degree of added value from the supplier, the mechanism for rewarding the supplier, and the means of interacting with the supplier.

Business as usual operates close to the origin in this 3-space. Moving in the X direction toward more extensive supplier involvement in design and fabrication of custom components requires similar movement in the Y and Z directions to have appropriate reward mechanisms and linkages to make the partnership effective. The vision of Agile Manufacturing transforms the definitions of customer, supplier and sale from their previous meanings. A customer is no longer the recipient in a one-time transaction, but a subscriber to the solutions of the supplier. A supplier no longer hands over goods in response to an order, but is a long term supporter of the customer. A sale is no longer a one-time event, but an ongoing transfer of products and services, and of payment, between supplier and customer. A work process is not isolated within a company, but connects to suppliers and customers. What motivates a company to move away from the origin? The need for a competitive edge is a powerful motivator.

Studies of aircraft design in the 1970s showed that early design decisions locked in most of the downstream production and operating and maintenance costs. It is now well accepted that 80% of the downstream costs are locked in the first 20% of design. At the prime contractor level, there is an intense focus on better tools and methods for the front end of the design process, where cost leverage is highest. In light of DoD's emphasis on affordability, defense firms are seriously pursuing the commercial practice of taking cost constraints into account from the earliest stages of design. The emerging insight from agile manufacturing studies is that much of a firm's competitive advantage in the future will come from its supply chain. A

supplier who requires "build to print" info on a forging 24 months in advance forces the prime early on to lock in that part of the design and associated interfaces. A supplier who can respond more rapidly, and who can participate in the design process to get information as it evolves, can allow design alternatives to be held open longer. The expected result is more iterations and better designs that still beat the competition to market.

Outsourcing has been a widely reported phenomenon in commercial manufacturing industries for the past ten years. As defense prime contractors have gone through downsizing, mergers and acquisitions, outsourcing has become an inherent part of the enterprise reengineering process. Recent investigations by Charley Fine of MIT suggest that the long term consequences of decisions to outsource technology, not just parts and services, can be a loss of core competencies at the prime contractor. In some cases this erodes the prime's ability to be a smart customer in the future—DoD is now facing this concern as we outsource to industry design decisions that used to be controlled by the government through MILSPECs. Aside from its effect on the ability to be a smart buyer, the choice of which competencies to outsource and which to retain has large unforeseen effects. For example, Toyota chose in the 80s to outsource electronics and retain in-house capability for sheet metal. Today, more than half the cost of the car, and the most profitable half at that, is in the electronics.

A popular classroom exercise at Sloan and other business schools is called "The Beer Game." The class is divided into three teams who play the role of a retail store, a distributor and a brewery, respectively. The instructor plays the role of customer, who generates the demand pattern. The rules of the game are that there are costs for holding inventory, costs for unfilled demands (which are backordered), and delays in the flow of information and cases of beer in the supply chain.

The game starts at the retail level with something like eight cases of beer in inventory, six on order, and a daily demand of six cases. Each "day" the retailer orders six more cases from the distributor, who delivers two days later. One "day" the instructor increases the demand to 12 cases, and keeps it at that level for the rest of the game. The retailer is uncertain how much to order. The delay in information flow results in a shortage a couple of days later, with backorders to be filled. Panic sets in and the retailer places a large order which triggers the distributor to place a large order with the brewery, who works in large batches. Quickly things deteriorate to the point where there are enormous mismatches between supply and demand at every level. Hundreds of MBA classes have learned from this experience. The beer game illustrates vividly that supply chains are complex dynamic systems that often exhibit nonlinear response to small perturbations. Models are needed to control this behavior.

Information technology has the potential to make the lag in supply chain information flow a thing of the past. In many large companies, electronic data interchange with suppliers has become routine. Replacing paper business transactions with electronic messages has reduced the large customer's purchasing costs by up to 75%. The Federal government is now implementing electronic commerce to realize similar savings. For the small supplier, the motivation to implement EDI is to avoid losing a large customer's business. The supplier's costs may actually go up in the near term. To make money with this new technology, the suppliers need to use automated transactions to drive internal business processes (which may not yet be automated). Moving up this spectrum of technology, DoD-

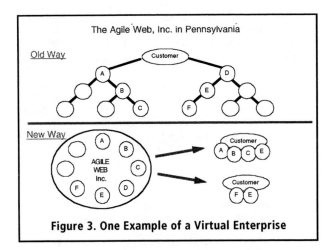

Figure 3. One Example of a Virtual Enterprise

sponsored demonstrations have shown the ability to share technical data, such as CAD files, to drive automated manufacturing, to browse parts catalogs and broker custom manufacturing over the Internet, and to enable design teams to collaborate across time and space. All of this is headed toward highly integrated "virtual enterprise" modes of operation.

The tough issues are not in the technology, but rather in changing traditional business practices to operate in this new environment. Decision models are needed help customers and suppliers select among a bewildering array of choices. Let's look at 2 examples: a company that is working its way up from the low end of the spectrum, and at a multi-company web that is trying to function as a virtual enterprise.

An Agile Manufacturing project at ASU is investigating the business case from the supplier's point of view. How can a supplier cope with change? The change in this case is that the NAFTA agreement opened small manufacturing shops in Phoenix to competition from companies across the border in Mexico, whose labor cost are a fraction of those in Phoenix. Dan Shunk of ASU put it bluntly to one of Motorola's suppliers, Catalina Printed Circuit board company: "You can win Motorola's business by making your products new, good, fast, and cheap. New is not an issue for a build-to-print shop. Good is assumed—your competitors have good quality. Cheap is hard to match when your Mexican competitors have such low labor costs. Therefore, your strategy must be to win business by being fast to respond to your customer."

The pilot project has implemented EDI and technical data interchange (TDI), reduced design changes, and shortened cycle times by 50%. In the longer term, the competition will also get fast. Therefore this supplier is positioning itself to add value as part of Motorola's design team as the next competitive strategy.

A virtual enterprise (**Figure 3**) is the business equivalent of an all-star team. There are many organizational models, but the newest is the web organization. The Agile Web in Pennsylvania is an example. Nineteen manufacturing companies, ranging from machine shops and sheet metal operations, to paint shops, to printed circuit board facilities, are linked in a consortium that can bid on jobs that none of the individual firms could undertake alone. These firms are still competitors in their "day jobs," so the major achievement in Agile Web has been to work out the business relationships and processes that enable them to function cooperatively as well as competitively. If you think about the sensitive information that had to be shared the

first time they priced a job as a team, you will get the picture. One of the Agile Manufacturing projects has developed a toolkit for virtual enterprise formation, dealing with rapid partnering agreements, finance and accounting procedures and the handling of intellectual property.

The Need for Further Analysis and Tools

The foregoing examples have been at a high conceptual level, but are indicative of what industry leaders are thinking. They may sound like problems to hand off to the behavioral scientists, but I think the OR/MS community has a big role to play, as well.

Some of the issues that managers need to deal with in designing and operating supply chains include outsourcing, partnering, product design, too lean vs. too fragile, and synchronization of production, inventory and distribution decisions. Most of these are at the strategic level, involve multiple criteria, and cannot be treated as traditional least cost optimization problems. Optimization and efficient transaction processing at the operational level is still a need, and robustness is a big concern. These kinds of issues point to a need for both technical advances in analytical capabilities, and new heuristic methods to guide decision makers.

There is still a need for fine grained OR models to optimize and control production planning, inventory, distribution and other processes. Much remains to be done in these areas through our normal OR development method of working on a bounded problem, then gradually finding ways to relax assumptions. Modeling dynamic conditions (as opposed to steady state), finite capacity systems, and extending to multi-echelon, multi-product, multi-customer situations remains a challenge for the community. There is also a need for higher level models that consider the supply chain as a whole. Managers today would rather find solutions that are globally good and robust than those that are locally optimal and fragile. Given the complexities of adding business relationships and human behavior to the picture, I believe we can best make progress on implementation by embedding these tools within a decision support framework. Populating such a framework will require a multi-discipline attack, integrating techniques from OR, Systems Engineering, Visualization, Distributed Collaboration, Expert Systems, OO Systems, etc.

Even with new analytical modules, decision makers will need new heuristic methods for making choices in the design and operation of supply chains. We expect great value from the case studies and knowledge bases being compiled by the Lean Aircraft Initiative and the Agility Forum. Nonetheless, more work needs to be done in developing business case templates, metrics and business practice standards for next generation supply chains.

Let me single out one key research issue: achieving a deeper understanding of trust-based relationships. Trust can be viewed as "my subjective probability that you will meet your commitments, given your past performance." Trust may also include "my confidence that, in response to some perturbation, you will consider my interests as well as your own."

Given the time it takes to build real trust, these relationships need to be long term in nature. The concept that the virtual company will be an instant partnership among strangers is unworkable. The relationship is a marriage, not a one night stand. Organizational and contractual models for such marriages are still in their infancy.

Conclusion

In summary, we have seen that supply chain management has enormous importance in the continued evolution of manufacturing enterprises. It is important both for commercial competitiveness and, from a public sector standpoint, for affordable defense. Challenges in this area abound for the Management Science and OR community, considering the new concerns about the strategic implications of supply chain design, about robustness in the face of change, and about the dynamics of supply chain operation. A multi-disciplinary thrust is required to provide the needed tools and analyses. I can think of no better organization than APICS to foster the development of new and better solutions.

About the Author

Michael F. McGrath is the Assistant Director for Manufacturing in DARPA's Defense Sciences Office. He is the agency focal point for manufacturing technology, and is the program manager for three ARPA programs: Agile Manufacturing, Electronic Commerce Resource Centers, and Affordable Multi-Missile Manufacturing. He also serves in leadership positions for several DoD-wide initiatives to improve manufacturing and reduce the cost of defense systems. Dr. McGrath has played an active role in strategic planning for the Defense Manufacturing Council and for the DoD Manufacturing Science and Technology program.

Before joining DARPA in 1991, Dr. McGrath was the Director of the DoD CALS Office, where he guided the Computer-aided Acquisition and Logistics Support program from its inception to be a catalyst for change in government and industry.

Dr. McGrath holds a B.S. in Space Science and Applied Physics (1970), an M.S. in Aerospace Engineering (1972) from Catholic University, and a doctorate in Operations Research from George Washington University (1985). He served as adjunct faculty at GWU in the late 1980s, teaching courses in Operations Research and Statistics.

Reprinted from APICS—The Performance Advantage, *November 1997.*

What Type of Company Are We?

Steven A. Melnyk and R. T. "Chris" Christensen

In past columns we have focused on areas such as capacity and inventory. In this issue, we address a question that is frequently asked of us, namely, "What type of company are we?" To understand this question, we must first understand the origins of this question. As most of you are aware, this magazine runs software surveys/directories on a regular basis. These directories contain listings of various packages found in such categories as MRP/MRP II, finite capacity scheduling and planning, warehousing, forecasting and simulation. These directories not only identify the various packages and their vendors, they also detail various features of their operation. One of the last set of categories pertains to the specific manufacturing settings for which the various packages are potentially suitable. Found within these categories are settings such as job shop, batch, repetitive, process/continuous, mixed mode, medical/drugs, food and automotive. For many readers, these categories are a source of major confusion. They are not clear as to the differences between the various categories. In this column, we will explore these various categories of manufacturing settings and their implications. We will carry out this exploration in two waves. In this column, we will focus on the categories of job shop, batch, repetitive and process/continuous.

Major Dimensions

Before we begin to explore the various manufacturing settings, it is important that we identify several of the major dimensions underlying these various settings. These include dimensions such as:

- Volume. This dimension refers to the level of output that the setting is capable of economically supporting. This dimension consists of two levels. The first is that of frequency, or the number of times during a certain period that we can expect to produce a lot of a specific part (i.e., a specific part number or stockkeeping unit). The second is that of repetition. This refers to the size of the typical production order. That is, whenever we release an order for a specific number, repetition refers to the size of the order. Using these levels, we can see that low volume can be generated by a combination of low repetition and low frequency, or very low repetition and moderate frequency, or moderate repetition and very low frequency. Volume determines the size of runs that the manufacturing setting can be expected to deal with.
- Variety. This refers to the extent to which the products built are standard or subject to modification. These variations show up in differences in routings that the manufacturing setting is expected to accommodate.

- Nature of flows. This refers to the extent to which there is a dominant flow through the manufacturing system. In some conditions, we must accommodate a setting where every order released to the floor has its own unique routing. In other conditions, nearly every order follows the same routing.
- Equipment type. This dimension refers to the type of equipment typically found in the specific manufacturing setting. Generally, this dimension runs from general purpose (GP) equipment (e.g., a drill, grinder, deburrer) to special purpose equipment.

In addition to these dimensions, it is also important to note that not every manufacturing setting is "pure." That is, we seldom see a pure job shop or a pure assembly line. Rather, we see a job shop that has elements of an assembly line in it. Under these conditions, what we tend to do is to describe ourselves in terms of that manufacturing portion that is either most critical or the largest.

Manufacturing Settings

Now that we have established the major dimensions underlying various manufacturing settings, let's examine the four types of manufacturing settings to be covered this month: job shop, batch, assembly line and process/continuous.

- Job shop. This setting anchors one end of the manufacturing spectrum (process/continuous being the other end). This setting is characterized by very low volumes, with production runs consisting typically of between two to 50 units. In addition, variety is very high in this setting (a result of the small runs), with each order being very different from the others in this system. As a result, software packages targeted towards this setting are designed to cope with this high level of product variety. The combination of low volume and great product variety results in a great deal of diversity in product routings. This diversity places a great demand on the ability of management (and the supporting software package) to manage the flow of work through the shop. This means that dispatching at the work center level is a critical task.

In general, the equipment in a job shop tends to be general purpose in nature. This means that while setups are relatively short, the processing times per unit tend to be longer than what one would find in an assembly line. This short setup time is consistent with the demands for flexibility made by the orders in this setting. Just as the equipment is general, the skill level of the employees tends to be very high. In most job shops, the key bottleneck tends to be labor, not equipment.

Layout in a job shop falls into one of two formats. The first format is functional. In this format, we lay out the flow so that all of the same or similar equipment is placed together in the same area. In contrast, the second format is process. With this layout, we organize and locate together all of the equipment needed to build orders belonging to the same part family (more about this trait later on in our discussion of batch). In general, most of the lead time in a job shop is consumed by queue time (i.e., orders waiting at various work centers waiting to be processed).

- Batch. In this setting, the volume is increased, with the typical run quantity ranging from 50 to 2000 units. Variety, while still present, is less extensive as that found in the job shop. With the larger runs and less variety, we find less general purpose equipment and more specialized equipment and tooling.

An important feature of a batch environment is that of the part family and machine cells. A part family consists of a set of parts which share commonalties or similarities in terms of processing (the most important from our perspective) or design. With part families, we must now recognize the presence of sequence-dependent scheduling. That is, the setup time depends on the order in which we group the runs. The ability of a software package to recognize and incorporate this feature into the resulting schedule is an important consideration.

Typically, MRP systems are most appropriate for this setting.

- Repetitive. Within this setting, we move into a high-volume manufacturing environment where the units of output are discrete (e.g., tires as compared to gallons of paint). Here the items are either standard or assembled from standard components and options. The presence of this standardization changes the requirements placed on the planning and control system. With such large volumes, we now find ourselves with dominant routings. That is, most of the orders follow a set sequence of operations (the machines and work centers are physically laid out in a manner that corresponds to this flow). Because of the volumes, we also focus our scheduling activities at two points—the master schedule and the first operation (frequently called the gateway).

In addition, large volumes combined with very short processing lead times require a very different fashion of inventory management. In the previous systems, we could track the inventory by focusing on the points in time when it was issued to the orders. In many repetitive systems, we use a backflushing logic. That is, we determine the number of end items we produce during a period of time. We then break this level of output into its components. Ideally, we should arrive at the ending inventory by taking the beginning inventory, adding to it the receipts received during the time period, and then subtracting from it the number of components needed to cover production (as based on the number of end items produced) and scrap allowances.

Equipment and tooling capacity within the repetitive environment tends to be specialized (again, due to the high levels of volume of standard items) with labor being either unskilled or semi-skilled. Within this environment, it is equipment and tooling capacity that tends to be the bottleneck, not labor.

Capacity planning is critical within the repetitive environment. Therefore, careful attention must be paid to the strength of the capacity planning modules.

- Process. Process is very similar to the repetitive except that the units of output are not discrete but continuous. Oil and paint are examples of items produced with a process environment. Here, volume is high with the products being fairly standardized. In addition, there exists a dominant flow that every product moves through. Because setups (or the change required to go from one product to another) are fairly time consuming and expensive, care must be made to ensure that those features are incorporated into the software package and into the planning and control system. Typically, we tend to see cyclical production scheduling.

Because of the high volumes, process settings are characterized by high levels of capacity utilization. In this type of environment, planning is the critical activity. Execution tends to be a reflection of planning.

Lessons Learned

In this column, we have focused on trying to help the reader understand the type of manufacturing setting in which they operate. We have seen the following:

- There should be a strong fit between the manufacturing setting and how the system is managed and controlled.
- The different settings are differentiated by factors such as volume, complexity, nature of flows and equipment type.
- The environments fall along a spectrum anchored at one end by job shop and process at the other.
- Each environment has its own requirements that must be recognized within the software decision.
- A mixed environment exhibits traits of different settings. Yet, there is a critical or dominant setting which can be used to identify the targeted setting if there is no package supporting mixed-mode production.

About the Authors

Steven A. Melnyk, Ph.D., CPIM, is software editor for *APICS—The Performance Advantage*. He is also an instructor in the Department of Marketing and Supply Chain Management at Michigan State University in East Lansing.

R. T. "Chris" Christensen is the director of the executive education program at the University of Wisconsin, Madison.

Reprinted from the 1992 APICS International Conference Proceedings.

Integration: Building the Foundation for Corporate Success

Steven A. Melnyk, CPIM, and William R. Wassweiler, CFPIM

Overview

As firms move into the 1990s, managers now recognize the need to change the paradigms underlying manufacturing and corporate systems. Previously, the major basis for competition was cost (with its attendant emphasis on cost reduction). In the 1990s, competition will be increasingly based on value (value maximization; waste minimization). This change in perspective will have an important impact on the firm and its organization. Previously, the firm was organized into functionally oriented groups; now the firm must be reorganized around products and customers. The firm must now change from emphasizing functional excellence to encouraging and building corporate excellence. This refocusing of the firm will require a major organizational restructuring. A critical element to this restructuring and to the manufacturing firm of the 1990s will be *integration*.

Integration is not an easy concept to implement. One reason is that it is not well understood and often ill defined. Second, integration runs counter to a corporate tradition built on functional orientations.

This presentation examines the concept of integration. It defines what integration is and discusses the four types of integration (functional, organizational, strategic and channel). It shows that the level of integration must be consistent with the nature of the product delivered and the competitive stance taken by the firm. This paper concludes by identifying the benefits to be gained from the successful implementation of integration and by discussing various guidelines for introducing integration into the typical American manufacturing enterprise.

Decision-Making: A Case Study

In *The Fifth Discipline* [9, Chapter 3], Senge describes a game developed at MIT's Sloan School of Management. This game, the *Beer Game*, involves managers in the production and distribution of a single brand of beer. The production and distribution system consists of three stages: a retailer, a wholesaler and a factory. The game examines how these stages respond to a sudden upward shift in demand for beer. For most players, the experiences and results are very similar.

In response to the increased demand for beer, the retailer increases the size of orders placed with the wholesaler. However, because of delays, the retailer finds himself with a dwindling stock of inventory. Larger and larger orders are placed in response. A similar reaction is shown by the wholesaler and the factory. Ultimately, by the time

that increased factory capacity comes on line and output starts to match demand, the entire system is faced with a problem. Inventory stocks are too high; orders are reduced or canceled; demand plummets. In spite of increased demand, the entire system is worse off than it was before.

The game illustrates a fundamental problem that plagues most manufacturing firms as they move into the 1990s. Each element of the production and distribution system is trying to achieve three important objectives: to serve their customers well, to keep the product moving smoothly through the system, and to avoid penalties. Each participant responds to their problems by making well-motivated, clearly defensible decisions. However, in spite of these considerations, the entire system breaks down. One reason for this breakdown is the lack of *system integration*.

The system described is one in which there is no integration between the components (retailer, wholesaler, factory). The retailer only communicates with the wholesaler when placing an order or when complaining (e.g., about missed or incomplete beer shipments). The communication between the wholesaler and the factory is likewise limited.

As a result, each component makes decisions that, while correct and logical from their isolated positions, are wrong when viewed from an overall systems perspective. Each participant assumes that the other elements of the system see the problem in the same way that he or she does. Each participant makes decisions that create problems elsewhere in the system (Gene Woolsey's "Good News/Bad News" syndrome). As a result, in spite of the best intentions and highest level of motivation, the system is unable to effectively serve its customers. Dissatisfaction (both from the customers and the participants) rises; costs increase; profits fall.

Some readers may be willing to dismiss these results as not being credible. After all, they are based on a simple game. However, the system described in the game is not that different from the systems found in most American manufacturing firms. Like the system found in the game, most firms are built around systems that are strongly functionally oriented and driven. These are systems in that decisions made are myopic and have limited breadth but great depth. The decision-makers can describe how the actions taken will affect their own areas; they are unable to anticipate or understand how these decisions will affect the other areas of the firm. These are systems that are ultimately slow to respond and, when they do respond, take actions that are highly inappropriate.

In short, the typical functionally organized firm found in American industry is ill-suited to survive and thrive in the 1990s. They lack the ability to provide a unified and highly integrated systems response.

Objectives of the Presentation

If integration is to be one of the major hallmarks of firms in the 1990s, it is first necessary to understand what integration is and what it is not. It is also important to understand why firms must change their organizational structures and reorient them so that they are business rather than functionally oriented. To understand integration and its need better, it is necessary that we address the following questions:

1. What are the organizational features and advantages offered by the functionally structural corporation?
2. What competitive pressures are forcing American firms to change the way that they are structured and to emphasize the need for integration?
3. How must firms in the 1990s be organized to meet these challenges?
4. What is meant by the term *integration*?
5. What are the major types of integration that management can implement?
6. What are the benefits and costs to be gained by integrating the modern enterprise?
7. What are some critical guidelines that management should consider when trying to integrate its company?

This presentation will show that in an environment where speed, flexibility and responsiveness are needed for survival, *no firm can hope to survive or grow unless it is integrated both internally (across functions and between top management and the functions) and externally (between its customers and suppliers). The costs imposed by the failure to integrate are simply too high and will not be tolerated by an increasingly more demanding customer and a very competitive marketplace.*

Organizing the Firm: A Traditional Approach

Until recently, many American firms were organized along *functional lines* with management control being exercised through a *hierarchical* structure. That is, the firm consisted of a number of distinct functional groups (e.g., manufacturing, engineering, accounting, finance, human resources). Each person who entered the firm became part of a specific functional area. Typically, advancement followed these functional lines. Manufacturing people achieved promotions by moving through a series of manufacturing positions (e.g., from foreman to shift supervisor to area manager to plant manager). Exposure to other functional areas was often very limited. There was little opportunity or need for incoming managers to be exposed to the other areas. It was only until the highest levels that the manager began to work closely with others.

By organizing the firm along functional lines, several important advantages were obtained. People within each line became very familiar with the needs and requirements of their areas. They quickly became experts in their areas (e.g., manufacturing). This structure also simplified the exchange of functional-specific information. It offered a basis for improving knowledge and skills [10, pp. 549-552].

By using a hierarchy, the firm took a triangular shape in that there were a number of management layers between the bottom (workers) and the top (e.g., executives). At the top, control was exercised by a relatively small number of people. In this structure, each higher level controlled the activities of those being done by the lower level. The use of hierarchical structure was important for several reasons. First, it offered an effective method of managing information flows. As information moved from the bottom to the top, it was filtered by each level. Ideally, this filtering condensed the information (i.e., eliminated unnecessary detail) and removed information deemed not important. As a result, the top was able to act on the basis of just the necessary information. In addition, the hierarchical structure reduced the span of control. Each manager in this structure had only a limited number of subordinates for which they were responsible.

The functionally organized hierarchy became the natural model for many American firms. First, it was the structure that had been used successfully by such American industrial leaders as Ford, General Motors and DuPont Corporation. Second, it was a structure familiar to many of its managers. Many of the managers that worked in American industry between 1950 and 1985 had previously been in the armed forces (primarily during World War II). They were exposed there to the *command and control* structure of the military—a structure that is functionally and hierarchically organized. They understood how this structure operated and how it could be used to achieve corporate objectives.

This method of organizing American manufacturing served industry well until recently. It offered managers an effective and efficient method of managing large volumes of information. It also offered greater control over uncertainty since each higher level knew exactly what the level below was to do (and not to do). This structure also helped managers reduce the time needed for making decisions. With a functionally organized hierarchy, there was no need to solicit input or acceptance from those below the decision-maker. Such a structure also provided for well-defined roles. Within the functionally organized hierarchy, everyone knew what they could and could not do. Finally, it offered managers a structure for reducing direct labor. These advantages, however, did not come without certain costs. The most significant of these included:

- **Increased Overhead**. As more management layers were added, more managers had to be hired to staff these new positions. These additional costs went into overhead. In many instances, the result was that there were more people involved in administrative and office positions than there were people working on the shop floor. For example, Rosencrance [8] noted that at General Motors, 77 percent of employees filled staff positions while only 23 percent handled operational, production jobs. Similar statistics were identified for companies such as Mobil, General Electric and DuPont. Increased overhead has pushed up the break-even point and decreased corporate flexibility.

- **Increased Redundancy**. Because each of the functional areas did not interact with the other areas on an ongoing basis, there was little sharing of information or activities. The result was a tendency for each functional area to have its own database and to replicate functions carried out elsewhere in the firm.

- **Internal Allegiances**. This structure encouraged people to identify with their functional areas and not with the product. People saw themselves, for example, as being engineers or accountants first and then as members of the firm. People evaluated problems and solutions in terms of how they would affect their own areas. They seldom considered how these issues will affect others in the firm.

- **Those who solve problems were distinct from those who had to work with the problems**. The people who worked on the line were not the persons charged with improving operations or with making the critical administrative decisions. This situation often resulted in the firm losing access to the expertise of its work force. Workers no longer felt responsible for their work. Morale often fell (as well as quality and productivity).

- **Sequential Problem Solving**. Each functional area tended to jealously guard their own tasks and decisions. There was often little sharing. Joint problem solving became the exception rather than the norm. As a result, decisions and processes were *sequential* in nature. Each area dealt with a task or problem in isolation. When it had addressed the issue to the best of its ability, it then passed the task on to the next function. When arriving at its decision, the functional area seldom sought input or suggestions from other areas potentially involved or affected by the resulting decisions. This type of "over-the-wall" decision making was most evident in the process of bringing a new product to market.[1] The product went from concept to product design to manufacturing engineering to manufacturing to distribution and then finally to sales. Input from the other areas at each step in the process was limited or non-existent. The result was that designed problems often have to be solved on the shop floor. A problem that might have cost $1,000 to correct during design now cost $10,000,000 to correct during final production.
- **Lack of Trust**. There was a tendency for employees to distrust anyone who was not in their functional areas. This lack of distrust was most evident when dealing with problems. Marketing people blamed production personnel for missed ship dates; production people accused marketing of either changing the manufacturing schedules too often or generating infeasible schedules.
- **Lack of Responsiveness**. The functionally organized hierarchy was slow to respond to changes. It often had difficulty responding to changes in customer demands or major competitive actions in a timely fashion.

The functionally organized hierarchy was often most effective when used in a stable environment characterized by long lead times. That is, this structure did well when product designs didn't change frequently, demand remained stable and product life cycles were long. However, these traits are not ones found in the manufacturing environment of the 1990s.

Competing in the 1990s

A large number of changes are now taking place. Product life cycles are becoming shorter. Quality, previously an order winner [3], is now viewed as a qualifier—everyone is now expected to provide its customers with well-built, well-designed products. Attention is shifting to time (in the form of *Time-Based Competition)* and flexibility. Managers everywhere are now thinking in terms of a global rather than a domestic marketplace. To compete successfully in this new marketplace, firms recognize that they must be able to compare themselves to the best in the market (not simply in a specific market niche). This realization has led to the phenomenon of *benchmarking.* It is no longer enough to be the best American firm. To win orders and market share, you must be the best. In the 1990s, the focus of attention is shifting. Previously, management was primarily concerned with cost minimization; the focus is now on value maximization.

Firms now see success in this new environment as the result of process by which the firm generates for its customer base more value than its competition. In generating this higher level of value, the underlying goal is to develop and maintain a *sustainable competitive advantage.*

Sustainable Competitive Advantage

A sustainable competitive advantage occurs whenever one firm has succeeded in developing such a dominant position in its market that it can be said that the firm "owns" the market. Its position in the market is both well-entrenched and protected. It has successfully erected high barriers to entry in the form of reputation, constant innovation (both in product and process), market share, capital base (necessary investments in plant, equipment and information) and a well established and extensive distribution system. Its source of competitive advantage cannot be easily nor readily duplicated by the competition. The firm is seen as an aggressive competitor in that it continuously pushes to enhance its position in the market by improving performance in such areas as cost, lead time, quality and flexibility. Its goal is to put its competitors into a reactive position—one in that they are constantly responding to initiatives taken by the market leader, yet never able to successfully mount a market initiative of their own.

Foundations of Value

Any strategy that management develops for building a sustainable competitive advantage must draw on four major elements: lead time, quality, cost and flexibility. How they are combined can result in very different strategies. There are, however, certain influences that can now be identified as fundamental in shaping these strategies [2, 6, 7].

- **Any Time**. Time has value for the customer. It influences the actions of the buyer. It is a resource, not a constraint. Customers are often willing to pay a premium for products that are quickly designed and delivered.
- **Any Place**. The firm must be able to reduce the distance between customer and supplier. It must be able to bring together in time and distance customers and suppliers. It must view the customer as a closely linked partner.
- **No Matter**. In the past, the buyer-supplier relationship was built on the flow of physical, tangible products. This relationship has now changed since suppliers now recognize that they no longer simply sell goods. Rather, they also provide their customers with such intangibles as security, information, goodwill and service.
- **Mass Customization**. Increasingly, customers demand systems that are able to customize their outputs on a mass scale. This capability must be offered without increasing lead time and cost.
- **No Risk**. Customers are becoming increasingly more sensitive to any risks (lead times, quality, quantities, cost) that their suppliers can create for them. They are willing to pay a premium to those suppliers who can offer them access to delivery systems that are able to reduce or eliminate the customer's exposure to these risks.

Recent developments such as Time-Based Competition, the Agile Corporation, Total Quality Management and Just-in-Time Manufacturing are all variants of these five factors.

Value and the Firm of the 1990s

These influences require a new and different type of organization. Unlike the functionally organized hierarchy of the 1980s, the effective firm of the 1990s must embody the following traits:

- **Highly Focused**. This firm must know exactly who its customers are and what its customers demand (i.e., what are the order winners, order qualifiers, and order losers). This knowledge must be reflected in the firm and its organization. The firm must be organized to serve its customer in the most direct and efficient manner possible. What this means is that the organizational structure of the firm must be regarded as *dynamic*. As the customer base changes, the organization of the firm must also change in response. Its structure can ultimately be described as being *plastic* in nature.

- **Shared Vision**. Just as it knows who it serves, the firm also knows what it is. It has a clear and well-defined view of how it competes in the market place. It knows what it does best and what its limitations are. This knowledge is not simply confined to the top managers. Rather, it is a vision to which everyone in the firm is party. As a result, everyone in the firm not only understands what they must do on a day-to-day basis (from the person on the assembly line to the marketing executive), but they also understand the links that exist between their actions and how the firm competes (i.e., there is a totality of vision). The tactical and strategic perspectives are found side-by-side at every level in the firm.

- **Flatter**. To be more responsive, a decision-making power has to reside with those who are most familiar with the problems and who are in the best possible position to identify and correct them. As decision-making moves from the top to the bottom of the organization, one result is a significantly reduced need for those many levels of management found in the functionally organized hierarchy. As these levels are eliminated, the organizational structure becomes flatter. Furthermore, as layers are eliminated, so are overhead costs. Finally, the reduced levels enhance corporate responsiveness.

- **Recognizes and is built about the "Manufacturing Paradox."** Every manufacturing firm must deal with a fundamental contradiction. It must "plan for change while simultaneously managing for stability." Every manufacturing firm must recognize that every development or system implemented today and considered to be leading edge or state of the art will be considered in the future and ultimately become obsolete. As a result, management must be willing to keep investing in its manufacturing system (planning, resources, information and capacity). However, these investments and the change that they bring must also live in harmony with the need to provide the stability needed for short-term production. This stability is needed for master scheduling, capacity planning and shop scheduling. These two forces must be recognized and balanced. The ability of firms to manage these two pressures can be expected to become a hallmark of the manufacturing firm of the 1990s.

- **Highly Integrated**. Finally, for the firm to compete effectively in the 1990s, it must be integrated. This integration must be both internal (among the various functional areas of the firm) and external (between the firm and its customers on one side and between the firm and its suppliers on the other). The arm's length relationships previously found must be replaced by a series of partnerships. The firm must know the needs and expectations of its customers. This requires that it develop a partnership with its customers. Once these needs are identified, the firm must act on them quickly. This requires a unified response. The sequential, "over the wall" approach of the past is too inefficient and time consuming. Finally, the firm must draw on the expertise of its suppliers to help it address the needs of its customers.

Failure to change the firm to incorporate these traits can adversely affect the firm in several ways: profit loss, loss of market share, and the move to *garbage niching* (a situation where your competitors take all of the desirable market segments and leave you with the remaining garbage). To implement these traits does require a complete understanding of each trait. Of these, the one that is most important but also least well understood is that of integration.

Integration: Defining the Concept

Integration is one term that many researchers and managers freely use but rarely define. As a result, a great deal of confusion surrounds this term. Our view of integration is relatively straightforward. We view integration as *the coordination and cooperation of systems, individuals, or organizational units within functional areas, between functional areas, and between firms* [7]. There are two critical dimensions underlying this concept—the application of integration and the types of integration.

Application of Integration: The first dimension describes how integration is implemented and supported. There are two levels to this dimension. The first, the *structure of integration*, refers to the formal and informal devices, structures and tools that management has introduced to encourage and support integration. Examples of such techniques include matrix organizations, cross-functional committees, common databases and large-scale communication networks (to encourage the spread and sharing of information and ideas). These techniques attempt to simplify and encourage cooperation and coordination by providing settings where these activities can take place. While a necessary condition for integration, they are not sufficient by themselves.

The second dimension, *the practice of integration*, refers to the practice or tradition of working together that is present in the firm. Considered within this dimension is not only the practice but also the attitudes of the people toward working together and solving problems jointly. It is in this dimension that we consider such factors as the degree to which people feel comfortable working together and the extent to which people from one area are willing to solicit suggestions and information from those in other areas when facing a problem and are willing to act on ideas generated elsewhere. This dimension also includes issues such as trust, openness, and willingness to share. In most organizations, this is the true acid test of integration.

Types of Integration

The second dimension deals with the different types of integration found in the firm. There are four basic types of integration present in most organizations [7, pp. 76-77].

- **Functional Integration**. This deals with the extent to which a functional area (e.g., marketing, manufacturing, accounting) is internally integrated. Within the context of manufacturing, functional integration deals with the linkages and feedback loops that exist between planning, scheduling, and execution on the shop floor. Closed Loop MRP II systems, for example, can be regarded as examples of functional integration within the manufacturing area.

- **Organizational Integration**. This deals with the links and extent of coordination existing between the different functional areas of the firm (e.g., between marketing and manufacturing or between manufacturing and accounting).

- **Strategic Integration**. The third type of integration involves the extent to which the processes of formulating, implementing, evaluating, and revising strategic objectives are coordinated with the activities of the various functional areas. With strategic integration, we allow for the presence of closed loops between the various functional areas and the strategic formulation process. The strategic process generates the objectives and milestones that direct the activities of the various functional areas. However, the activities, problems, capabilities and limitations of the various functional areas can and do influence the specific objectives selected by top management and the process by which they were identified.
- **Interorganizational (Channel) Integration**. The final type of integration deals with the linkages that exist external to the firm. Specifically, this type of integration considers two different directions for channel integration. The first *is forward integration*. This involves the coordination of activities between the firm and its customers. The second type, *backward integration,* focuses on the integration of activities between the firm and its supplier base.

These four types of integration represent investments that the firm may make. Management may choose to invest in one, two, three or all four forms of integration (for a detailed discussion of the integration investment decision as it pertains to CIM, see Reference 7.) In those settings where the environment is stable, product life cycles are long, and how the firm competes well known, the firm may decide to limit its investments in integration to functional and organizational. However, when the environment is unstable, life cycles short, and the basis of competition highly unsettled, the firm must invest in all four types of integration. Organizational integration enables marketing to communicate directly to manufacturing those traits demanded by the firm. Strategic integration ensures an ongoing consistency between corporate strategy and manufacturing capabilities. Functional integration is needed to keep the shop floor in step with manufacturing planning. Channel integration is needed to maintain the constant flow of information and communication between the supplier, the firm and the customer.

Integration: Identifying the Benefits

Integrating the functionally oriented hierarchy is a major undertaking. It requires not only putting in place the structure for integration (for all four types of integration) but also changing the way people and organizations interact with each and the way that they think. It requires changing people's allegiance from the function to the product (and the customer). It demands that walls between the various components of the total system (between functions, between the functions and top management and between the firm and its suppliers and customers) be torn down. The various barriers to change (obvious and hidden) are great. As a result, this is a long-term undertaking. For example, Frost, Inc., of Grand Rapids, Michigan, took over four years to integrate its organization along only three dimensions (functional, strategic and organizational). Ingersoll Milling of Rockford, Illinois, has been working on building linkages between itself and its customers and suppliers since the mid 1980s. If the barriers are so great and the time for implementation so long, then why do it? The answer is that the potential benefits offered by effective integration are very great and include:

- **Integration is necessary to implement such new developments as Just-in-Time, Time-Based Competition and Computer Integrated Manufacturing**. Many of the new developments that managers are now exploring require the presence of an integrated enterprise. For example, in Computer Integrated Manufacturing (CIM), the major element and requirement for success as noted by Melnyk and Narasimhan [7] was not the technology, nor was it manufacturing. Rather, it was integration. In Time-Based Competition (TBC), several of the strategies used to reduce lead times require the prior existence of integration (within the firm or between the firm and its suppliers and customers). For example, simultaneous engineering is built around integration [1].
- **Integration facilitates improvement**. Integration brings people, functions and organizations together. It promotes on-going communication between people. As a result, people share their own unique insights. They begin to teach each other and the other functions about what features they value and what features create problems. Manufacturing teaches marketing about the importance of schedule stability (at least in the short term); marketing teaches manufacturing about who buys the firm's products and what they want. This interaction is important because it enables the firm to overcome a basic limitation of the functionally organized hierarchy—*no one person and no one function is an expert about every aspect*. Instead, by bringing people from various functions and areas (both within and outside of the firm), various insights can be brought to bear on problems and issues involving process and product design. This melding of views has several important implications for the firm, its products and its process. First, better products and more effective and efficient processes can be made right "the first time." For example, in designing the manufacturing process layout for a new facility, management can form a design team consisting of representatives from manufacturing, industrial facilities management and process engineering. The result is that the design will reflect the inputs of these three areas—each with their unique perspective. The new design should lend itself to the efficient flow of material through the system. It should also be easily manned, staffed, managed and maintained by manufacturing. Finally, it should ensure easy removal of waste and complete compliance with governmental regulations (a concern of industrial facilities management). Similar results can be observed for new product design through the use of simultaneous engineering. Second, because less time is spent in correcting the problems created by poor product and process designs, the ongoing costs of manufacturing product are reduced (as are the various lead times).
Third, because of the ongoing communications and interactions over issues concerning design and problems, each of the parties involved develops a familiarity with what is going on. They have a chance to provide a flow of suggestions on how the problem (or problems) can be either corrected or avoided in the future. They can reflect on past experiences and identify potential improvements. These factors not only reduce the time required to effectively resolve problems; they also encourage *continuous improvement.* These improvements are often small improvements in the status quo and are consistent with Kaizen [4]. These small incremental improvements often create the greatest increases in corporate productivity and effectiveness. Integration does not preclude the discovery of large-scale innovations.

Rather, it provides a very fertile ground for these smaller incremental improvements.

- **Less internal stress and frustration**. Within the functionally organized hierarchy, frustration and stress are frequently present. Each function is unable to understand why the other areas of the firm don't seem to understand what it is doing. It also sees the actions taken by other areas as adversely affecting its operations and processes. It also seems confused when accused by others of "causing havoc" elsewhere. This frustration and stress reflect the myopic perspective with which everyone views problems and issues. Manufacturing people see problems from a manufacturing perspective, not a marketing, finance or customer view. With integration, much of this stress and frustration is reduced. The myopic perspective is replaced by a broader corporate or product point of view. Marketing begins to learn why frequently changing schedules make it difficult for manufacturing to meet on-time delivery requirements. Product engineering can see how a small change in the designs that it releases to a supplier can significantly increase the scrap rates experienced by the supplier.
- **More effective problem resolution**. In the functionally organized hierarchy, problem solving is frequently very time-consuming and inefficient (especially if the solution to the problem requires the cooperation of two or more areas). There are several reasons for this. First, none of the parties has access to all of the information or facts. Since information is not shared extensively, each of the involved parties tries to capture some of the missing information. The result is that there is a great deal of redundancy of information with much of the information not being correct. When the groups meet, valuable time at the start of the meeting is taken up with comparing information and determining what information is correct and what information is still missing. This time detracts from problem solving. Second, the mutual distrust and suspicion (as noted in the previous discussion) tends to encourage "finger pointing" as the various parties try to assign blame (to each other). Again, this distracts from problem solving. With integration, less time is spent on information assessment and finger pointing and more time is devoted to identifying what factors caused the problem and formulating a plan for solving the problem.

There are many other potential benefits attributable to integration. These include more focus on the processes rather than symptoms, better products, effective processes, a more responsive organization (especially since information and decisions do not have to travel up and down functional hierarchies), less overhead, and change in orientation (from the function to product—the most logical method of integrating the firm with its customers and suppliers). Integration offers management an effective structure by which it can develop and maintain a sustainable competitive advantage in the marketplace.

Obstacles to Integration

If the potential benefits offered by integration are so great and the costs imposed by the functionally organized hierarchy so high, then why have so few firms been successful in integrating their operations? The reason for these failures is that there are many obstacles that must be first overcome before integration can effectively take place. These include:

- **Fear of Change**. For a person working in a functionally organized hierarchy, the current structure offers certainty.

Each person knows what is expected of him or her; each person knows how to manage; each person knows what he or she can and cannot do; he or she knows who reports to him or her and to whom he or she reports in turn. The new integrated structure, with its reduced number of levels and more decision-making at the lower levels, represents change. It offers to take away the security of what he or she knows and replace it with a new structure that has less structure and is less well defined. People may not see the benefits to be gained by moving to this new integrated structure as being sufficient to offset the perceived higher costs of change. This fear of change with its attendant resistance to change may be greatest at the lower and middle management levels. It is these levels that are to be affected the most by the introduction of integration.

- **Perceived Loss of Power**. Closely related to the preceding point is the loss of power (influence) that the new integrated structure may bring with it. Under the functionally organized hierarchy, the power of many managers (especially at the middle and lower levels) comes from their functional expertise. They know more about their functions and their operations than others outside of their functions. By controlling access to this knowledge, managers can exercise influence or control over what takes place in the firm. But integration threatens to remove this source of influence. Information is now shared; mutual education now takes place. These factors threaten to erode the manager's basis of power and influence.
- **Resistance by Top Management**. Many top managers know how to manage the functionally organized hierarchy. However, few know how to manage the integrated firm.
- **Lack of Role Models**. One of the major obstacles to integrating the American firm is lack of many successful examples of the integrated enterprise. Currently, only a handful of firms (e.g., Frost, Inc. of Grand Rapids, Michigan; and Ingersoll Milling of Rockford, Illinois) have been able to successfully integrate their firms. The management of most of these firms is still learning how to manage this new type of enterprise. As a result, there are few guidelines or examples that other managers can study and learn from.
- **Lack of Properly Trained and Educated People**. The new integrated enterprise requires a new type of personnel. These are people who identify with the product and not the function. They are also people who can cope with stress and high levels of ambiguity (especially on the shop floor where the shop personnel will now be taking over much of the decision-making previously done by management). These are people who are driven by a strong strategy view of what is required (i.e., CEOs on the Floor). They share a common vision of the firm; they understand the needs of the firm; they know the customers. Finally, these are people who can view problems from different perspectives. These people are different from those found in the functionally organized hierarchy. At present, there is no well-established source for producing such people.

For example, many American business schools are structured around functionally oriented curricula. People are trained in finance, accounting or operations management. The only integration that takes place occurs at the end (just before they graduate) when the students are exposed to a single or two-term class in strategy/policy. In spite of this class, these people are primarily functionally oriented.

- **Inappropriate Performance Measures.** Most of today's performance measures are functionally based. That is, they deal with how the function carries out its tasks. Even in a recent study of performance measurement for world class manufacturing [5], many of the measures presented dealt with how manufacturing carried out its tasks with attributes such as production flexibility, process time, and quality being monitored. Without product-based performance measures present, there is no support for integration. As Oilie Wight wisely noted, "You get what you inspect, now what you expect."

Integrating the Firm: Some Guidelines

Integration is no longer a luxury; it is a necessity and a requirement for corporate survival and growth. However, one of the problems surrounding integration is that it is the general lack of guidelines and suggestions. The following are some very general guidelines that should be followed when trying to integrate the firm:

- **Begin with a Base Line.** One of the first steps is to carry out a self-assessment of your firm and the level of integration now present. This assessment should examine the extent to which problem solving is joint. It should examine the various databases used by each of the functional areas (and determine the extent to which these databases are redundant or overlapping). It should assess how access to these databases is managed, who is given access, what information is passed out and under what conditions information is shared. The assessment should also examine *indicators of integration*. Tooling and Engineering Change Notices/Engineering Change Orders (ECN/ECOs), for example, are strong indicators of the lack of integration (specifically organizational). Increases in the number of tools per active part number or ECN/ECOs often point to "over-the-wall" problem solving. The self-assessment should determine how prevalent "workarounds" are. A workaround is often created by one function in response to a problem originating from elsewhere. A high level of workarounds indicates a lack of integration. The self-assessment should examine the process by which problems are identified and resolved within the firm. This process should be documented using a tool such as *process flow analysis*. The assessment should also examine in detail the processes by which the firm introduces new or modified product and process designs. Finally, the self-assessment should involve feedback from customers and suppliers as to the receptiveness of the firm to suggestions and comments. Suppliers should also be asked at what stage they become involved in the firm's designs and problem-solving activities.

  Carrying out this self-assessment is important for several reasons. First, it helps to make everyone aware of the current state of affairs within the company. Second, it identifies the costs and problems created by the existing system. This self-assessment also helps identify where integration (either formal or informal) is strongest and where it is weakest or non-existing. Finally, it provides a base against which future changes can be compared.

- **Determine what level of integration is required.** The self-assessment is internally oriented. It describes what is but it does not set out what should be. To do that, we must start with the customer base. We must identify who our customers are and why they buy from us (as compared with our competition). These requirements must be broken into *order qualifiers* (those traits that we

must satisfy at a certain level to be considered for an order), *order winners* (those traits in which we must excel relative to our competition if we are to win orders) *and order losers* (those traits that will cause us to lose orders and business) (for a more detailed discussion of these traits, see references 3 and 6). In addition, we should benchmark our firm against the best in the industry. The purpose of this assessment is to determine what types of integration are required (both now and in the future) to serve our customer base better. Integration is an investment and should only be made when it can be justified from a strategic perspective.

- **Focus on the Corporate Databases.** Any integrated system is built on an integrated database. To integrate the database is a major undertaking since it requires merging the various databases managed by the various functional areas. Redundancies and inaccuracies must be identified and eliminated. The corporate database must offer a conversion capability so that financial decisions can be translated into terms meaningful to manufacturing and marketing people.

- **Institute an Ongoing Training and Education Program.** Successful integration requires not only an integrated database, but also extensive training and education. This training and education should include all levels of the firm. It may even include certain suppliers and customers. This training should target the lower and middle managers and help them understand the impact of integration on their tasks. It should also present them with models and frameworks for managing within the integrated firm. This task is not something that can be carried out by such external resources as universities. It is something that must be done internally. The reason is that there are very few external experts when it comes to integration. One effective way of training people is to emphasize (and reward) cross-training. That is, encourage people at the various levels of the firm to take assignments outside of their functional areas. Encourage horizontal rather than vertical movement within the company. Develop a training program, for example, for incoming manufacturing managers that will expose them to assignments in marketing, engineering, and purchasing. Remember that cross-training is currently done very effectively for cost accountants.

- **Encourage integration by focusing on certain key processes and activities.** Key to successful integration is the development of the practice of integration. One way of encouraging the development of this practice is to have people work together on certain activities of mutual interest. These activities include product and process design and problem solving. Management should consider implementing (on a small scale) developments such as *simultaneous engineering* [1] and simultaneous process design (involving manufacturing, process engineering and industrial facilities management). It should also consider the introduction of cross-functional problem solving teams for addressing problems involving manufacture, design and delivery. These teams may involve both representatives from key customer accounts and key suppliers. The key to the successful implementation of these activities is to start with small, well-focused problems and designs and to build only when people are confident that they can work within the new integrated structures.

- **Recognize that integration is a long-term undertaking.** Integration is a major undertaking. It will require several years before some of the benefits will be realized. The reason is that management practice and habits have to change. Top management must have the patience to allow people to experiment, make mistakes and learn. It should be prepared to view investments in integration as strategically, not financially based. The financial benefits will be realized, but not in the short term. However, without integration, there is no long-term financial benefit to be gained.

- **Restructure the performance measurement system.** Most performance measurement systems focus on functionally generated outputs. They do not reward integrated behavior. They rarely reward people for working together. As a result, a new set of measures must be formulated and introduced. These measures should reward product-based activities (e.g., the length of time needed to introduce a new product, reduction of unnecessary tooling, percentage reduction in product response time). People do only those things for which they are rewarded.

Concluding Comments

As we enter the 1990s, we must recognize that our ability to survive and grow will be greatly influenced by how we organize the firm and the relationships that we develop both internally and between ourselves and our customers and suppliers. We must recognize that the new foundations for competition in the 1990s (e.g., JIT, TQM, TBC) require a firm that is tightly integrated. These developments are not consistent with the functionally organized hierarchy of the past. This structure has served us well in the past. However, for many firms, it is no longer a viable structure. As Sir Leuan Maddock noted in 1982: "To cherish traditions, old buildings, ancient cultures and graceful lifestyles is a worthy thing—but in the world of technology to cling to outmoded methods of manufacture, old product lines, old markets, or old attitudes among management and workers is a prescription for suicide."

References

1. Charney, C. *Time to Market: Reducing Product Lead Time.* Dearborn, MI: Society of Manufacturing Engineers, 1991.
2. Davis, S. *Future Perfect.* Reading, MA: Addison-Wesley, 1987.
3. Hill, T. *Manufacturing Strategy:* Text and Cases. Homewood, IL: Irwin, 1989.
4. Imai, M. *Kaizen: The Key to Japan's Competitive Success.* New York, NY: Random House Business Division, 1986.
5. Maskell, B.H. *Performance Measurement for World Class Manufacturing.* Cambridge, MA: Productivity Press, Inc., 1991.
6. Melnyk, S.A., and Narasimhan, R. "Developing Manufacturing Excellence through Integration: Uniting Capacity, Shop Floor Control and Strategy." *APICS 34th International Conference Proceedings.* Seattle, WA: October 20 - 25, 1991, pp. 267 - 270.
7. Melnyk, S.A., and Narasimhan, R. *Computer Integrated Manufacturing: Guidelines and Applications from Industrial Leaders.* Homewood, IL: Business One-Irwin, 1992,
8. Rosencrance, R. "Too Many Bosses, Too Few Workers," *New York Times,* July 15, 1990, p. 11.
9. Senge, Peter M. *The Fifth Discipline.* New York, NY: Doubleday/Currency, 1990.
10. Wagner, John A. Ill, and Hollenbeck, John R. *Management of Organizational Behavior.* Englewood Cliffs, NJ: Prentice-Hall, 1992.

About the Authors

Steven A. Melnyk, CPIM, is Professor of Operations Management at Michigan State University. Steven Melnyk is the lead author of five books in the area of production and inventory control. These include *Shop Floor Control* (Dow Jones-Irwin, 1985), *Production Activity Control: A Practical Guide* (Dow Jones-Irwin, 1987), *Shop Floor Control: Principles, Practices and Case Studies* (APICS, 1987), *Computer Integrated Manufacturing: A Source Book* (APICS, 1990), and *Computer Integrated Manufacturing: Guidelines and Applications from Industrial Leaders* (Business One-Irwin, 1992). He has also edited the first conference proceedings dealing with tool management and control (Tool Management and Control: Manufacturing's Ignored Resource—LA ADSIG, 1990). Dr. Melnyk has also signed a contract to write a textbook on Operations Management (to be published through Austen Press-Irwin, 1995).

In addition, Dr. Melnyk is the author of numerous articles that have appeared in journals at the national and international level. He sits on the editorial boards for *the Journal of Operations Management* and *Production and Inventory Management.* He serves as a member of the CIRM committee on manufacturing processes. He is also the software editor for *APICS—The Performance Advantage.*

Dr. Melnyk is a member of the Grand Rapids Chapter of APICS. He is also active in such professional societies as NAPM, DSI and SME. His research interests include Shop Floor Control, Tool Management and Control, Just-in-Time Manufacturing, and Time-Based Competition.

William Wassweiler is the Manufacturing Industry Specialist for J.D. Edwards & Company, a leading supplier of applications software for IBM midrange computers. He has over 30 years of experience in manufacturing operations and materials management and is known as a pioneer and innovator in the field of automating manufacturing systems.

He developed the first successful shop floor control system driven by Material Requirements Planning that was installed at Twin Disc, Inc. Consulting assignments have been worldwide. Areas of expertise include Process, Repetitive, Make-to-Stock, Assemble-to-Order, Job Shop and Just-in-Time.

Mr. Wassweiler is a member and past president of the Milwaukee Chapter of APICS. He is certified at the fellow level in production and inventory management. He has developed and presented courses pertaining to material management and MRP II at the University of Wisconsin and Marquette University.

For the last twenty years, Mr. Wassweiler has been a member of the University of Wisconsin Business Management Advisory Board. He was chairman of the committee that developed the APICS Shop Floor Control Certification Program and he is currently chairman of the CIRM Manufacturing Processes Committee. In 1974, he received the APICS Communication Award. He helped author the APICS Shop Floor Control and Cycle Counting Training Aids. He is also the author of the MGI book and course on Shop Floor Control and contributed to the Production Activity Control book from the Business One-Irwin/APICS series in production management.

Reprinted from the 1994 APICS International Conference Proceedings.

Supplying the Demand Chain

Roger T. Miles

Over recent years, the term "supply chain" has been used increasingly to describe the logistics process. This has now become so much a part of the logistics language that "Logistics" is in great danger of being renamed Supply Chain. Is this the best term to describe the process of moving material through a value-added chain to a customer? In my view, the word Supply gives totally the wrong inference and therefore before Supply Chain becomes totally accepted it is, I suggest, beneficial to change from Supply Chain to "Demand Chain." In this paper I will explain why the change in word is important, what demand means in the logistics sense and how the often overlooked service demands, both ideal and perceived, can be measured. Achieving a thorough understanding of the demands placed on a company is the all important first step in achieving world class status in logistics.

What's in a Name?

During the eighties, the term "logistics" grew in usage although the functions included varied considerably from one company to another. The level of understanding of what were the important elements of world class logistics invariably decreased the higher one went in an organization, and many attempts were made at using a more readily understandable term. For many years the term Supply Chain had been used by a firm of consultants (Booz Allen Hamilton) to describe the logistics processes of a company, and it was a logical step for the term Supply Chain Logistics to be coined and to be used increasingly to help explain the logistics function.

Unfortunately, Supply infers manufacturing or supplier "push" into the marketplace and indeed the term was first used in the seventies when the emphasis was very much on manufacturing. In the nineties, with the shift of power to the customer and the Total Quality drive impeaching companies to be much more customer focused, optimizing a supply chain can imply that it will be optimized to the suppliers or manufacturer's benefit. What World Class Logistics companies practice is optimization of the DEMAND CHAIN, i.e., they understand the needs of their customers in terms of the volume of orders and service level requirements and supply these demands at the lowest cost.

Why Is the Nature of Demand Important for Optimum Logistics?

Demand is the key driver of logistics. If there is no demand there is no requirement for moving any materials through the value added chain. In order to optimize an organization's logistics, it is necessary to understand the full nature of the customer's logistics demands both in the two major components, volume and service. Once a thorough understanding of the customer's real needs has been achieved it is then possible to manage the demand better. World Class Logistics companies practice Demand Management; many of the second league practice Supply Management.

The manifestations of Supply Management are high levels of stock and poor service levels. Companies with a thorough understanding of Demand Management, on the other hand, are able to operate with lower stock levels through the total value added chain and provide competitive service levels that the customers actually need.

Demand Management falls into two discrete parts, volume demand and service demand. Volume demand requires the logistics team to be closely involved with sales and marketing in order to fully understand the nature of the customer's volume demand: seasonality, geographic location, order size, delivery size, etc. While most companies can supply endless sales data analyzed every possible way, very few companies have real service level data of sufficient depth to enable the total customer's demands to be properly managed. The remainder of this article will focus on the important aspects of service demand.

Understanding Service Demand

Logistics can easily represent from five to twenty percent of the cost of sales and the key logistics challenge is "Does the logistics function provide value for money in terms of the logistics service provided in the marketplace?" There should be no unknown product give-away.

The service level is the product of the logistics function and as such the product must be specified and monitored to ensure that there is no unnecessary "product give-away." On a recent review of a major oil company's logistics we were interested in the computerized vehicle scheduling system and its impact on customer service level. In effect the company was scheduling better, which in their terms meant bringing orders forward so that more deliveries were made on day 1 than previously. The stated oil industry service level in that market was two days and the company rarely exceeded that. During a long discussion with the Managing Director about balancing cost and service, a capital expenditure item was waiting for signature on his desk. This was for an expensive piece of refining equipment that would reduce the product give-away on 98 octane petroleum. Despite the price of the equipment the MD felt confident in authorizing the expenditure as the benefits could be quantified. Investments in service level improvements were much more difficult to justify for the simple reason that no meaningful measures were in place.

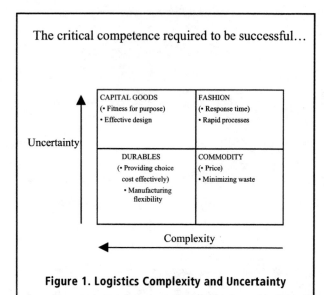

The critical competence required to be successful...

CAPITAL GOODS	FASHION
(• Fitness for purpose) • Effective design	(• Response time) • Rapid processes
DURABLES	COMMODITY
(• Providing choice cost effectively) • Manufacturing flexibility	(• Price) • Minimizing waste

Uncertainty

Complexity

Figure 1. Logistics Complexity and Uncertainty

The nature of the ideal logistics service is a subtle blend of a number of different attributes, and individual service packages can vary enormously. The cost implications of two slightly different service packages can be enormous. For example, the cost of providing a 24-hour delivery service as opposed to a 48-hour one is probably double, and yet if the customer is happier with the total 48-hour service there is clearly no point in overspecifying the service. In some marketplaces, a 24-hour service is the accepted norm; and yet in others a slower service may be quite acceptable provided that other factors, or attributes, are met. For a logistics function to be optimized it is vital to understand the nature of the service package and how it changes from market group to market group.

In broad terms, manufacturing logistics can be segmented into the four quadrants of a classic two-by-two grid (see **Figure 1**).

This grid is a powerful means of understanding the differences in customer demands. The vertical axis is a scale of uncertainty of demand. An example of a market with high demand uncertainty would be ice cream, where demand can soar in a matter of hours. An example of low uncertainty would be the bread market, where the peaks in demand (public holidays, etc.) are predictable. The horizontal axis represents logistics complexity as represented by the complexity of the bill of materials, the number of manufacturing processes, the packaging variety, the number of distribution points, etc. Manufacturing and selling own label TV dinners has a much greater degree of complexity than manufacturing and selling a branded dinner.

Clearly, each of the four quadrants of this grid has different demand characteristics, which give rise to totally different logistics demand requirements.

How Can Service Level Demands Be Established?

The essential key to developing a competitive logistics strategy is to gain as good an understanding as possible as to what the customer measures in terms of service performance and how this varies by channel, by sector, by geography, etc. There are different views of this performance:
• needed—what does the customer want?
• perceived—what does the customer think he gets?

• agreed—what is agreed between the customer and supplier?
• achieved—what does the supplier actually deliver?

The customer measures the gap between the first and second while the supplier measures the gap between the third and fourth; consequently, there is often a significant and expensive dissatisfaction. The fundamental cause of this is the fact that many companies think that they know precisely what their customers want in terms of service. The first step towards meeting the customer requirements therefore is to actually ask the customers. Although this seems blindingly obvious, all too often we find that the supplier thinks they know precisely what their customers want, only for a customer survey to show a quite different picture of attributes and their respective levels within attributes.

A second short case study illustrates this need to talk to the real customers and not to assume that the marketing department knows best. A national service company had 23 depots to cover the total U.K. The Marketing Director, the Operations Director and the Managing Director all felt that 23 depots gave them a competitive advantage as they knew that their customers needed to be near a depot. We convinced the client that we should test the service level requirements including this important attribute of nearness to depot. We therefore carried out an independent market survey on a wide range of customers with a questionnaire covering some fourteen different service level attributes. "Nearness to depot" came thirteenth in importance with delivery reliability and completeness of order being clearly the two most important attributes. Once the impact of that fact had been absorbed we were able to develop a logistics strategy that halved the number of depots. This produced significant financial savings and also raised the service level as the company was able to tune its efforts on the key factors of service.

How to conduct such a customer service survey has been a problem as with the traditional approach there is a considerable risk that the customer will mark everything as important. Customer Preference Modeling is a fairly recent development which actually reflects the customer saying, "Everything is important, but some things are more important than others."

The technique is a software package that includes some very clever programming which essentially forces the interviewee to make "Trade-offs" between different groupings of attributes and levels. For example, the computer screen may show two service packages:
• package A where 100% of orders arrive on time but 1 - 2 months from order to receipt of product
• package B where 70 - 79% of orders arrive on time but 1 to 2 weeks from order to receipt of product

The interviewee then has to score his preference on a scale of 1 (strongly prefer package A) to 9 (strongly prefer package B). The programmer decides which packages to offer the interviewee on the basis of single choice questions earlier in the interview. The advent of highly portable computers has made the interview process extremely convenient to conduct, and interviewees find the technique interesting, nonthreatening and relatively quick.

Customer service incorporates a number of attributes, each with different possible levels, for example:
• lead time—from 15 minutes (computer engineer) to three months (steel sections)
• delivery precision—10-minute delivery window to specified week
• order drop size—single carton to complete truck load

- delivery completeness—100% only to lower levels of acceptance.

In practice we have used as many as twenty-five different attributes although typically we use only ten to fifteen.

The actual attributes and levels are agreed with our client at a preliminary workshop where the overall demographics are established. We develop the client specific interview and trial it before agreeing on the final version. If appropriate, we will train the client's staff to conduct the interview and then commence the interview program. The individual interviews are downloaded and the overall results produced. The output can be represented in a variety of ways, depending on the size and complexity of the sample base. A typical interview would last between 30 and 45 minutes.

This example is of an assignment for a steel company where the results of the logistics survey showed that there were two attributes that were equal first in importance and by a significant margin. 'Delivery reliability' was one of these and that came as no surprise to our client; however, the customers placed 'Documentation' equally important, which was a surprise. It was also interesting to find that 'Product Development,' which our client would have placed in the middle of the league table, came last and by a comfortable margin. Once again the importance of talking to real customers can be clearly appreciated.

Having determined that a particular attribute is important the next question is, "What is the critical level within that attribute?" Lead time may be the most important attribute but is lead time measured in minutes, hours, days or even weeks? The analysis is able to answer these types of questions in a very clear way.

It is interesting to note that in this case the importance of order lead time increases steadily as the lead time shortens to two days but that there is only a minimal increase in importance when moving from a two-day to a one day lead time. The logistics cost implications of providing a one-day service as opposed to a two-day service will be appreciated by this audience but without the benefit of this analysis our client would have continued to strive to provide a one-day service when in the total picture the customer would rather have improved performance in other attributes.

It is possible to establish an Ideal Performance Profile for each relevant market sector. Having established this picture of the ideal world the next important question is "How well does the supplier match his service package to this ideal?" This benchmarking exercise is relatively straightforward to include within the interview process and enables the supplier's strengths and weaknesses to be identified and therefore improvement opportunities to be examined. At the same time it is also possible to obtain the customer's perception of one, or more, competitor's performance against the ideal. Figure 5 is an example of a recent assignment and clearly shows that both our client and the competition were failing to meet the customer's real service level requirements.

Plotting the relative performance of the "Client versus Competitors" with the "Characteristic Importance" on a simple two-by-two grid enables the competitive actions to be identified. There are four discrete sectors:
- review—those attributes that are low in importance and where the competitive position is also low
- rescue—attributes where most improvement is required as the customer perceives these attributes to be important and rates the company lower than the competition

- sustain—where the company has a competitive advantage in attributes that the customer rates highly important
- restrain—attributes that the company is scored higher on than the competition, but unfortunately these attributes are not perceived to be of great importance to the customer and therefore further efforts to improve the attribute would have minimal benefit. Indeed, there are cases where this analysis has led to a reduction in the level of that particular attribute of the service package with a consequential saving in logistics costs.

In an example from a telecommunications company, there are five attributes where attention should be focused: "Spares availability for new equipment," "Lead time," "Quality and timeliness of stock information," "Closure for stocktaking" and "Opening hours of stores."

Customer service level is a complex but very important element of establishing a competitive demand chain logistics strategy. We have shown how it is essential to:
- ask the customer what he thinks are the important factors
- use a forced trade-off analysis technique to obtain the ideal total package
- benchmark the company's performance against this ideal
- benchmark competitors against the same ideal
- identify priority actions to gain competitive advantage.

The case study that follows illustrates the impact that a thorough understanding of the customer's demands, both in terms of volumes and service requirements, can have on major strategic questions.

Case Study

The company is a major manufacturing enterprise, and this strategy was developed for the principal division from which the company has grown. The products made are consumables and, in the main, commodity items. Hundreds of millions are produced each year and at the start of the assignment they were made in a large number of factories throughout Europe. The company developed their own manufacturing equipment and were convinced that future profitability was dependent on the next generation of machines which would be able to produce at twice the rate of the current machines. Faster meant cheaper and cheaper meant more profit was the logic. Unfortunately, implementation of this new generation of machine throughout their manufacturing base was estimated to take a number of years and it was at this stage that the company approached our applied research laboratory to see if we could identify a faster route to full implementation.

To understand the business needs that this equipment was designed to meet, we undertook a short preliminary study. This revealed that while the end, packed product was made in a two-stage process and the new equipment was aimed at making the basic, unpacked product faster, this wasn't the right solution for the total business. Making the products faster had less than a 3.0% impact on the cost of product made, whereas the cost of packaging, the second process, was over 12%. This had been largely overlooked in terms of development work and analysis showed that equally important cost reductions could be achieved much quicker. We subsequently were commissioned to develop a total European manufacturing and logistics strategy, the core of which was dependent on understanding the demands in the marketplace and the changing nature of these demands across different distribution channels and regions.

As part of the first phase of the strategy development we carried out a market survey of the different countries including a customer service survey. This showed:

- the market had changed considerably over the previous ten to twenty years, and in particular, the importance of the supermarket channel had grown enormously
- this growth was not uniform across Europe, with southern Europe being served by a greater number of traditional outlets
- the supermarkets' product range was only some 200 of the total 2000 unpacked products available; however, each supermarket required its own packaging and different multi-packs
- this packaging complexity increased the total number of end-product code numbers from 2,000 to in excess of 10,000
- the results of the service level survey showed that lead time, delivery reliability and flexibility were the important attributes and that neither our client nor the competition met the customers' requirements.

Approximately 70% of all the products sold were of the supermarkets' "200" range which, while having a steady demand throughout the year at this 200 code level, exhibited considerable weekly variations at the packed code level when own label and multi-packs were recognized. There are two traditional manufacturing solutions to this problem. One is to have sufficient manufacturing capacity to meet the short lead time variations; the second is to forecast demand and make to stock. It was this latter approach that the company had chosen and operated a European Central Warehouse which held, on average, four months' stock of end code products.

From our complexity and uncertainty picture and our customer service surveys, it was clear that we had to find some way of reducing the complexity and uncertainty of this major part of the throughput. The answer came from realizing that all this extra complexity came from packaging for the supermarket channel and that if we decoupled the process and held a buffer stock of common product we could provide considerable flexibility with a world-beating service offering.

Development of this approach showed that there were many benefits:

- large stocks of finished product were replaced with smaller stocks of unpacked product held closer to the market-place
- the European Central Warehouse was redundant

- decoupling the two processes allowed the primary process to be concentrated in two focused factories instead of the previous large number and ensured that the packaging process received the attention it required
- the company was able to provide a level of service that the competition found difficult to match
- the focused factory required drastically simpler planning and control systems.

Conclusion

Supply Chain Logistics gives the impression that all the forces of Manufacturing Push will be brought to bear on the customer. As such the "We know best" suppliers end up misunderstanding the real needs of the customers with resultant loss in revenue and profitability. Demand Chain Logistics implies that the supplier recognizes that the customer is king and that he, the supplier, must understand all the variations in customer demand that the market has to offer.

Of all the demand factors, service level has been the most difficult to analyze and understand. Customer Preference Modeling now provides a means by which the real customer needs can be assessed and a truly competitive logistics strategy developed.

About the Author

Having joined PA Consulting Group (Europe) in 1983, Roger Miles is now responsible for managing major logistics assignments and developing the Distribution Logistics practice in Europe. He has carried out a large number of logistics assignments in the U.K., Europe, Australia, and elsewhere in the world. These assignments have been undertaken on behalf of companies in all major industry sectors and have included all elements of logistics. During this time he has published a number of articles and spoken on a number of platforms around the world.

Before joining PA, he worked for seven years for a major U.K. food group with overall responsibility for distribution logistics. Prior to this, he worked for two years in North Africa as a distribution consultant on secondment to the Algerian National Oil Company. This had followed four years of European distribution logistics experience with Esso Petroleum and a Ph.D. thesis on motor vehicle-generated air pollution. Roger joined Esso from City University, where he studied chemistry and completed a Ph.D. thesis on motor vehicle-generated air pollution.

Reprinted from the 1994 APICS International Conference Proceedings.

Top Management's Role in Fostering and Managing Positive Organizational Change

Timothy M. Mojonnier, CPIM

"If you don't know where you're going, you might end up somewhere else." —Casey Stengel

Overview

For many businesses, our current knowledge of computing technology, manufacturing processes, machine capabilities, integrated information systems, and P&IC principles will be outdated in a few years. "The only constant we face," said an ancient philosopher, "is change."

For top management, success depends on more than merely being able to articulate a vision of where and what the organization needs to be. This presentation will focus on showing how top management must develop a solid approach and methodology that managers will use for fostering and implementing positive change throughout the corporation.

The clear delineation of a vision for the organization's future is a key role for top management. But all too often, this vision has focused mainly on achieving certain financial results such as gaining market share, return on investment, and inventory to sales ratios. Envisioning what the business needs to be requires that the vision be aligned foremost with customer requirements and an assessment of the organization's current status and overall ability to achieve the long term objectives.

If top management is to successfully manage change, what needs to be developed is a description of issues such as:

What will the company look like when working inventory turns are increased by 80%?

What will be required of self-directed, small work groups to achieve throughput reduction targets?

How will we interact differently with vendors and distributors after integrating our information systems and business functions?

How will management processes change? What skills will our workforce and managers need? How will people be measured and rewarded when goals are achieved?

Asking these kinds of questions will help top management better define the vision of what things the organization will need to do and how it will have to do them. This is the basis on which a solid methodology for managing change depends.

How to Implement a Major Change

Whether you are implementing Just-in-Time (JIT), total quality management (TQM), manufacturing resource planning (MRP II), distribution requirements planning (DRP), or some combination of these management philosophies, you are introducing a major change into your organization.

1. Create a vision statement that clearly defines what your organization should look like in 3 to 10 years.

2. Ascertain your company's current condition by assessing your core competencies, your competition, your people's strengths and weaknesses, technological trends, and other variables.

3. Develop the critical strategies—including specific milestones—that will take you from your current condition to the condition described in the vision statement.

Figure 1. Three Steps Required for Successful Change Management

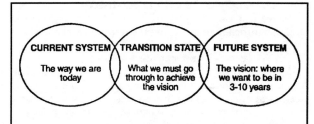

Figure 2. The Three Elements for Achieving Successful Organizational Change

There are three steps—critical to achieving lasting performance improvements—that are preconditions to successfully bringing about any major change (see **Figure 1**). These three preconditions to successful organizational change are logically interlinked.

First, you begin by creating the vision statement. Then, you assess where the organization is today. Finally, you develop strategies that move the organization from its current condition to what will exist when the vision is actualized.

Figure 2 graphically depicts the interrelationships among the three elements pertinent to every major organizational change.

Current System

There are attributes of your current system that you will want to maintain. For example, in one company, the culture inculcated the view that everyone was ultimately responsible for serving the customer. If the people in order entry needed help, other departments would willingly share resources in order to ensure high levels of customer service.

When converting to a DRP system, top management determined that they wanted to reinforce these positive behaviors. So it is important to determine what attributes of the current system you want to keep before planning a new management system.

The analysis of the current management system should be detailed and comprehensive. An effective way of gathering this information is through a cross-functional project team. The final report provides top management with an indication of what shouldn't be changed as well as what needs to be changed.

Transition State

As indicated in Figure 2, the vision of what the company will look like takes place in a 3 to 10 year time frame. This is realistic when implementing major systems changes, e.g., TQM. Despite this long time, you will need the complete commitment and energy of all employees today. To harness this energy, it is essential that you develop, with the input of the workers, goals that relate to improved operational performance each year. The establishment of intermediate term goals must be specific and detailed. They need to be developed for all areas of the corporation.

The Vision Statement

Whether it's TQM, JIT, DRP or MRP II, or some combination of these management philosophies, a new management system usually requires that our business is conducted in a radically different way than at present. Given that we face culture change, top management must do more than simply sign a check: the new way of doing business cannot be simply packaged and purchased.

Instead, it's the responsibility of top management to spend significant amounts of time to create a vision statement. Indeed, the greatest impediment to change is a poorly concocted vision statement.

In this process, top management must be willing to challenge the conventional wisdom, and analyze what is needed in order to make the business successful at some point in the distant future. As such, the vision statement becomes the organizational glue that holds everyone together during the transition from the current system to where you want to be in 3 - 10 years.

The vision statement has several purposes. First, it moves managers and employees away from attacking the symptoms of problems. Instead, it directs their efforts towards taking the actions that are required to make the organization truly effective.

Second, the vision statement serves as a motivational tool. The current reality may appear to be fraught with problems. By having a detailed vision of where the organization is headed, each person develops a better sense of his or her role in the future organization. Conversely, without a clearly articulated vision, the prospect of major changes will leave most employees unsettled. As a result, during the transition to the new system, these employees will end up resisting change.

Finally, the vision statement gives people direction. There are, for example, times when an employee must take actions that are not clearly prescribed by departmental procedures or corporate policy. In these instances, a sufficiently specific vision statement provides employees with direction to take those actions that are consistent with the organization's mission. For example, without a vision statement, a steel buyer may use lowest price as the primary criterion for choosing suppliers. In contrast, in a company

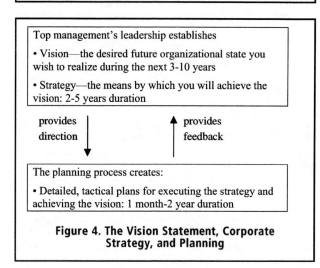

- Customers and markets
- Technology and its characteristics
- Performance review systems
- Compensation systems
- Organizational structure
- Competition
- Personnel policies
- Financial position
- Macro and micro economic variables
- Information systems

Figure 3. The Elements of Corporate Strategy

Top management's leadership establishes

• Vision—the desired future organizational state you wish to realize during the next 3-10 years

• Strategy—the means by which you will achieve the vision: 2-5 years duration

provides direction → provides feedback ↑

The planning process creates:

• Detailed, tactical plans for executing the strategy and achieving the vision: 1 month-2 year duration

Figure 4. The Vision Statement, Corporate Strategy, and Planning

where the vision statement indicates that serving one's customer is a primary value, the buyer will tend to place greater emphasis on the supplier's quality, because lesser quality steel could create problems for the buyer's customer, namely, the internal department that fabricates the steel.

Strategy

The creation of a vision statement is a necessary condition to achieving positive organizational change, but it is not a necessary and sufficient condition. For example, part of a company's vision may be to achieve dominance in the marketplace attaining a #1 market share position in 5 years. If this vision is not realistic, then the vision statement will not be believed by employees. As such, it will tend to demotivate employees and thus be counterproductive.

Instead, top management must create a vision that is realistic and attainable. The "how to" is the corporate strategy, and it must address the issues listed in **Figure 3**.

The development of a corporate strategy and the attendant planning that is required are not a substitute for a vision statement. Indeed, the creation of a vision statement precedes the development of a corporate strategy. Once the strategy and vision statement have been finalized, then it is possible to produce detailed plans for each business unit. The relationships between the vision statement, corporate strategy and the planning process are depicted in **Figure 4**. As indicated in Figure 4, the planning process provides feedback on the reality of the company's vision and strategy.

For example, an appliance manufacturer in the Southeast embraced a vision that included becoming a world-class manufacturing company within 3 years. An element of the strategy involved implementing SPC during the first year. In doing the detailed planning for the SPC implementation, it became apparent that the math skill level of the average factory worker was at the 6th grade level.

The planning process indicated that the company had to provide basic training in math prior to implementing SPC. Thus, the time table for implementing SPC in one year had to be pushed back, and this in turn impacted the timetable for reaching the corporation's vision.

Lining up Your People Behind the Vision

To overcome the obstacles that will invariably come in the way of achieving the vision, it is essential that your employees buy into the vision. Moreover, you want them to be highly motivated towards achieving it. To create this high intensity level, begin communicating the vision to them when it starts taking shape. By getting them involved in the process, you will be able to win over their enthusiastic support.

Communicate! Communicate! Communicate! Use every opportunity and medium (company newsletters, teleconferencing, personal appearances, etc.) to get the message out. Use public recognition to reward those individuals who are demonstrating behaviors that strongly support the company's vision of where you want to be.

To unify your people behind the vision, they must share in the rewards. Compensation systems must be realigned with the vision and changed so that desirable behaviors are reinforced.

Summary Cases

Specific case studies illustrating these principles will be presented, Space limitations do not permit inclusion of these examples here.

Conclusion

It is often said that improving performance should be viewed as a journey rather than a destination. But it is also true that when we do not know where we are going, any road will get us there. All too often, when implementing a new management system, restructuring a new division or undertaking a major project, we have focused on the "quick fix."

Each of our businesses is different. Thus, the monolithic implementation of a panacea program will not bring about the results that we seek. Instead, when contemplating a major change, we need a different mindset—a different approach.

---

1. Create a detailed vision statement.

2. Assess your current organizations' total culture.

3. Develop a strategy for achieving your vision.

4. Establish mid-point goals to motivate your troops.

Figure 5. Top Management's Role in Fostering Positive Organizational Change

---

The approach described in this paper has four essential elements (see **Figure 5**).

References

1. Beckhard, Richard, and Reuben T. Harris, *Organizational Transitions: Managing Complex Change,* Addison-Wesley Publishing Co., 1987.
2. Imai, Masaaki, *Kaizen,* McGraw-Hill Publishing Company, 1986.
3. Kotter, John P., *A Force For Change,* New York: The Free Press, 1990.
4. Prahalad, C.K., and Gary Hamel, "The Core Competence of the Corporation," *Harvard Business Review,* May-June 1990.

About the Author

Timothy M. Mojonnier is President of Mojonnier & Associates, Inc., a management education and consulting firm located in River Forest, Illinois. He provides education and consulting services to manufacturing and distribution companies in a variety of industries within the United States and internationally, primarily in South America and Central America.

He has helped both small and large companies—including AT&T, Baxter Healthcare and FMC—with a variety of innovative performance improvement strategies and tactics. Recently, he designed, developed and produced a complete education program for AT&T.

Mr. Mojonnier has a BA degree from Lafayette College and an MBA degree from the University of Chicago. He is a Lecturer in the Management Science Department at Loyola University of Chicago.

Mr. Mojonnier is on the Board of Directors of the GF Marchant Co. He is a frequent speaker at professional society meetings and events, both at the local and national levels.

Learning to Learn: The Key to World Class Manufacturing

Helene J. O'Brien, CPIM

The relationship between World Class Manufacturing (WCM) and Continuous Improvement continues to be explained, expanded, and attempted. Volumes of information have been published about the various approaches, mindsets, and measurements needed to achieve the performance advantages experienced by a few companies who have embarked upon the WCM odyssey. The literature also attests to the expanding realm of strategies, systems and technologies jockeying for prominence as the single-most important element to competitive advantage in the marketplace.

The observation of leading-edge companies in the United States, as well as our formidable competitors, substantiates that no strategy, system or technology can secure a permanent performance advantage in the marketplace. Sustainable competitive leverage requires ceaseless improvement at a faster pace than competitors. Thus, rapid and continuous improvement is directly associated with and inseparable from rapid and continuous learning. Continuous learning may be the economic imperative for industry in the 1990s.

This paper will explore the concept of Continuous Learning. What is it? Why is it important? Is it a new idea and who should be responsible for providing it? A review of popular learning methods will highlight four program characteristics that currently hamper the learning process within industry.

Following the definition of successful learning, nine critical factors will be proposed that should be in place in order to reap direct application within the workplace. Several innovative measurements of educational investment will be suggested and expanded.

What Is Continuous Learning?

Understanding *Continuous Learning* requires the review of the traditional terms of education and training. "Education" can be briefly defined as a process (not an event) that provides the knowledge, skills and attitudes to produce cause and effect understanding and support long-term behavioral change; e.g. education in medicine or law. "Training" is a transfer of mechanical expertise in response and reaction to a given situation; e.g. training in use of specific software. The "Learning" process combines both education and training and implies mastery gained through education and experience. Learning prepares individuals to educate themselves.

Continuous learning at a faster rate than one's competitors is required to achieve sustainable competitive leverage that results from rapid and continuous improvement.

The learning rate of competitors can therefore be assessed by the observation of their improvement rate. This information is gained through careful identification and surveillance of key competitive companies and compiled within a company's competitive analysis. This top management process includes gathering data from a variety of sources along with an in-depth analysis of strengths, weaknesses, opportunities and threats surrounding self as well as each competitor. The benefits derived are dependent upon regular reviews and contributions from all functional representatives within a formal and documented process.

Why Is Continuous Learning Important?

Peter Drucker predicts that "the factory of 1999 will allow rapid changes in design and product, rapid response to market demands, and low-cost production of 'options' or 'specials' in fairly small batches."[1]

Hauser and Clausing define House of Quality as "a process that gets people thinking in the right direction and thinking together." For most U.S. companies, this alone amounts to a quiet revolution, while implementation of Quality Functional Deployment (QFD) may require an organization capable of absorbing elegant ideas[2]

The justification and explanation for continuous learning in the manufacturing enterprise can be capsulized as follows:

- The changing nature of the future of business
- System and technology proliferation
- Workforce changes characterized by well-educated individuals who often feel like victims that have no control over decisions made
- Occupational evolution resulting in many obsolete positions and emerging responsibilities and roles
- Communication barriers resulting from decades of self-serving fiefdoms of Engineering, Marketing, Manufacturing, and Finance
- The natural human resistance to change [4]

Interfunctional planning and communication require different communication patterns and information flows. The flow is sideways, not upwards, and demands team members who are mindful of the whole. The work climate of the future will be characterized by people who collaborate, communicate, and commit to execution of agreed upon decisions. [1] An organization's infrastructure—systems, policies, and practices—must be ordered in such a way that doing the right thing is the easiest thing to do. Continuous learning will provide the skills, knowledge, and practice to apply sound analysis and decision-making in support of company goals and objectives.

Is Continuous Learning a New Phenomenon?

Education and training is certainly not new to the American manufacturing industry. During the 1940s, then President Roosevelt instituted the Training Within Industry (TWI) program that allowed for basic training in job instruction, job methods and job relations. Industrial psychologists promoted the concept of "whole company wellness" during the very period in which the U.S. experienced flourishing industrial strength.

During the 1950s the first computers were introduced into manufacturing. Much learning occurred as employers grappled with the application of statistical and scientific techniques for forecasting and inventory control. Later in the decade, the birth of the American Production and Inventory Control Society, Inc. (APICS), the professional society dedicated to education within the manufacturing realm.

The need for education and training was so strong in the 1960s, spearheaded by the development and installations of MRP, that APICS undertook a massive educational effort entitled *MRP Crusade*. With the evolution of Master Production Scheduling in the 1970s, came well-developed formal company-wide education and training programs in support of closed-loop MRP.

The 1980s provided a staggering array of philosophies, systems and technologies—MRP II, JIT, CIM, FMS, EDI, Imaging—to name a few—as well as the undeniable realization of lost markets and new intense competitors. American companies now experienced the beginning of faddish educational efforts. Education and training programs, often canned and nearly always unrelated, were offered in response to competitive crisis and some recently released concept of salvation for the manufacturing community.

The 1990s promise still further technological developments and implementations as well as several emerging bodies of knowledge focusing on the interfunctional development of a manufacturing firm. APICS' concept statement for the new Certified in Integrated Resource Management (CIRM) certification program states: "Managers of the future will need a better overall understanding of the integrated manufacturing enterprise—a guiding architectural blueprint—to effectively move the organization forward. They will encourage simultaneous decision making—or teaming—between multiple functional areas, focus on quality and customer service, and require continuous education at all levels within the organization to master changing technologies and market realities."

Accordingly, new educational offerings will be introduced with the repeated marketing promise of providing a competitive advantage for the next century. Such promises have not served as industrial salvation in past decades, nor will they do so in the future. Companies must begin to exhibit "sanity" in the development, selection, delivery and measurement of learning opportunities that are offered at ominous expense. There exists an ever-widening gap between the systems and technologies available and those that are understood and successfully applied. Appropriate, rapid and continuous learning in the 1990s is not an option!

Companies are responsible for identifying and developing competitive advantages. An enterprise that must compete aggressively requires a Continuous Learning strategy formulated to utilize all employees as contributors to performance advantage. Why would industry consider any outside sources, such as universities, colleges, etc., capable of providing competitive leverage in the marketplace?

Popular Learning Methods

Some of the popular vehicles for learning used in American manufacturing companies are listed below.
- Distribute information about "approved" educational offerings
  - Home-study programs
  - Internally developed instructional programs
  - computer-based
  - video-assisted or -led
  - instructor-led
- Externally developed or consultant education programs:
  - computer-based
  - video-assisted or -led
  - instructor-led
- Cross-functional rotations
- Training on tools and techniques
- New employee orientation
- Library administration
- Train-the-trainer
- Programs of professional societies (local and national)
  - Certification
  - Fundamentals
  - Tuition reimbursement
  - On-the-job training

Billions of dollars are spent each year providing education and training programs that are poorly selected, poorly coordinated, and poorly delivered despite many good intentions. The lack of demonstrated performance advantage may result from the following program characteristics:
- Fact-transfer only
- Biased programs
- Schedule or content conflicts
- Misapplication of education and training

Fact-Transfer Only

Many programs, regardless of internal or external development, assume that exposure to a fact; e.g., the independent and dependent nature of demand, will (1) have relevance to the learner; and (2) cause the learner to do something different when he/she returns to the workplace. The mere transfer of facts never alters workplace behavior.

Biased Programs

Many programs have been developed with a bias for a specific theory, software routine, or group of books. These programs are very often characterized by "right" or "wrong" answers and offer limited application potential. An example is cycle-counting education, which includes software forms and procedures and alludes to its unparalleled success. The learner is hampered because of a mismatch in data availability. The changes of successful application are minimal.

Conflicts

In large companies where each functional group sponsors educational offerings and schedules participants (sometimes mandatory), schedule conflicts as well as content clashes are sure to prevail. Example: The Human Resources function has scheduled a mandatory six week program on supervision for all supervisors. The Materials group schedules a mandatory ten week program on Inventory Management. What is the Production Control Supervisor to do?

Misapplication of Education and Training

Not only are many education and training programs short-term events that transfer facts in a biased manner, it is also important to note that education and training are often misapplied. In short, training is often substituted for education and, less frequently, education for training.

Example: In specifying a system architecture, a project team identified a need for the historical performance of each operation. The team was informed the data might be unacceptable due to prevalent "gang clocking" activity. Investigation showed that 30 classes were held each year on "clocking of work" and that all operators had attended at least two sessions. Attendance at one class proved that each person was indeed instructed in the mechanics of using the clocking equipment and associated cards. No amount of training, however, improved the accuracy of the clocking data.

In desperation, for accurate data was critical to the success of the new system, the team developed a detailed educational program that included *why* clocking data were important and the various uses within the company. This program did not include any training on the mechanics of clocking. Within two months, most of gang-clocking had ceased (without any harsh warnings or threatened punitive action) and the data were deemed to be "accurate."

The misapplication of education and training can be very dangerous and very pricey.

Defining Success

Our formidable competitors, the Japanese, practice a custom where all new people begin their employment in factory positions for several years. Since we cannot realistically revert all employees to the shop floor for several years, we must utilize the process of continuous learning if we are to compete effectively in the future. We must also clearly understand the definition of successful learning in an industrial environment. Learning in a manufacturing enterprise is significantly different than learning in an academic environment because the objective is not only to learn things but, most often, to unlearn acquired habits.

The primary test of learning achievement is the ability and willingness to apply learning to the work environment in support of a firm's competitive strategy. Companies can no longer afford to provide educational opportunities as an employment benefit for personal development.

In order for a competitive strategy to be supported within the manufacturing sphere, a company must integrate a manufacturing strategy into their business strategy. Manufacturing strategy can be defined as a series of coordinated decisions that act upon the deployment of manufacturing resources to provide a competitive advantage in support of the firm's strategic initiative. (3)

The global competitive environment does not require individuals with more refined thinking processes. Workers must do things and they must do things differently.

Characteristics of Successful Learning

Some of the following practices and attitudes are currently demonstrated in companies. Only a handful, however, have been successful in integrating and implementing a broad range of continuous learning elements. The nine critical factors that should be in place in order to reap the rewards of direct application within the workplace are expanded below.

1. Strategic Learning Plan Linked to Future Direction of Business

A Strategic Learning plan must be linked to decisions about the future direction of the business. This ensures that the knowledge and skills acquired will be required, appreciated and utilized. The Chief Executive Officer must monitor all continuous learning efforts to ensure that program priorities support the business strategies and that skill and knowledge objectives are valid and met in a timely and cost-effective manner. The costs associated with Continuous Learning are included in the cost of gaining competitive advantage.

2. Regular Top Management Verification

Learning that will be directly applied to the workplace requires top management verification regularly as well as line management initiative. This can best be accomplished with management and workers learning together. Additional benefits include shorter response time for implementation of improvements and first-hand management knowledge of manufacturing strengths and weaknesses. This learning is critical for managers participating in the company's competitive analysis and strategy determinations.

3. Learning Objectives Included in Performance Review

Learning is an integral part of each job. Individual learning objectives are part of the periodic review process between all employees and supervisors. Employees participate in deciding what skills and knowledge they must acquire to support the firm's business strategy.

4. Work Team Organization

Where possible, work teams are organized to contain a mix of skills and knowledge. Teaching and learning become a part of each job and provide informational job rotation and job coverage during absences

5. Qualified Instructors

Instructors are selected from the employee base. These content experts are provided with strong instructional expertise. This effort serves to multiply the instructional capacity and the quality of existing resources. These individuals create an educational environment that positively influences individual and group motivation. Learning must be attractive and appealing. A skilled instructor will always introduce the unfamiliar through the familiar.

6. "Process" Approach to Education

For most individuals, an honest analysis of our professional and personal growth will force an acknowledgment that we learn, first and foremost, by doing. We do things that succeed and we do things that fail. Repeated experiences, combined with the help of coaches and mentors, some independent learning, and much frustration, yields a seasoned person with expertise.

Instructors utilizing a "process approach" empower learners with the self-esteem and knowledge to make the correct decisions. In many cases, there are no "right" or "wrong" answers. One can no longer just provide information— there's too much of it. A "process approach" provides the knowledge and practice to select the appropriate information, apply analysis and make appropriate decisions.

Continuous Learning efforts must provide learners with simulations and exercises—laboratory-like learning experiences where groups collectively evaluate real opportunities and propose real solutions. Content must include honest representations of current practices and clear vision of strategies selected for future positioning. A portion of the learning process is accomplished on the factory floor since future success requires moving responsibility for the manufacturing process and control of it to the shop floor.

7. Learners Feel a Sense of Choice

Learners feel a sense of choice in selection of skills and knowledge to be acquired. Without choice, motivation is affected. Motivated learners seek out opportunities for improvement, organize appropriate teams and propose and implement improvements. Adults have a strong need to apply what they have learned and to be competent and confident in the application.

Learners with choices experience less absenteeism and reduced job-hopping: both traits of bored, unmotivated employees who feel like victims rather than contributors; individuals who cease to value what they think.

8. Learners Trust Management

Any existing distrust will be eliminated by implementing #2.

9. Measure the Right Things!

Measurements

If rapid and continuous learning is directly related to and inseparable from continuous improvement, and continuous improvement is the single greatest contributor to performance advantage, then we must learn to quantify a new set of business elements. Measuring the learning process within an industrial setting is very difficult—perhaps impossible. The measurement of fact-transfer serves no purpose to the firm. This is often demonstrated by exams and pass-fail grading techniques.

The test of relevance for continuous learning? Does the firm's competitive strategy require it? Systems and technology are not self-implementing nor self-regulating. Their utility and contribution depend upon the skills and knowledge of those individuals who direct, operate, and maintain them. The only pertinent learning is that which contributes to the performance advantage of the company. Measuring "learning" is not as important as measuring "improvement."

Continuous learning breeds continuous improvement and is demonstrated by improvement projects that are coordinated by motivated workers. The volume of projects is measurable as is the output.

Example: An effective inventory management program generates two project teams: one embarked upon a lot size reduction project, the other on a set-up reduction effort. The specific education program yielded two improvement projects that support the firm's competitive initiatives of delivery speed and flexibility. The output of the lot size reduction project, e.g., the number of lot sizes reduced and the accompanying lead time reductions serve to support other strategic measures of the firm. In short, continuous learning can be measured by the following:

- Linkage to the firm's strategic initiatives
- The number of improvement projects
- Output and results of improvement projects

This measurement scheme will support both the correct changes in corporate culture and cause appropriate behaviors throughout the organization.

Conclusion

The competitive strategies of a corporation determine what specific skills and knowledge are needed to determine what products and services should be offered, what kinds of technology will be used to produce them, and which systems will be required to support them. Specific knowledge is also needed to apply new technologies profitably and competitively. These competitive requirements provide the foundation for continuous learning and demand the active intervention by the highest levels of management.

Restrictions on education and training encourage counterproductive behavior and impair the ability of the organization to respond to change. Change is the prerequisite to performance advantage and a strong contributor to the friction and controversy about companies as "institutions of continuous learning."

References

1. Drucker, Peter F., "The Emerging Theory of Manufacturing," *Harvard Business Review* (May-June 1990, vol. 68, num. 3).
2. Hauser, John R. and Clausing, Don, "The House of Quality," *Harvard Business Review* (May-June 1988, vol. 66, num. 3).
3. Roscow, Jerome R. and Zager, Robert, *Training—The Competitive Edge* (San Francisco, Jossey-Bass Inc., 1988).
4. Pannesi, Ronald T., "Promoting Manufacturing Strategy Through the Right Measurements," *32nd International Conference Proceedings* (American Production and Inventory Control Society, 1989).

About the Author

The work experience of Helene J. O'Brien, CPIM, includes a variety of line and staff positions within marketing, manufacturing, and distribution. Her involvement in business planning, manufacturing planning and control systems, materials, customer service, order processing, and education and training spans the high volume, high technology, aerospace and defense, and metal fabrication industries. Prior to her industrial experience, she contributed to the field of public education as an educator, administrator and curriculum developer.

Qualified by the American Production and Inventory Control Society (APICS) as a national course presenter and instructor trained for the Applied Manufacturing Education Series (AMES), Ms. O'Brien conducts national workshops for manufacturing executives and managers. She is a frequent speaker at local APICS chapters as well as national conferences and has served as adjunct faculty for two New England colleges. She holds certification in production and inventory management.

Ms. O'Brien serves as a member of the APICS Systems and Technology curriculum and certification committee, as well as the APICS Dictionary committee. She is listed in the 1989 edition of Who's Who in Finance and Industry. She is President of P.M.L. Associates of Exeter, New Hampshire, a firm that provides educational services to the manufacturing community throughout the United States.

Reprinted from the 1994 APICS International Conference Proceedings.

ISO 9000: A Fail-Safe Approach to Successful Compliance

Robert E. Olsen, CPIM

C ertification and registration to ISO 9000 standards or requirements are one of the highest priorities in many companies today. Yet, for all of the urgency and focus, it is still, in many cases, a misunderstood and therefore misinterpreted requirement. This paper focuses on the resolution of key issues relative to understanding and successfully implementing a program leading to certification. The paper is divided into the following key sections:

I.   Determining the need
II.   Understanding the requirements
III.   Establishing a structure, plan, and schedule
IV.   Establishing and maintaining consistency and uniformity
V.   Avoiding typical pitfalls
VI.   Education and training requirements
VII.   Self-evaluation
VIII.   Continuance

I. Determining the Need

The ISO requirements were established to provide an international standard of conformance to certain key criteria. The intent is to establish a base of common expectations and disciplines. Auditable conformance is then expected with continued adherence. Basically, conformance and certification are necessary if you do, or plan to do, business in the European Community. However, the application of ISO 9000 may very well spread to all business areas since the intent is for universal application. It is probably a safe strategy to assume that its application will be expanded and that, unless your market is totally domestic, certification and registration will sooner or later be required.

Another decision that must be made concerns the level of ISO 9000 required for your specific company. This is a decision that is determined by your company type, your level of activity, and the scope of certification that you desire. **Figure 1** defines the different levels of conformance required for different levels of business activity. Conformance criteria can also be a function of what level business unit you require to be certified and registered. A total company program may require adherence to a different level of criteria than a plant or division level application.

For example, a company that designs, manufactures, distributes and services product will require adherence to the requirements of ISO 9001. What level and what scope you decide necessary is a function of your company's structure, its geographical deployment and the markets within which you do, or intend to do, business.

- ISO 9000—Guidelines for selection and use—which model is appropriate?
- ISO 9004—Systems elements guidelines for implementation
- ISO 9001—Applies to activities involved in design/development, production, installation and service
- ISO 9002—Applies to activities involved in production and installation
- ISO 9003—Applies to activities involved in final inspection and rest

Note: Guidelines and standards applicable to all industries.

Figure 1. ISO 9000 Series Defined

II. Understanding the Requirements

ISO 9000 requirements are written mainly in a generic or broad sense. This is because of the universal applicability objective which detail beyond a specific level would make impossible.

The requirements are also written in the sense that the overall intent is accomplished. Specifically, this means that what you do is documented, how you do it is verifiable, and that control of documentation is established and maintained. **Figure 2** lists the categories and their applicability to difficult levels of certification.

Another important point to understand is that ISO 9000 has no relationship to continuous improvement, has nothing to do with the Malcolm Baldrige Award or with World Class performance measurements. It is a step of standards to provide consistency and standardization of approach.

The following is a basic outline concerning definition of the key conformance elements:

1. Management Responsibility—relates to management role in policy creation, maintenance and conformance.
2. Quality System—requires a clearly documented quality system including a quality manual, clear procedures and work instructions, new product quality plan, measurements, capability, and inspection or monitoring methods.
3. Contract Review—involves verifying customer process needs, schedule, and cost, plus process conformance.
4. Design Control—involves clear documentation concerning the engineering change system. Specific areas include responsibility for changes, effectivity management, and design/process verification.

Title	Corresponding Paragraph (or Subsection) No.		
	9001	9002	9003
Management Responsibility	4.1	4.1a	4.1b
Quality System Principles	4.2	4.2	4.2a
Contract Review	4.3	4.3	4.2a
Design Control	4.4	—	
Purchasing	4.6.	4.5	—
Purchaser Supplied Product	4.7	4.6	—
Product Identification and Traceability	4.8	4.7	4.4a
Control of Production	4.9	4.8	—
Inspection and Testing	4.10	4.9	4.5a
Inspection, Measuring and Test Equipment	4.11	4.10	4.6a
Inspection and Test Status	4.12	4.11	4.7a
Control of Nonconforming Product	4.13	4.12	4.8a
Corrective Action	4.14	4.13	—
Handling, Storage, Packaging and Delivery	4.15	4.14	4.9a
Quality Records	4.16	4.15	4.10a
Internal Audits	4.17	4.16a	—
Training	4.18	4.17a	4.11b
After-Sales Servicing	4.19	—	—
Statistical Techniques	4.20	4.18	4.12a

a = Less stringent than 9001
b = Less stringent than 9002
— = Element not present

Figure 2. Cross-Reference List of Quality System Elements

Procedure Category	Primary	Secondary
Management Responsibility	Management	
Contract Review	Marketing	Manufacturing
Design Control	Engineering	Manufacturing
Purchasing	Purch/Matls	Quality
Purchaser Supplied Product	Materials	Quality
Product Identity & Traceability	Quality	Mgf/Matls
Process Control	Manufacturing	Quality
Inspection and Testing	Quality	Manufacturing
Inspection, Measuring, and Test Equip.	Quality	Manufacturing
Inspection and Test Status	Quality	Manufacturing
Control of Nonconforming Product	Quality	Mfg/Matls
Corrective Action	Quality	Mfg/Matls
Handling, Storage, Packaging & Deliv.	Materials	Quality
Quality Records	Quality	Manufacturing
Internal Quality Audits	Quality	Manufacturing
Training	Management	Qual/Mfg
Servicing	Marketing	Quality
Statistical Techniques	Quality	Mfg/Matls

Figure 3. Responsibility Matrix

5. Document Control—concerns data base management and control, scheduling control and accuracy. Most important requirements relate to the creation, review, approval and maintenance of documents. These include responsibility and conditions under which documents can be changed.
6. Purchasing—involves the evaluation, selection, certification, and control of suppliers. It also involves maintenance and verification of documentation and data.
7. Purchaser Supplied Product—concerns the storage, control, and accuracy of purchaser supplied items.
8. Product Identification and Traceability—looks for defined levels of traceability and specific controls. It also concerns methods of establishing and monitoring product identity.
9. Control of Production—concerns process identification, process control, process documentation, and documented work instructions.
10. Inspection and Testing—looks for actions and controls in conformance with quality manual instructions and inspection/test instructions. These are specifically related to incoming, in-process, and final.
11. Inspection, Measuring, and Test Equipment—involves conformance to required calibration and adjustment. Also requires protected storage, control, and accurate records.
12. Inspection and Test Status—concerns documentation relative to conformance and reporting status.
13. Control of Nonconforming Product—involves storage, control, dispositioning and reporting of non-conforming product. It also involves customer coordination of disposition.
14. Corrective Action—defined procedures relative to failure analysis (internal and external), corrective action responsibility and control. Also look for verification of implementation and prevention of re-occurence.
15. Handling, Storage, Packaging and Delivery—involves packaging procedures, warehouse storage procedures and disciplines, and controls to prevent product deterioration and obsolescence.
16. Quality Records—involves quality record maintenance, storage and availability.
17. Internal Quality Audits—concerns conformance to quality manual and management directive. This requirement also requires corrective action procedures as the result of an audit.
18. Training—requires documentation on training scope and content, responsibility for planning and coordination, authorization and funding.
19. After-Sales Servicing—involves the need for policies and procedures to meet contractual and committed guarantees, warranties and other service activities.
20. Statistical Techniques—as necessary, but well documented; to meet customer and/or internal performance standards. Does not require SPC or other specific inspection or monitoring techniques.

III. Establishing a Structure, Plan and Schedule

The Excelsior Corporation, recognizing the need, and understanding the requirements, created the following structured approach to implementation:

1. Appointed a project team with a full-time project team leader. This team reported to the top management steering committee. Its main objectives were to obtain resource commitment, maintain schedule integrity, provide necessary resources, and to maintain system and procedure interface integrity, conformance and compatibility.
2. Implementation teams, reporting to the project team, were multifunctional and responsible for the actual documentation and verification of ISO 9000 requirements. These were the working groups, and although not full-time, they did commit approximately 50% of

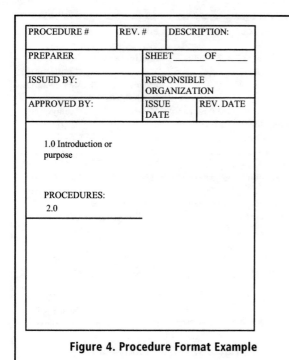

Figure 4. Procedure Format Example

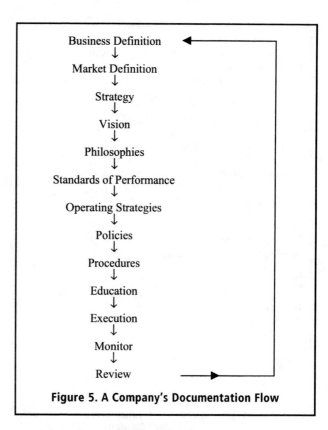

Figure 5. A Company's Documentation Flow

their time to this project. Because Excelsior needed to implement as soon as possible, two teams were created to operate in parallel.

3. Developed understanding of requirements: An outside consultant was hired to conduct in-house education sessions.
4. Determined level of certification required: In Excelsior's case, ISO 9001 was necessary because they designed, manufactured, installed and serviced their product.
5. Translated requirements into specific internal activities: This amounted to a list of requirements that must be met for internal conformance. Included were all the areas where documentation was needed. A matrix was developed to show the interrelationship and interface points of activities and/or procedure documentation. Also, a responsibility matrix was developed, as shown in **Figure 3**.
6. Conducted an internal evaluation: Teams did an internal assessment, developing a list of items where conformance was missing or inadequate.
7. Decided corrective actions: Teams created a list of corrective actions required and, using the responsibility matrix, responsibility for corrective action was established.
8. Obtained commitments: Each team member was responsible for obtaining commitments from their particular areas of responsibility.
9. Developed an implementation schedule: This was developed by the project team because of the need to prioritize and synchronize tasks. It was also necessary to ensure the proper coordination of resources.
10. Followed-up to ensure commitments were met: Leader of each implementation team reported to project team weekly, presenting position to schedule, any problems, and where intervention by top management is necessary. These meetings were considered high priority and attendance was mandatory.
11. Scheduled pre-evaluation visit.
12. Took corrective action based on pre-evaluation visit.
13. Scheduled final compliance survey.

14. Certification and registration.

From beginning to end, the total time required was nine months. This was a relatively accelerated program, with a more likely time in many companies being a minimum of twelve months. Total cost to Excelsior was approximately $250,000 including internal effort, external evaluation, outside consulting services (two days per month) and estimated top management time.

IV. Establishing and Maintaining Consistency and Uniformity

1. Develop a consistent procedure format and structure (see **Figure 4**).
2. Coordinate with all procedure writing responsibilities.
3. Minimize wordage and maximize flow charts, checklists and simple work instructions.
4. Always provide, within the procedure, what occurs when the procedure must be violated, on an exception basis. An example of this would be when an urgent engineering change muse be processed on a "fast-track" basis. Always spell out how the formal system is later accommodated.
5. **Figure 5** is a flow chart reflecting the documentation flow of a typical company.
6. Clearly spell out how a procedure can be changed, who is responsible, and who must approve.

V. Pitfalls to Avoid in Implementing an ISO 9000 Program

1. Do not create procedures that are long, overly complicated and difficult to understand.
2. Ensure that procedures created are followed.
3. Do not misunderstand the intent of ISO 9000 requirements. The requirements are intended to be universally applicable, therefore they are largely generic in nature.

This means that a level of interpretation must be used to clarify applicability in a given industry or company environment.

4. Ensure the uniformity, compatibility and interface accuracy: Make sure that procedures follow the same format and are compatible at interface points.

VI. Education and Training

Education initially should involve management and the project team in understanding the requirements of ISO 9000 and which are applicable. This group should also be educated in the best approach toward structuring an implementation process, the key issues to be addressed, and the pitfalls to be avoided.

Training should be conducted to ensure the following:
1. A clear understanding of procedures by those involved in their execution.
2. Actions taken are in conformance with the established procedures.

Responsibility for education and training is the responsibility of each member of the project team as it applies to his or her area of responsibility.

VII. Conducting the Internal Evaluation

When conducting an internal evaluation, it is important to ensure the following:
1. Everyone knows the intent and purpose.
2. Communicate that you are not evaluating personal performance, but systems or process performance.
3. Do not be arrogant.
4. Ensure that procedures that do exist are followed.
5. Do not assume conformance. Look for tangible, verifiable evidence of conformance to requirements,
6. The people conducting the internal evaluation have the knowledge and expertise to evaluate in an objective, efficient manner.
7. The internal evaluation results in corrective action where nonconformance is agreed and verified.
8. Corrective action is followed up and verified.

Meeting the requirements of ISO 9000 should not be an insurmountable task for any reasonably well-disciplined company. However, even if the requirements are not completely met, they force a company to get its act together relative to disciplines, documentation conformance, and predictability. It perhaps is a good first step on the road to improvement.

About the Author

Robert E. Olsen is currently President of Robert E. Olsen, Inc., a firm specializing in Management Consulting and Education Services. In addition to his consulting experience, Bob has over fifteen years of Materials and Operations management experience for a variety of companies and products, including lengthy involvement with both military and commercial product environments. Bob also has ten years of experience in Production Engineering Management with United Technologies. The Wall Street Journal article, "Bob Olsen's Wonderful World of Inventories," has created significant management interest and response. He has counseled many companies in the U.S., Mexico, Canada and the U.K. in the areas of J.I.T. implementation. Manufacturing Strategies development, Supplier Certification, and Inventory Management.

A widely utilized international speaker. Bob has conducted a broad range of educational seminars for a variety of industries and universities, including the California Institute of Technology Industrial Relations Center. Among the topics included are: Just-In-Time Manufacturing, Manufacturing Resource Planning, Manufacturing Strategies, Inventory Management, and Supplier Certification.

A former President and Board Member of the Hartford (Conn.) County Chapter of APICS, Bob also has had extensive speaking experience over the past fifteen years at numerous APICS and B.P.I.C.S. chapter meetings, seminars, national and international conferences. He is a speaker at N.A.P.M. and A.S.Q.C. conferences, and is a member of APICS, B.P.I.C.S., A.S.Q.C. and S.M.E.

Bob holds a Bachelor of Science Degree in Mechanical Engineering and an M.B.A. degree from the University of Hartford (CT). For six years he served as adjunct professor at the University of Hartford, teaching courses in Operations Management and Industrial Production.

Reprinted from the 1990 APICS International Conference Proceedings.

Promoting Manufacturing Strategy Implementation Through the Right Measurements

Ronald T. Pannesi, CPIM

Manufacturing strategy has become increasingly popular as a means of creating and sustaining a competitive advantage for today's firms. With increased focus on the formulation of manufacturing strategies that support market initiatives, attention has begun to shift to the measurement systems of the firm and the degree to which they are consistent with strategic initiatives and manufacturing deployment in support of those initiatives. This paper proposes a model for measurements and their linkage to strategic resource deployments and reports measures that firms have used to support their manufacturing strategies.

Competitive Initiatives

For most firms, advantages in the marketplace can be gained through a variety of strategic initiatives. These include:
1. Being the low **price** manufacturer
2. Providing superior **quality** conformance
3. Having greater **delivery reliability** than competitors
4. Providing greater **delivery speed** usually through shorter lead times or faster distribution
5. Having more **flexibility** to changes in volume and variety of product offering than the competition
6. Providing a **product design** with more attractive features and options or with greater technical capability than the competition
7. Providing better **after-market service**.

These strategic advantages can be thought of in two groups for any firm. They can either be classified as *qualifiers*, those characteristics that are needed to be a viable competitor, and *order winners*, those characteristics that cause the firm's customers to prefer it over its competitors.

Not all of the characteristics will necessarily come into play for every firm or competitive situation. In fact, it is nearly impossible to provide all the characteristics simultaneously. So in spite of the urgings or desires of marketing, the firm must focus its resources on a few vital characteristics that provide the order winners and qualifiers to gain competitive advantage.

Manufacturing can assist by making the proper decisions on the deployment of its resources to support competitive advantages in Price, Quality, Delivery Speed, Delivery Reliability and Flexibility. The decisions to support one or more of the preceding characteristics have become the basis of manufacturing strategy.

Manufacturing Strategy

Manufacturing strategy can be defined as a series of coordinated decisions that act upon the deployment of manufacturing resources to provide a competitive advantage in support of the firm's strategic initiative. The key words in that definition are coordinated decisions, resource deployment and competitive advantage. Manufacturing strategy implies that all the decisions related to how the resources of the firm will be configured or deployed must be coordinated with a specific goal in mind; that of establishing a competitive advantage for the firm. This means that manufacturing takes its cue from corporate and marketing strategy and acts to support those strategies with actions that cause the firm to be better in the ways that will sustain an advantage over its competitors.

But manufacturing strategy, like all strategies, is formulated within the corporate culture of the firm. And it is this corporate culture that can either help or hinder the achievements of manufacturing and its strategies.

Why is this so? If we define corporate culture as a set of behaviors and beliefs that are used by all employees to make day to day decisions in the firm, it becomes clear that the role of measurements is critical. Ollie Wight, among others, once said that "anything you measure" will improve. Perhaps a better statement is that the measurements of the firm provide the key evidence of its corporate culture.

When asked why a worker was producing 6 months supply of a particular part when the carrying cost of that part would greatly exceed the labor cost of the worker to do nothing or to produce only a short supply, an auto industry foreman replied: "Because I get paid for labor productivity, not inventory!"

Clearly, the accounting measures of this firm that were focused on micro measures of individual workers were not consistent with the greater goals of the firm, in this case, inventory reduction. Further, if the firm had chosen one of the strategic variables listed above (such as quality) to compete on, measurements such as labor productivity would work directly against those initiatives.

A quick look at the traditional measures that firms use to measure manufacturing reveal a large number of conflicting objectives. Most firms, for example, use some sort of variance based cost accounting system that reports labor cost variance, labor quantity variances, material cost and quantity variances and a large variety of overhead variances. In addition, one of the most common measures used to assess manufacturing performance is inventory levels or inventory turns. A purchasing manager who is being measured on material price variance may be motivated to increase quantity buys of material to reduce price. This would cause conflict with manufacturing objectives to lower inventory levels.

Perhaps the biggest problem with these traditional measures is the assumptions that underlie them. When cost is measured so closely and so individually, the assumption is that the firm is competing on low cost. Since only

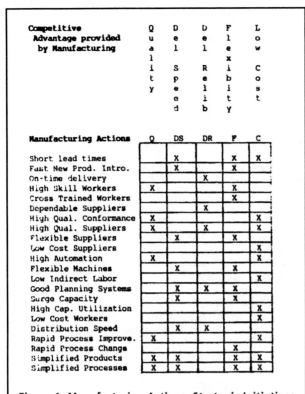

Manufacturing Actions	Q	DS	DR	F	C
Short lead times		X		X	X
Fast New Prod. Intro.		X		X	
On-time delivery			X		
High Skill Workers	X			X	
Cross Trained Workers				X	
Dependable Suppliers			X		
High Qual. Conformance	X				X
High Qual. Suppliers	X		X		X
Flexible Suppliers		X		X	
Low Cost Suppliers					X
High Automation	X				X
Flexible Machines		X		X	
Low Indirect Labor					X
Good Planning Systems		X	X	X	
Surge Capacity		X		X	
High Cap. Utilization					X
Low Cost Workers					X
Distribution Speed		X	X		
Rapid Process Improve.	X				X
Rapid Process Change				X	
Simplified Products	X	X		X	X
Simplified Processes	X	X		X	X

The column headings read: Quality (Q), Delivery Speed (DS), Delivery Reliability (DR), Flexibility (F), Low Cost (C).

Figure 1. Manufacturing Actions, Strategic Initiatives

one firm in an industry can gain that position and since most firms use these traditional measures, conflicts are bound to arise. An even more important assumption is being made when the traditional cost measures are used. That assumption is that by focusing on individual cost measures, total cost will be reduced. Nothing could be further from the truth.

But it is often not the measures themselves that cause errant behaviors, It is the *interpretation and use* of these measures that is often the culprit. For example, a firm may use full absorption accounting as a means of measuring performance.

In a very simplified form, absorption accounting would estimate the sales for the firm over a year and also determine the expected overhead costs for the same period. If, for example, a firm expected to sell 120 of its products for the year, then each product would bear 1/120th of the total burden. On a monthly basis then, each unit produced would bear 1/10th of the total burden cost for the month. By itself there is little problem with this approach. However, the use of this simple assignment of overhead is often abused.

Let's assume, for example, that in the first month, 10 units are produced and sold. All is well. Overhead is fully absorbed and everyone is happy. But what happens if in the second month only 6 units are sold and the manufacturing manager produces only 6 units as he or she would logically do to meet other objectives of minimum inventory. This is when the potential for abuse occurs. Usually a report is shortly issued that condemns the manufacturing manager for under-absorbing overhead. Depending on the severity of that sin, the manufacturing manager may be motivated to produce 10 units every month thereafter, *regardless of sales*. By doing this, he or she is fully absorbing burden and avoiding criticism. The conflicts are clear.

But the problem is not with the measure but what is done with it. When less than the full 10 per month are sold and burden will not be fully absorbed, the correct response would be to either improve sales by increasing efforts to sell the product or reduce overhead. But neither of these actions are the usual response for many firms.

Perhaps the most important conclusion that we can draw from the above discussion is that with existing measures mostly based in traditional cost systems, little attention can be given to strategic objectives other than cost. This means that firms must turn their attention to providing new measures that are consistent with manufacturing strategies that focus on strategic initiatives such as delivery speed, quality, delivery reliability and flexibility and that measures of cost must be focused on total cost rather than individual costs.

Manufacturing Resource Actions

There are a number of actions that a firm can take to deploy or concentrate its resources to support various strategic directions. **Figure 1** lists down the left hand axis some of those actions. The list is not meant to be exhaustive but only representative of the kinds of actions that the manufacturing manager has at his or her disposal to support strategic initiatives.

At the top of the figure are the strategic initiatives the firm may choose that involve manufacturing. Where actions on the left coincide with initiatives along the top, the intersection is marked with an X. This means that manufacturing action would directly support that strategic goal. Nearly all of the actions may indirectly affect each strategic goal but the only ones marked are those with direct effects to indicate a primary relationship.

The idea is to develop measures for each of the X's to support a particular initiative. For example, if the firm wishes to compete on quality conformance, then the required manufacturing actions are:
1. Use highly skilled workers.
2. Put systems in place that assure high quality conformance such as SPC.
3. Create supplier relationships and work with suppliers whose quality is best.
4. Ensure rapid process improvement to produce stable, repeatable processes that assure high quality outputs.
5. Simplify products to ensure manufacturability that will support high quality conformance.

Now, for each of those actions, appropriate measures can be developed to support that goal,

Measurements

Choosing measurements is a critical process that should follow a few simple rules.
1. Multiple measures are better than single measures
2. Measurements should provide an agreed upon basis for decision making
3. Measurements should be immediately understandable
4. Measurements should be easily and correctly interpreted
5. They should be economical to obtain and apply
6. Measurements must cause the correct response from a strategic perspective

For each strategic initiative we can identify critical activities that need to be measured in some way.

For quality, the following are characteristics that represent quality related problems.

1. Rejects of parts, subassemblies and finished goods
2. Mistakes in paperwork, schedules & data bases
3. Warranty claims and customer complaints
4. Machine downtime and repair time
5. Yields
6. Time spent in repair
7. Supplier performance
8. Cost of quality
9. Design errors
10. Personnel capabilities and attitudes
11. Customer attitudes

For all the above characteristics (and many more not mentioned above) there are appropriate measures. Some suggested measurements include:
- Number of consecutive parts produced without failure
- Number of Bill of Material errors
- Defects of a part, component or subassembly measured in parts per million
- Hours of machine downtime due to breakdown
- Consecutive lots received without rejects
- Number of Order Entry errors
- Number of Engineering changes
- Number of employees educated in quality
- Trust and Confidence Index

There are, of course, a large number of other measures that can be used to keep manufacturing focused on quality. If the firm has quality as either an order winner or a qualifier then these and other appropriate measurements will cause a corporate culture to exist that supports these goals.

In like fashion, we can identify a number of characteristics of the firm that related to delivery reliability. They may include:
1. On-time delivery
2. Worker training
3. Supplier dependability
4. Planning system performance
5. Distribution speed

Along with those characteristics there are a number of measurements that may be appropriate if the firm is focusing on delivery reliability as an order winner or qualifier. Some are:
- Percent Master Schedule achieved per week
- Percent Sales and Operations Plan achieved per month
- Percent final assembly schedule achieved per week
- Production Worker Skills acquired
- On-time supplier delivery performance per period
- Number of lots received where the count is perfect
- Percent of customer promises met (first time)
- Hours of expedite time
- Number of changed delivery promises
- Number of "emergency" orders placed per week
- Number of customer order changes requested per week
- Number of outside subcontracts placed per month

For the firm that competes on flexibility, the characteristics that may apply include:
1. Responsiveness to change
2. Production lead times
3. New Product introduction speed
4. Worker skill level
5. Worker training level
6. Supplier flexibility
7. Machine flexibility
8. Surge capacity
9. Process change capability
10. Process simplification

Measurements that relate to the above characteristics and help maintain focus on flexibility include:

- Product changeover time
- Process changeover time
- Machine changeover time
- Production lead time
- Design to produce time
- Number of process steps
- Number of parts per product
- Number of parts produced per machine
- Flow path changes per period
- Worker skills acquired
- Excess capacity available against goal
- Supplier acknowledgment time for changes
- Time to process change orders
- Number of parts produced in-house

Again a similar list of characteristics can be developed for firms who are competing on delivery speed. They may include:
1. Manufacturing lead times
2. Total lead time
3. Distribution speed
4. Supplier performance
5. Machine flexibility
6. Capacity availability

These then imply a number of actual measures that support the goals of delivery speed. Some suggested ones include:
- Cycle time per operation
- Cycle time per part
- Cycle time per product
- Delivered lead time
- Order entry time
- Set-up times
- Supplier lead times
- Supplier response time to changes
- Number of planning changes
- Surge Capacity
- Distribution time
- Payment schedule time
- Acknowledgment time
- Receiving time
- Quality of received product
- Quality of produced product

Finally, there are characteristics that keep the firm focused on low cost as an objective. Importantly, the traditional measures of labor productivity and labor efficiency do not necessarily lead to low cost because as noted above, total cost is the issue and it is not necessarily true that the sum of the costs that are minimized with the variance cost system will produce a minimal total cost. The characteristics to focus on, however, may include:
1. Indirect labor costs
2. Direct labor costs
3. Quality conformance
4. Supplier conformance
5. Degree of automation
6. Capacity utilization
7. Rapid process improvement
8. Product simplification

The measurements that may correspond to the above characteristics include but are not limited to:
- Direct labor hours per good product
- Indirect labor hours per good product
- Number of engineers required per new product
- Marketing and Sales hours per shipped product
- Finance and Accounting hours per shipped product
- Number of shipments received without rejects
- Number of shipments produced without rejects
- Machine hours per good product

- Raw material dollars
- Work-in-process dollars
- Finished goods dollars
- Process cost in hours or minutes
- Number of parts per product
- Capacity index
- Product lead time
- Down time of machines
- Labor cost
- Transit time in house
- Hours of automation per product

While there are many measurements that are repeated above, each has a primary and each has a secondary focus. For example, activities that improve delivery speed may also contribute to flexibility and actions that focus on quality improvement may also contribute to improvements in delivery speed, cost, delivery reliability and flexibility.

In putting together measurements that support one or more of the strategic initiatives, it is highly likely that many attempts will be needed before the best set of measurements can be compiled for a particular operating environment. Most importantly, the firm must continue to experiment until it finds the right combination of measurements that support strategic goals without while supporting a corporate culture that is tuned to support of the customer and worker in that order.

Examples of Measurements Applied

There has been increasing interest among leading firms in altering their measurement systems to accommodate the strategic goals of the firm. Two examples of firms with changed measurements are given below. The first of these is a telecommunications manufacturer whose competitive initiatives include quality, delivery reliability and new technology introduction. Their measurements include:

In new product introduction
- Total time to introduce
- Interval time between products
- Schedule performance In meeting cost goals
- Mature first cost
- First Pass Design
  In quality
- Customer Satisfaction Index
  In delivery reliability
- Rate of on-time delivery
- Rate of order completeness
  Other measures
- Operations overhead
- Inventory reduction

A brief examination will indicate that cost measures are also part of the goals even though they were not announced as primary.

An electronics manufacturer applies values to each of its measures. If the measurement improves, the value assigned is a + 2. If the measurement is the same when compared to the last period during which it was measured, or against some standard, the value is + 1. For measures that

worsen, the value is -1. The sum of the values then gives the firm some idea of its progress, and improvement in one measure can make up for slippage in another. The measurements taken are:
- Plug to Play
- Percent meeting target values in R & D
- Percent on time to schedule
- Time to market
- Process Time
- Waste rate index
- Quality index
- Schedule change index
- Material availability

What strategic initiatives do the above measurements focus on? We leave it to the reader to consider.

Conclusions

For most firms, measurements have focused on every traditional characteristics such as cost and turnover. This means that, for the most part, initiatives for control of the manufacturing operation have been abdicated to accounting.

If we wish to both seize the initiative back and help provide a strategic advantage for the firm, manufacturing must support its strategies with specific measurements that bring about both a change in corporate culture and cause behaviors to focus on actions that support marketplace actions.

The key to this change is the formulation of specific strategies and the support of these strategies with measurements that either replace or supplement the traditional accounting measures that are no longer appropriate with the change that has come about in the manufacturing environment.

Further, it is not enough to focus only on manufacturing actions. The actions of each functional group in the firm must be measured with the strategic goals of the firm in mind.

Finally, cultures will not change over night, nor will one set of measures remain in place, unchanged over time. New measures will be constantly needed as the firm's environment changes and the focus of the actions of the firm in the marketplace shifts.

About the Author

Ron Pannesi is Assistant Professor of Operations Management and Director of the Center for Manufacturing Excellence at the University of North Carolina, Chapel Hill. He received his Ph.D. in Operations Management from Michigan State University and is also past president of the Triangle Chapter of APICS in Raleigh, North Carolina.

Ron has over twenty years experience in business and industry where he served in a wide variety of managerial functions in Manufacturing, Materials, Quality, International Marketing, Sales and Engineering.

Ron is a frequent speaker at local, regional and national meetings of APICS and other professional societies.

Reprinted from The Production and Inventory Management Journal, *Fourth Quarter 1999.*

How a Measurement System Change Motivates Performance Improvements

Gerhard Plenert, Ph.D., CPIM

The author has long felt that the key to successful performance is not in systems and procedures such as ISO certification. Rather, successful performance is found in a meaningfully structured measurement system focused on results rather than on data collection. With that idea in mind, the author was awarded an APICS grant funding research focused on the relationship between motivation and measurement, with the belief that the measurement system directly affects employee performance.

In October 1997 the author went to work for Precision Printers, Inc., a company that was structured and focused on volume. Quality, which was secondary, was not used as a measure of employee performance. A shift was made to eliminate the volume measure and focus on measuring quality performance in the belief that driving for quality would result in volume increases, but driving for volume would not improve quality. The transition occurred as a series of stages: production planning training, total quality management (TQM) training, goal/measurement system redesign, setting up "Quality Week," team-based empowerment, and ongoing continuous improvement programs. Each of these areas will be discussed, but first we should briefly describe Precision Printers, Inc.

Company Background

The company opened its doors in 1982 as Marshall Marketing under the guidance of its founders Don and Frank Marshall. Later that same year they renamed the company Precision Printers and within five years replaced the garage they started in with a 5,700 square-foot facility. By 1989 they had increased their initial $100,000 per year in sales to $1,000,000 and their workforce of 4 employees to 19. This was accomplished by acquiring customers like Freightliner, Infocus, Fender Musical, and Grass Valley Group/Tektronics producing primarily overlays and membrane switches.

In 1992, with the acquisition of an aggressive new customer, IGT, the face of PPI changed dramatically. IGT doubled PPI's sales and moved the company into the world of high-volume mass production with stringent quality and registration requirements. Many of PPI's original customers also grew their businesses.

By 1994 PPI had 50 employees and the following year was awarded ISO 9000 certification. By 1996 sales had increased to $5,000,000, and by 1997 PPI had grown to the extent that a second move was necessary.

The company, which now has 108 employees and a 16,000-square-foot facility, believes that thrilling the customer means delivering product that is on-time, defect free, or it should be free. PPI has incorporated systems that focus on a competitive, leading edge stance in technology.

This technology includes the following internal systems and procedure technologies:

- ISO 9000 certification—PPI was recognized by *Quality Digest* for its excellence in achieving certification.
- Facilitywide total quality management (TQM) system that involves everyone, from CEO to the newest employee.
- Corporatewide enterprise resource planning (ERP) system that is manufacturing resources planning (MRP II)–based to improve production scheduling and responsiveness.
- Quality initiative that focuses the entire company on continuous improvements through teaming.
- Improved quality testing procedures with tools such as integrated switch testing and bar coding.
- Customers involved with and integrated into company processes through site visits and improved communication.

Transformation

The transformation that occurred at PPI was accomplished by removing the volume/revenue–based measurement system. PPI had built up one million dollars of unshipped customized finished goods inventory because the measurement system focused on revenue to be produced. The measurement transformation changed the focus of the company to quality units produced while limiting inventory to no more than 30 days worth.

That measurement change was initiated by implementing an extensive training program focusing on production/inventory management. Training concentrated on the way in which the inventory buildup was destroying profitability. It showed that managing inventory was more important for profitability than managing labor and that quality could improve only if it was measured and motivated by an incentive program. It also pointed out that the then-current defect rate was costing the company money and chewing up valuable capacity. Employees were taught how quality should be measured and that quality improvements came from employees, not from management. Total quality management (TQM) training, which focused on cross-functional team building with empowered ownership, was included as well.

The next phase of the program required setting up Quality Week, the implementation point. During this week the goal was to "produce only perfect parts." The employees were given the freedom to tear anything apart, move anything, or meet with anyone. It didn't matter if only one part was produced, but that part had to be perfect.

PPI also had to construct some new goals and objectives. Quality was the new goal, with the following objectives:

- Reduced defect rate
- Reduction in number of customer complaints
- Improved delivery performance
- Reduced cycle time
- Reduced inventory level

All these measures have a direct effect on profitability and customer satisfaction.

The week began with a great deal of fear and trepidation. Management was concerned that employees would stand idle, unsure what to do. Employees, however, were excited; they had always wanted to have the time and freedom to examine the machinery and find out why they were having certain problems and how they could be fixed. Teams formed spontaneously. Employees enjoyed the experience; several commented on how much fun they were having.

Figure 1 is a performance report distributed by PPI. It's an example of some of the improvements made in a typical day during Quality Week. The following definitions explain some of the abbreviations used in the report:

- TQM—total quality management.
- Parts Prep—Parts Preparation Department cleans, folds, and stacks product for shipment.
- Touch Switch—Touch Switch Assembly Department.
- Reg Lam—Registered Lamination Department laminates materials to metals.
- Pos $ sheets—Positive dollar sheets are reporting mechanisms that track costs.
- PCU—Pre-Cut Department prepares materials by cutting them down to production sizes.

The Quality Week program taught employees about teaming, goal setting, and empowerment. At first they were skeptical, but once they saw the rewards for their performance, they became seriously involved in the process of improvement. The continuous improvement process that was kicked off by Quality Week is ongoing. Teams still form spontaneously to attack quality and performance issues.

The total transformation from volume to quality took about eight months. The first three months were spent preparing for the shift to quality (quality week), and the last five were focused on implementing the transition. Some of the measurable results can be seen in the following charts. **Figure 2** shows how the defect rate was steadily increasing from May 1997 to about October 1997. Then around November of that year there was a sudden shift, both in the direction of the trend and in the level of the defects. This figure demonstrates the most dramatic effect of the quality improvement process.

Figure 3, which records customer complaints, shows a decrease due to the new emphasis on quality. **Figure 4** shows that on-time shipment performance had also improved in that there were fewer late shipments. This is directly related to **figure 5**, which illustrates how quality improvements directly reduced cycle times. All these measurable improvements are directly linked together, including the performance on the FGI (finished goods inventory)

QUALITY WEEK – DAY 2
THOUSANDS AND THOUSANDS OF IDEAS AND SOLUTIONS

Think about it...10 things a day multiplied by 200 working days equals 2000 things that got done. WOW!!! Because of the success of the last two days, a company meeting at 2:00 PM today has been called to see what the next level is.

AWARDS ISSUED:

TQM TEAM	WHO	ISSUE	ACTION	PRIZE
Parts Prep / Touch Switch	Josh, Wendy, Nancy B, Scott, Sherri, Steve	Parts sticking together, removing protective cover from windows	Slip sheeting instead of recovering windows	$20
Die Cut, Touch Switch, Quality, Print	Justin P, Rob, Jeff, Steve, Joe, Judy, Matt, John V, John C, Skip, Brandon, Derek, Josh, Wendy	Touchswitch conductive layer registration	Season polyester prior to print to reduce variance	$20 Music Certificate
Stencil	Bill, Ralph, Tyson, Karl	Masking tape falling apart, shredding into ink	Use box tape	$20
Print Coordinators	Judy, Heath, Mike, Greg, Jesiah	Wrong ink getting into wrong screen	1-3 cans of ink at each press, provide only the necessary amount of ink	**Movie Passes**
Reg Lam	Skip, Randy, Stacy	Difficult assemblies – requiring highly skilled hand / eye coordination	Making tabs and jigs, improved quality and efficiency	$20
Touch Switch	Gerhard, Karen, Steve, Rich P	Order requirements, late list qty's, WIP qty's	Using correct tools to track quantities and due dates, filling out pos $ sheets, using 456.	**Movie Passes**
Touch Switch	Nancy, Scott	Clean room environment	Made a cleaning schedule	$20

The awards in bold above were ideas implemented from yesterday's update. I'm sure there were more!

IDEAS:
- Someone interested in a job has the opportunity to spend a little time in the area of interest.
- Job switching / trading
- Identify the areas
- Artwork drying racks – cleaning films in the loop
- Clamps for the vacuum table (exposure room) in stencil – safety and stability and better locking
- Preventing adhesive from tearing when pulling large amounts of parts out of the matrix (parts prep)
- Advanced work orders to PCU from purchasing may help PCU be able to schedule their work better

This is great stuff! I am sure more challenging and things to "get out of the box" will make themselves apparent. One of the great things notes were the statistics and data and measurements used yesterday to confirm solutions were effective. Having valid and accurate measurement makes it easier to showcase our efforts. Keep it up everyone!

Figure 1. Quality Week—Day 2

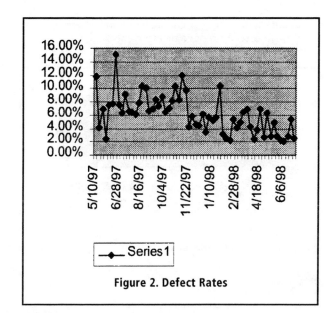

Figure 2. Defect Rates

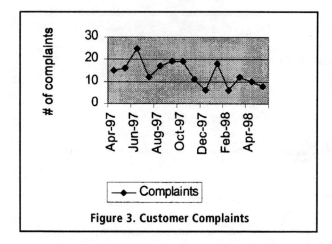

Figure 3. Customer Complaints

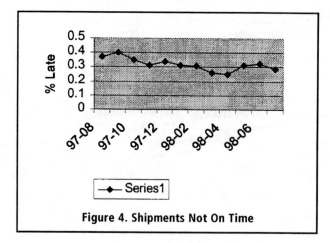

Figure 4. Shipments Not On Time

balance which, according to **figure 6**, has been steadily going down. Cycle time reductions produced reduced lead times, which made the organization more responsive to customer demands. Cycle time reductions also increased on-time performance. It is interesting how all these performance efficiencies were triggered by a measurement system modification.

There were also some nonmeasurable improvements resulting from the shift to a quality measurement process: a strong shift from departmentalization to interdepartmental efforts occurred, engineers were working on the production floor, teams were spontaneously organized to solve specific problems, the culture of the company shifted to being "one big family," and communication greatly improved as did customer relations.

Research Findings

The findings of this research project include many additional lessons learned at PPI:

1. Corporate Vision and Mission statements (goals) tend to have very little to do with the measurement systems. Tradition does more to dictate the measurement methodologies than do goals. For example, some companies have slogans and banners all over their facilities promoting customer-oriented quality, but are still measuring and paying employees based on the number of units produced. These employees, therefore, care very little about quality, since spending more time checking quality will directly reduce their paychecks. [5]

2. Financial measures promote short-term thinking. Managers are numbers focused and will do anything to make the numbers look good in the short term. Long-term investments are discouraged since they negatively affect the short-term numbers by increasing debt and costs. The result is that a "fix and patch" strategy wins out over a "replace with newer technology" strategy because the former costs less in the short term. [4, 5]

3. Blanket international measurement systems dictated by the corporate office don't reflect the local management style or culture and are often demotivating rather than motivating as desired. [3, 6]

4. Measurement systems are still thought of as data collection systems and all data are considered good. One company, for example, has been running SPC for one year now and wanted some recommendations on what to do with all the data. When told to throw the data out because SPC is a process tool for continuous improvement, not for data collection, they were very frustrated. Many companies have not yet realized that the measurement system is what directly motivates employee response, and that measuring the wrong things (e.g., units produced per minute) brings the wrong results. [1, 2, 7, 9]

5. There seems to be no understanding of the relationship between goal achievement and resource efficiency. For example, in most discrete manufacturing, labor is less than 10% of the value added product content, whereas material is more than 50%. Yet, when cost-cutting measures are enacted, we still hack more on the 10% and tend to ignore the 50+%. In one situation I encountered,

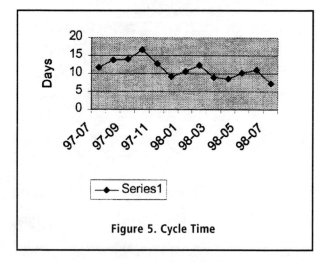

Figure 5. Cycle Time

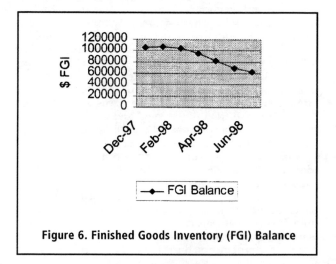

Figure 6. Finished Goods Inventory (FGI) Balance

a company that increased labor productivity (employee throughput) by 10% did so at the cost of decreasing materials efficiency (lower inventory turns) by 5% (increased labor efficiency required more materials availability). Simple mathematics shows us that the increased labor efficiency increased profits by 1% overall (10% times 10%), but the decreased materials efficiency hurt profits by 2.5% overall (50% times 5%). Therefore, increased labor productivity cost the company a 1.5% reduction in profitability. [5, 8]

Summary

This research project has been enlightening. The initial premise that the measurement system directly affects employee performance has been proven by the PPI example. Employees tend to focus on keeping their jobs and getting a raise and consider the measurement system as the primary tool in determining their personal goal achievement. Employees have the ability to make any measurement system look good. The trick is for management to identify what that measurement system should be to maximize corporate goal achievement.

References

1. Lockamy, A. III, and J.F. Cox III. *Reengineering Performance Measurement*. Burr Ridge, Ill.: Irwin Professional Publishing, 1994.
2. Marsh, and Meredith. "Changes in Performance Measures on the Factory Floor." *Production & Inventory Management Journal* 39, no. 1 (1998): 36–40.
3. Plenert, G. "Installing Successful Factories into Developing Countries." *The International Executive* 32, no. 2 (Sept–Oct. 1990): 29–35.
4. Plenert, G. "Leading Edge Production Planning Philosophies and their Effects on Productivity and Quality." *Productivity and Quality Management Frontiers - V*, ISPQR (Feb. 1995): 476–483.
5. Plenert, G. *Plant Operations Deskbook*. Homewood, Ill.: Business 1 IRWIN, 1993.
6. Plenert, G. "Productivity and Quality in a Developing Country." *Productivity and Quality Management Frontiers - V*, ISPQR (Feb. 1995): 194–202.
7. Plenert, G. "Successful Factory Management Systems." *Produktiviti, Bil.* 42 (Jul/Ogos 1992): 2–6.
8. Plenert, G. "What Manufacturing Resources Are Critical?" *Produktiviti, Bil* 42 (Jul/Ogos, 1992): 14.
9. Staff. "Finding Your Way Through Performance Measurement." *News for a Change* (July 1998): 1, 4, 6.

About the Author

Gerhard J. Plenert, Ph.D., CPIM, is senior principal, AMS. He has spent 20 years working in executive level management. He has traveled extensively, giving seminars and solving industrial management problems. His books include *Concept Management, World Class Manager, International Management and Production-Survival Techniques for Corporate America*, and *Plant Operations Handbook*. During the past few years, Dr. Plenert's consulting and seminar work has included programs for companies such as Ritz-Carlton, Hewlett Packard, Seagate Technologies, Precision Bearing, Applied Magnetics, and Motorola. Dr. Plenert experienced 12 years in an academic setting and has now returned to a full-time executive management and consulting career. His current projects include the books *Finite Capacity Scheduling* and *International Operations Management*.

Reprinted from APICS—The Performance Advantage, *November 1995.*

Managing Your Suppliers: A Commonsense Approach

Philip E. Quigley, CPIM

Managing suppliers is the new operations imperative. It's always been an integral part of materials management, but over the last 10 years it has become obvious that suppliers, or rather the management of suppliers, is a key contributor to a company's success or failure.

The current buzzword is "partnership." All suppliers are partners and everyone is going to work together as one "team." Suppliers can also become "certified." But in reality, developing suppliers in today's competitive world is not easy. It takes a lot of work and patience and it doesn't have to end in a partnership. Reality is that managing suppliers and developing a relationship with them is a process with four steps, and not every supplier will become a partner.

There are four stages in managing suppliers and implementing a partnership approach. But take notice of a few points. You will not necessarily have a pleasant and orderly one-way flow where everything moves along nicely. You can easily move along and then fall back. Why? Maybe the supplier isn't performing. Maybe the supplier has decided it doesn't want you as a major customer. Maybe you're not big enough, or you're too demanding, or they just don't like you. Also, you don't have to move to the final stage of partnership as defined here (I realize some other people may have a different view of what a supplier partnership is). With these comments let's look at the stages.

Stage 1—Traditional Adversarial Relationship

There is no relationship here. Every purchase order is let out for bids. Suppliers are pitted against each other and the main criterion for selection is price. This stage still exists, mainly because companies either think they have no choice or the materials management group is rewarded by cost measurements only.

Obviously, this stage is not the one to be in. Quality and delivery become major problems—usually because the supplier has "lowballed" the price and tries to make up for it with expediting fees or other bogus charges, or because the supplier didn't know what it was getting into and now can't perform.

At this stage there are high transaction costs to support purchasing. Transaction costs? Take a look a what's going on:

- Requisitions have to be placed by planners—one at a time.
- Quotes are sent out—one at a time.
- Purchase orders are issued—one at a time.
- Material is received and inspected—order by order.
- Bills are paid—one order at a time.

All of these transactions are time consuming and ripe for error.

For a case study, let's look at an oil tool company that has castings as one of its major purchased components. In the beginning of this process, the company has more than a dozen suppliers of castings in the U.S. and Asia. There are no long-term contracts and purchase orders are released one part number at a time. In theory, each order is sent out for bids to every supplier, but in reality, certain suppliers are preferred for certain parts.

Lead times are long—three to six months—and every casting received is inspected. The relationship between the companies is good.

But there are problems. Costs seem too high, especially for the American suppliers. Lead times are considered excessive and there are nagging quality problems. Everyone agrees that it takes too much paper, too many phone calls and too many meetings to make things happen.

In other words, this is a typical situation for a lot of companies—even today. Agreeing that this isn't a good place to be in, let's go on.

Stage 2—Building the Relationship

This stage is a building and transitioning one. Dramatic changes take place in this stage, both for the company and its suppliers. The key activity at this stage is the development and implementation of long-term contracts/purchase agreements. What are long-term contracts or agreements? Typically, you will set up a year-long contract with a total quantity required and a dollar amount. Price will be a major issue, but quality and delivery terms are now explicitly stated. The contracts must be carefully drawn up. Some points are:

- A total requirement for each part is called out. But be careful to explain that this quantity is for planning purposes only. The requirement could be exceeded, or it may not be met. When you have high volume for one part, this is relatively easy to negotiate.
- A dollar guarantee is made part of the agreement. Here you guarantee the supplier a dollar amount of business. Again you state the amount as a range—high, low, and expected.
- The agreement lays out a schedule of receipts requirements. You will be calling out whether you will want daily, weekly or monthly deliveries. You can specify type of freight, etc., at this time.
- Order placement details are spelled out in the agreement. You do not want to send out a P.O. You may use a phone call, fax or a computer printout with several weeks of demand and forecast, etc. Do what makes sense for your business, but keep it simple.

- Some sort of inspection process is still required. You may have an incoming inspection or have your inspectors at the supplier's plant. But the agreement should explicitly lay out requirements for handling quality problems and improving quality. You are building a foundation for a long-standing relationship through which you can test the supplier's desire and ability to improve quality.
- The agreement should provide some mechanism for rating suppliers, as well as a process for the supplier to review the grading with you. Also make a provision for the supplier to grade you—Do you pay your bills promptly? Do you answer calls concerning technical questions?

As you can see, the relationship with the supplier has changed greatly. There is more up-front planning work being done by purchasing, but less day-to-day expediting and paper chasing.

Now you implement the contract and monitor results. If the supplier performs well, the relationship can go on to the next stage. If the supplier doesn't perform, then it must be dropped. This stage should be considered an interim toward Stage 3 or certification, and the supplier should be aware of this.

Let's look at our case study of the oil tool company. It has analyzed demand for castings. It can project its requirements out 12 to 18 months and can estimate reasonably well 18 to 36 months out. It now calls in its suppliers and lets out bids for 12-month rolling contracts for castings. But these aren't standard contracts. The purchasing department has done its homework—listening to its own MRP planner and talking to foundries. The contracts call out the following:
- Contract will be for pounds of casting delivered each week. There is a total pounds required and then a breakdown of parts into three sizes—large, medium and small.
- Two weeks before delivery date, the foundry will be given a detailed delivery schedule by part number.
- Minimum and maximum delivery amounts are specified.
- Provision is made to review the min/max amounts every quarter based on market forecasts.
- The min/max amounts have been carefully calculated. The minimum amount can easily be met and the maximum amount has been carefully thought through.
- As part of the agreement, all of the suppliers know that the oil tool company wants to be between 10 to 20 percent of each foundry's business. This number has been agreed to by both sides. Neither wants to depend too heavily on the other.
- Quality requirements are called out, both initial quality specifications by which the castings will be inspected and a procedure for a joint problem-solving process when problems arise.
- A grading system has been created to measure supplier performance.
- The purchasing department, after working with accounts payable, guarantees payment within 10 working days of receipt of material. The oil tool company negotiated purchasing releases to six foundries, reducing its supplier base by half. The six were selected on a basis of past performance in the areas of quality, cost and schedule.

Stage 3—Certification

The key points in this stage of supplier development are

Quality: You now drop requirements for incoming inspection. The supplier has performed so well that inspection is not required. The key is performance. It doesn't matter that the supplier has applied for the Malcolm Baldrige Award or has become ISO 9000 certified, even though they should be required to do one or the other (and ideally, both). Companies can have certificates on the wall and still shut down your line.

Electronic data interchange (EDI): The supplier now receives order and forecast information directly from your system. They may invoice and receive payment electronically.

Design input: The supplier is encouraged to provide input into design of parts. They may make suggestions on a routine basis or they may be asked to review prototype designs. Agreements will have to be made on sharing cost reductions and confidentiality.

This stage should be a goal for all of your suppliers. The benefits of a stable of certified suppliers are tremendous, both in cost, quality and cycle time.

It is now a year later in our oil tool company. There has been constant communication back and forth between the oil tool company and its suppliers. Performance has been carefully monitored and measured. Purchasing has decided that two of the suppliers have not been performing and are dropped. The remaining four are considered excellent suppliers and the decision is made to move them to "certification."
- Contracts are released but they now contain new provisions for quality improvement, EDI and design input.
- Quality improvement now has requirements for statistical process control, ISO 9000 or Malcolm Baldrige.
- Incoming inspection on a routine basis is dropped. Audits are called for instead.
- EDI is now required with supplier.
- Design review of new castings and improvements to existing drawings are required.
- Provision is made in the contract that cost improvements due to suggestions from the supplier will be shared.
- The contracts are released and again performance is measured.

Based on performance and need, you may now move to the final stage—partnership.

Stage 4—Partnership

The final stage—the new buzzword. But not every supplier should get to this stage. The main points are

Design responsibility: The supplier now has responsibility for design of the parts as part of the new product development process. They are members of the design team, attend meetings and may well be located in your plant. They know your specifications and marketing plans. This means the supplier must have the technical ability to design parts and the ability to keep your secrets.

Sharing of cost data: The supplier now has an understanding of your product costs and the commitment and ability to work with you to cut costs on a proactive basis. The supplier knows you will share the cost reductions equally with him and it's not always coming out of his pocket.

Material ownership: The supplier now owns the material until it's consumed, not delivered. This is a new concept and it is generating a fair amount of controversy. The supplier is not paid when the material is delivered but when it is "consumed" in the manufacturing process or sold to the customer.

As you can see here, partnership means just that. The supplier knows all of your secrets, plays a key role in developing your new products and thus, in your new markets. Their ability to perform will have direct impact on your bottom line.

This requires that you carefully manage this partnership and realize several points:

- Not every supplier will or can move into partnership with you.
- Partnership also means that you must be deserving of partnership. (This point needs some clarification. Partnership means equality—the supplier is benefiting equally from the relationship. If not, the relationship will sour quickly, with potentially disastrous results for both parties.)

What do I mean that you must be deserving of partnership? Well, do you say you want quality, but then place orders based on price only? Are your systems set up to work with suppliers? Do you use EDI and is it easy to work with? Do you want supplier input on quality and design but never respond to their ideas, or worse, steal them and not reward the supplier? Do you get supplier input and then give it to a competitor to use? Do you pay your bills promptly or do you keep suppliers hanging?

Let's take a final look at our oil tool company. Another year has gone by. The foundries have performed well and a very good relationship has been developed with them.

Purchasing has reviewed performance and decided two of the foundries should move to the partnership level.

- Two are selected because they have developed their own internal design capability, the other two have not.
- All four foundries will be kept as suppliers.
- Also, the nature of the business and the competitive situation negate the foundries owning the material until it's shipped. But they have agreed to daily shipments of some parts that are in high demand.
- An ongoing continuous improvement process is also in the works. Cost savings are shared between the supplier and the company.

This process took two years, and out of 12 original suppliers, only two became partners.

A final lesson then is: Partnership takes time and is a two-way street. Think hard about it before you blindly send out a letter to all suppliers saying you want a partnership with them.

About the Author

Philip E. Quigley, CPIM, is a senior consultant with KPMG Peat Marwick in Southern California. He has 20 years of experience in manufacturing and has directed master scheduling, material and production planning, stockrooms, quality improvement projects, new product teams and systems implementations.

Reprinted from the 1994 APICS International Conference Proceedings.

Business Process Reengineering—Making the Transition

Ravi Ravikumar, CPIM

Business Process Reengineering is being embraced by most corporations as the savior in a highly competitive, global marketplace Mired in age-old practices and organizational structures, these corporations are working hard to find new ways to muster the flexibility required for success and survival through the 1990s and beyond. Reengineering offers tremendous potential for these corporations. However, the transition has been extremely painful and somewhat tricky. More than seventy percent of the reengineering efforts are reported to have failed to achieve their objectives and promised benefits. Most of these efforts have not even gone through all the requisite phases to complete the transition. Organizational stamina and focus have been among the major stumbling blocks. The recipe for successful reengineering initiatives is not an "off-the-shelf" commodity. The good news is that there is a wealth of information on what works and what doesn't from the consultants and professionals who have been courageous enough to be the early adopters of this activity.

Background

American companies are expected to spend an estimated $32 billion on reengineering projects. Nearly two-thirds of those efforts are predicted to fail.[1] Such gloomy predictions do not seem to slow down these corporations from aggressively pursuing reengineering programs. Peter Drucker, an eminent management expert says "reengineering is new and it has to be done."[2] Michael Hammer, who is credited with coining the term "reengineering," defines it as "the fundamental rethinking and radical redesign of an entire business system—business processes, job definitions, organizational structures, management and control systems and values and beliefs—to achieve dramatic improvements in cost, quality, service and speed." The overriding philosophy guiding the reengineering efforts is a disbelief in the traditional ways corporations are organized in planning and executing work. Steep organizational hierarchies preached and practiced during the industrial era seem to be no longer suitable in the information era which is characterized by intense global competition and value creation for customers. Quality and continuous improvement initiatives that attempted to deliver 5% or 10% improvements, though still essential, are no longer sufficient. To survive in today's competitive environment, firms have recognized the need to make dramatic improvements—10X rather than 10%. Thomas Davenport in his book on *Process Innovation* says, "Businesses must be viewed not in terms of functions, divisions, or products, but of key processes. Achievement of order-of-magnitude levels of improvement in these processes means redesigning them from beginning to end, employing whatever innovative technologies and organizational resources are available."[3]

Results

Many success stories have been published to hail the benefits of reengineering efforts. Union Carbide has used reengineering to scrape $400 million out of fixed costs in just three years.[2] Many of the process-focused change programs in corporations are delivering notable improvements in cost, quality and time. Major efforts in a variety of industries to redesign core processes such as customer service, order fulfillment, or new product development have begun to pay handsome dividends. However, for every success story, there are numerous horror stories and failed attempts at making this non-trivial transition.

Other success stories characterize reengineering efforts, with very little improvement to the critical factors. Reengineering the Accounts Payable function in one of the industrial firms, for example, did not have much impact on the overall performance although it achieved substantial percentage improvements within the function. Accounts payable, in this case, was not one of the few core processes that determined the success or failure of the company's business.[4]

What then are the critical success factors for these sweeping, enterprise-wide initiatives? What did the successful organizations do right? What lessons can the other firms, both those considering launching such programs, and ones that are deeply entrenched in it, learn from such successes and failures?

Reengineering Phases

The four broad phases of reengineering programs are identified in **Figure 1**. It is important to study past successes and failures in the context of these phases. The success of a reengineering program depends on effectively managing the organizational dynamics through each of these phases. Change management issues play a significant role in identifying and dealing with some of these challenges.

Reengineering Critical Success Factors

Even the best-laid reengineering plans often go astray. Despite bold commitments of blowing up the status quo, some companies end up merely tinkering with well-entrenched business processes. Others try to drive radical changes from the bottom up and quickly get stymied by functional managers defending parochial interests.[5]

Some of the issues and challenges from each of the major phases are discussed below.

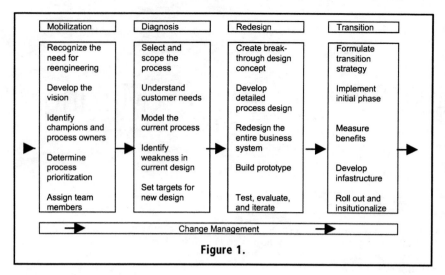

Mobilization	Diagnosis	Redesign	Transition
Recognize the need for reengineering	Select and scope the process	Create break-through design concept	Formulate transition strategy
Develop the vision	Understand customer needs	Develop detailed process design	Implement initial phase
Identify champions and process owners	Model the current process	Redesign the entire business system	Measure benefits
Determine process prioritization	Identify weakness in current design	Build prototype	Develop infastructure
Assign team members	Set targets for new design	Test, evaluate, and iterate	Roll out and insitutionalize

Change Management

Figure 1.

Phase 1: Mobilization

This is a very crucial phase in any reengineering activity. Key activities include identifying and articulating the need for change, determining the true potential for reengineering, identifying and prioritizing core process, enlisting the executive sponsor who has the necessary clout and commitment to carry this through, and identifying the process owners and project team members.

The Need for Change

The foundation for successful transition is built in this phase through identifying and articulating the need for change. First and foremost, the company must establish a change imperative. The need for change has to be so compelling that it serves to sustain the much needed momentum throughout all phases. Tremendous discomfort with the status quo must be established. Most reengineering efforts seem to fail for lack of this rallying point. Although one may get started into a major reengineering effort, organizational focus and commitment will not be sustained unless there is a strong sense of urgency. In the case of Chrysler, for example, the change imperative was simple: change or go out of business. Senior management plays a key role in establishing this environment and in frequently communicating this into the organization.

Communicating the Vision

Even after the need for change has been established, the vision that is compelling, specific, and measurable must be broadly communicated. Vision must first be validated in terms of its relevance, particularly from a strategic value point of view. For example, if the firm decides to reengineer customer processes, customer perspectives may be very important to formulate the vision. Designing from the outside in may be a prudent approach. In the case of AT&T, the company enlisted several customers who served as the focus group, critiqued plans, participated in trial runs and gave regular feedback.[2]

Prioritizing the Process

In order to achieve the levels of performance breakthrough, it is essential to identify all activities that drive key elements of performance. The fact that most businesses are organized along functional lines only makes it harder to identify appropriate processes that drive performance. Thomas Davenport defines a process as a structured, measured set of activities designed to produce a specified output for a particular customer or market. It implies a strong emphasis on how work is done within an organization, not emphasizing only what is being done.[3]

Typically, there are only a few (five to seven) core processes in any enterprise that delivers value to its customers. Order fulfillment, which may include the traditional manufacturing functions, is a good example of a core process. This process typically includes order entry, order management, manufacturing and logistics functions. In many instances billing and receivable functions have also been included.

Positioning the Reengineering Effort

Many corporations involved with reengineering have also deployed quality initiatives of one kind or other. At American Express, Total Quality Management (TQM) was a major focus at the time reengineering was being introduced. This caused a major debate about which one of the two was more important. There was a perception that the reengineering was replacing the TQM methodologies. These two methodologies maintain different perspectives. The TQM approach focuses on improving the current functions, whereas the reengineering approach fundamentally questions why that particular function should exist and whether it should be eliminated. At American Express, process mapping issues got bogged down into disputes. Says Randy Christofferson, VP of Quality and Reengineering at American Express, "we burned up an inordinate amount of time arguing over how many processes and how big the boxes were."

American Express was apparently not prepared to deal with this conflict. Finally the disputes were resolved by redefining reengineering with Baldrige award terminology. Essentially, reengineering was positioned to be a subset of TQM. Lessons learned from similar experiences show us that these issues have to be proactively addressed and the reengineering effort appropriately positioned to avoid significant time and energy loss.

Phase 2: Diagnosis

Key activities in this phase include scoping and modeling the current process and activities, and establishing targets for the new process. Some of the questions answered in this phase are: what is the process all about; what does it take to get the process done; what is needed from the new design; why does the current design not perform better; and what opportunities exist for redefining the output of the process.

Reengineering Training and Education

One of the areas overlooked by most companies engaged in reengineering is training the teams early in the process. Workshops have to be conducted with the senior executives to create the awareness and to help them get prepared for the long journey ahead. Right level of expectations will also be set at the executive level. The reengineering teams will have to be trained on the methodology for reengineering. There is no substitute for this early learning at all levels.

Scoping the Process

Most companies must consider reengineering the core business process that has the greatest potential for delivering significant competitive advantage. While prioritization of the process itself should be done in the earlier phase, the scoping of this process must be a major activity in this phase. Companies that get started with reengineering activities without fully scoping the process end up fighting scope issues through all remaining phases. The scope of the process has to be developed very carefully. First, a clear vision of the end state has to be identified along with the definition of the value to be created. This has to be then balanced with the breadth of functions and the capacity of the organization to sustain the effort. The boundaries for selected process must be dearly defined. If process limits are not clearly defined, you can end up with analyses that are never completed, or a reengineering process that requires such far-reaching and complex changes that it simply cannot be implemented.[6]

Current Process Analysis

Before designing the new process, we need to understand what's wrong with the current process. The team needs to identify the value-adding steps associated with the current process and understand the problems related to performance of these activities. Current performance measurements have to be identified and related to inherent process limitations.

Current processes have to be examined from a customer's point of view. It is important to keep a high level perspective and not get bogged down in details. One of the major mistakes in reengineering is spending far too much time on analysis of current processes. Dr. Hammer says people get stuck in up-front analysis very often, because they don't know how to proceed through a reengineering effort.[1]

There usually is a great deal of resistance in most companies to perform a current state analysis. This is usually perceived as a non-value-added activity. Such analyses would have been done many times under various initiatives, most recently perhaps with the TQM projects. Even in such cases, one would find that the analyses performed with prior initiatives to be more narrow in scope, typically at a functional level. It will be therefore worthwhile to map the process at a high level, characterizing it from a customer's perspective.

Phase 3: Redesign

This is the phase team members seem to enjoy the most. Details of the new process are identified, tested and prototyped during this phase. Team members are usually encouraged to "think-out-of-the-box" and start the design with a blank sheet of paper. Starting from scratch, companies can plan and build the new infrastructure required to realize the new design. This new infrastructure should include programs like comprehensive training and skill-development plans, performance measurement systems that track how well the organization is meeting its targets and how employees should be rewarded based on those objectives; communication programs that help employees understand why and how their behavior must

change; information technology development plans that capture the benefits of new technology, and finally, pilots that test and redefine the redesign as well as its implementation.[7]

The Reengineering Team

The reengineering team takes on a very significant role during this phase. The team must be led by the business community members, not outsiders, who have the business savvy, organizational skills, knowledge and clout to make changes happen. Outsiders include members from the IT group and external consultants. A common mistake made by most companies is to have the reengineering efforts led and managed by the IT organization. While the IT function is a very important component, it will not have the wide influence required to make radical changes that are needed. The team must be responsible for scoping, structuring, and managing the construction and implementation of related systems, technologies, procedures and human resource enablers from the reengineering proposal. The team must maintain the balance between the elements—people, process, and technology.[6]

The members from the business community, besides bringing all of the stated benefits, also bring a personal stake in the outcome. One of the most difficult challenges is to obtain the necessary level of involvement from these people. While these people may not be available full-time for this effort, they have to be involved more than half-time, at a minimum, during the program. There is some value in having these people removed from their current positions to be full-time on the reengineering effort to enable them to be objective in redesigning the new process. However, they need to stay in touch with the business as well. The outsiders—whether they be consultants, or IT members-play an invaluable role. They bring a fresh perspective and the creative naïveté to ask, "Why do we do things this way?" Consultants, in addition, bring the methodology, discipline, and requisite experience to avoid some of the common pitfalls.[8]

The Role of Benchmarking

In order to jump start the process of "thinking-out-of-the-box," benchmarking other companies for similar processes have proved to be valuable. Typically, best-practices from other industries can be an eye-opener. Texas Instruments, for example, used the pizza company process and the airline industry models for reengineering their order fulfillment processes for custom, semi-conductor business. In so far as it enables companies to look outside for alternative ways of designing processes, benchmarking can help to break a company's inwardly focused mind-set. Benchmarking can identify realistic performance objectives and target characteristics for companies to match or surpass best practices from other companies or industries.[3]

Information Technology as an Enabler

Conventional wisdom, among reengineering practitioners, is that process design and development should occur before commencing the design of the supporting information system solution. While this sounds logical, this approach misses the opportunity of using information technology as an enabler. Since most of the reengineered processes take advantage of current capabilities with IT such as distributed or client/server computing, work-group computing, etc., it has become more important to take into account the potential of IT to influence the new process design. Information is an extraordinarily powerful lever for the redesign of core processes. Changing where you deliver information, how you deliver it, and what you deliver can have a dramatic impact on performance.[9] As Thomas Davenport says: "But IT can play an even more important role in process innovation. When we understand how companies in many industries have used technology in innovative ways to improve their processes, we can better design new processes."[3]

A recent reengineering article cites a company failing three times to bring off a reengineering effort. The article quotes: "It spent a lot of time building castles in the air regarding process redesign without paying attention to information technology."[1]

Information Technology—Make vs. Buy

Classical reengineering approach will suggest that the design of the new solution be completed to the required level of detail before beginning the design of the enabling information system solution. In reality, however, this may not be a practical choice. Many companies get impatient with the long drawn out reengineering program and end up selecting the information system to be implemented, somewhat prematurely. And then they learn to simultaneously reengineer the business processes in the context of the system solution. This may indeed be a more effective approach, if coordinated effectively, due to the long time taken for developing a custom solution. Motivation to sustain the effort will fade quickly if it takes longer to deliver the reengineered solutions. Well-designed integrated solutions may in fact offer rich ideas that may speed up the reengineering design and implementation activity.

Solution Component: The "Social" Design

Most reengineering efforts are primarily focused on the "technical" design and not on the "social" design aspects. The technical design includes the process design, linkages with other processes and functions, information requirements, etc. Social design, on the other hand, is where Human Resources (HR) can play a crucial role. As Dr. Hammer puts it, "the soft stuff is the hard stuff." Unless social factors are included in the reengineering, the designs will most likely remain as designs that may not get implemented. Some of the tasks in developing the social design include: empowering customer contact personnel, defining jobs and skills, specifying the management structure, designing career paths, designing change management activities, and designing appropriate incentive structures.

Phase 3: Transition

After prototyping the new process, the organization must evolve to institutionalize the new capabilities. This phase has to be meticulously planned because this is when most of the organization will actually experience change. Many important decisions have to be made regarding the rollout strategy and sequence, particularly in global environments. There are significant risks and tradeoffs in implementing the solution in a "big bang" fashion vs. in a phased manner. The phasing of implementation can get very tricky. It is often not easy to decide whether to roll out the implementation one product division at a time, or one geographic location at a time. Cultural issues will have a significant bearing as well.

Transferring Ownership

The reengineering team makes the transition, during this phase, from a design focus to working within various organizations supporting the rollout. Management teams from individual organizations should lead the implementation efforts. The reengineering team provides the expertise and experience required for successful transfer of ownership. Many of the change management issues pertaining to this phase are covered below.

Change Management

One of the common causes of reengineering failures is the inability of the organization to manage change effectively. There will be tremendous resistance to change from key people at all levels who will be affected by it. These people are usually worried about losing their power base or even their jobs, uncomfortable with the ambiguity of the new ways of doing business, and cynical from past failures. Good ideas do not implement themselves. To overcome organizational resistance and inertia, managers of reengineering need to meticulously plan the organizational change campaign. To make reengineering happen, the "soft" human resource issues need to become hard—with clear goals, steps, measurements and outcomes.[5] To be successful at reengineering, the organization must anticipate the resistance beforehand, and know how to defuse it by gaining the trust and backing of key individuals who will play major roles in the new process. These change management activities must run in parallel through all phases of the reengineering effort.

Managing Stakeholder Resistance

Stakeholders include people affected by the radical change in the business process—the CEO, senior management teams, middle management, and the "owners" of the process to be reengineered. Early activities for managing stakeholders include mapping the roles of all affected players in the organization. Executives must respond to sources of resistance that emerge at various phases.

During the mobilization and diagnosis phases, skepticism and fear occur at all levels of the organization. Resistance usually takes the form of dismissal and denial. Frequent communication with the stakeholders is mandatory to address such natural concerns.

During the redesign phase, resistance becomes more intense as the new processes are being designed. Middle management shows a greater deal of resistance at this stage because their jobs are being threatened by new management structures and empowerment of front-line workers. During this stage, resistance takes the form of rejection.

During the transition phase, resistance comes from all levels. By this time the organization may be losing the steam to complete the effort. Several roadblocks will be thrown to abort the effort from various executive's levels. The senior executive's role at this time is very critical. Since reengineering activities cut across organizational and functional boundaries, accountability for development, testing and implementation must be clearly defined.

The Role of Communications

One cannot overcommunicate during reengineering; it requires constant communication at all levels. Communications campaign must be designed early in the reengineering process. Specific company events have to be leveraged, such as employee quarterly meetings, staff meetings, executive briefing sessions, etc. Communications must come from the top. Several companies have successfully published reengineering newsletters. Many companies see this as a "make it, or break it" program that is of strategic importance to the enterprise.

Communications breakdowns occur for many reasons. One of the more common reasons is that the need for change is unknown. Executives tend to overestimate the capacity of the organization to understand and accept the need to change.

Summary

Reengineering is here to stay. Age-old practices are not applicable anymore in today's world, which is getting increasingly "connected" with powerful information technology enablers. Companies will have to undertake serious reengineering to reap the hard work they have put in over the past decade, with continuous improvement initiatives within manufacturing. These companies realize that there is greater potential in integrating various processes to deliver their products and services effectively and profitably to the ultimate customer. Reengineering, however, is very painful. Organizational stamina and focus backed by strong will and executive leadership are necessary ingredients. By understanding what reengineering entails and getting prepared and organized for the venture, we can ensure a higher probability of success.

References

1. Bruce Caldwell, "Missteps, Miscues," *Information Week,* June 20, 1994
2. Thomas A. Stewart, "Reengineering: The Hot New Managing Tool," *Fortune,* August 23, 1993
3. Thomas H. Davenport, "Process Innovation, Reengineering Work Through Information Technology," Harvard Business School Press, 1993
4. John Hagel III, "Keeping CPR on Track," *The McKinsey Quarterly,* 1993 Number 1
5. Steven Stanton, Michael Hammer, and Bradford Power, "From Resistance to Results: Mastering The Organizational Issues of Reengineering," *Insights Quarterly,* Fall 1992, Volume 4, Number 2
6. John Farrell, "A Practical Guide for Implementing Reengineering," *Planning Review,* March/April 1994
7. Gene Hall, Jim Rosenthal, and Judy Wade, "How to Make Reengineering Really Work," *Harvard Business Review,* November - December 1993
8. Mark M. Klein, "The Most Fatal Reengineering Mistakes," *Information Strategy: The Executive's Journal,* Summer 1994
9. John Browning, "The Power of Process Redesign," *The McKinsey Quarterly,* 1993, Number 1
10. Ravi Ravikumar, "Business Process Reengineering: The Competitive Advantage," *APICS International Conference Proceedings,* 1993

About the Author

Ravi Ravikumar is a Senior Manager with the Information Technology practice at Ernst & Young. Ravi is currently involved with reengineering and system implementation efforts with the firm's clients in the western area of the United States. Prior to joining Ernst &Young, Ravi managed a reengineering program for Applied Materials, a leading manufacturer of semiconductor wafer fabrication equipment. Ravi has also worked with various other high-technology firms such as Digital Equipment Corporation, leading their consulting practice in the western area. He has over fourteen years of experience in the information technology area and has managed many MRP II implementations.

Ravi regularly teaches CPIM fundamentals and certification courses at the APICS Santa Clara Valley Chapter. He has an M.B.A. from the University of Texas and a B.B.A. in Accounting from India, in addition to the CPIM from APICS.

Reprinted from the 2000 APICS International Conference Proceedings.

What Gets Measured—Gets Done!

John Reichwein, CFPIM

My session is entitled, "What Gets Measured—Gets Done!" And I believe that to be a very true and a widely accepted concept. People understand that if something is important enough for you to measure its success, they had better pay attention to it too. But just as important as the measurements and accountability is the understanding. Do your employees truly understand what is important, what is your organization's vision, what are your goals, what's their role, and how they will be measured?

So I'm saying that although measurements are incredibly important to the success of all of our organizations, there are a lot of foundation steps to be completed before you start that process. Measurement is just part of a cyclical process, not an end in itself.

Today I am going to tell you the story of my company, Revcor, and how we have implemented a process, which we call performance alignment. I'll share the history of the implementation and the results that we achieved. But, in the process of developing my presentation, I did a little research to help support the Revcor processes and to validate some of our fundamental theories about which I'll speak.

We at Revcor have developed some unique tools and methodologies, but they are based upon concepts subscribed to by many forward-thinking companies. In other words, we didn't originate any theories or create new ways of doing business. We simply developed a process to drive and manage what many successful companies are trying to achieve, the performance alignment of the entire organization.

In doing my research, I came across some articles on *IndustryWeek*'s annual competition called "America's Best Plants." The articles explored the winning entries and endeavored to find common traits shared by these very successful organizations. The articles obviously talked about measurements, but there were an amazing number of powerful quotes, talking about the importance of the organization's understanding of the vision, the goals, and then the measurements.

Here's a good one with which to start: *"Effective and open communications play a huge role in creating a trusting organization. It's amazing what people will do, if they just know why they are doing it."* (Porter-Cable Corp.)

I have personally found this to be a very accurate observation. If employees understand your vision, in other words, you've communicated your strategies and translated them to meaningful "line-of-sight" goals; you've empowered them to achieve and to act independently.

We at Revcor have found that communication of our vision and our goals, that which will ultimately be measured, cannot be overemphasized. It has to happen effectively, often, and not just in a traditional top-down fashion. This belief is shared by Halliburton Energy Services,

another quoted winner from the *IndustryWeek* competition. *"Whatever form communication takes within your company, make sure it is 'multidirectional'—that is, up, down, and through all levels of the organization. Open lines of communication develop trust, encourage new ideas, eliminate intimidation and skepticism, and aid in building a brighter future for employees and the company."*

At Revcor, in addition to traditional communications, we have also added a software tool that acts as both a broadcaster of organization goals and a repository for translated versions of those goals as they apply to each group and individual. In other words, we have a goal warehouse in which individuals can view, manage, and share goals throughout our organization. So our efforts to communicate goals through this mechanism actually evolve into an alignment process.

"Communicate frequently, personally, and through multiple vehicles to ensure that the message gets across and that you obtain understanding…but don't forget that listening is the more important part of communication." (Alcatel Network Systems—*IndustryWeek* winner)

Alignment starts with employees using our software tool to define their working relationships in the organization, first hierarchically, identifying their boss and their staff members. Then, they identify their relationships along the supply chain: providers, teammates, and customers. The tool notifies those identified and requires them to reciprocally agree (or disagree) that there is a material business relationship, and confirm the interdependence. (See **Figure 1**.)

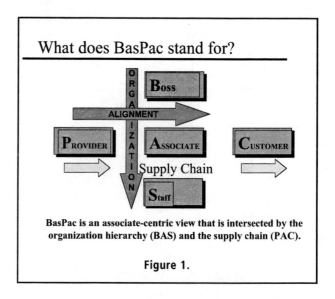

What does BasPac stand for?

BasPac is an associate-centric view that is intersected by the organization hierarchy (BAS) and the supply chain (PAC).

Figure 1.

It is through this process that you will see some early returns for your efforts. The organization-wide dialogue that is facilitated is the foundation of the alignment process. The dialogue initiated by the employee, or associate as we call it, between providers, customers, teammates, boss, and staff begins to clarify working interdependencies, and creates a better understanding of how work flows through the supply chain and hierarchically. Procedures begin to make more sense, and refinements start to become everyone's business.

At Revcor, the process was eye opening. The downside was that work came to a screeching halt for almost two days. People were fully engaged in the company-wide dialogue that I mentioned earlier. The discovery process was amazing. Light bulbs went on all over the organization. So, I guess that the upside was also that work came to a screeching halt for two days. Instead of simply and maybe robotically going through our established procedures, we took the time to understand what we needed from one another to succeed.

"Make sure that everyone is aligned to the same goals, alignment of common goals throughout the organization stops turf wars, and lets all departments and levels of the organization focus on what is truly important to the success of the operation." (Cooper Industries)

Once these relationships are set up and reciprocally confirmed, the goal assignment process can begin. Our tool helps us to systemize and manage this process. But maybe even more importantly, it enables us to communicate to everyone in the organization our vision in terms of strategic goals. Our strategic goals are communicated and translated for every department and individual associate in our organization. In other words, not only does everyone know what the company's strategies are, they know their role in the strategy.

How does that happen? We have three levels of goals: organizational, group or departmental, and associate or individual. Organizational goals are created by the CEO or by a steering committee and are communicated through our software tool to everyone in the organization. Group goals are assigned by the group or department managers. And individual associate goals may be assigned by the person's group and/or taken on independently by the person himself. This is a unique practice that we've developed at Revcor. Associates are empowered through our software to build their own goal set. They are empowered through our goal warehouse concept.

How's it work? Well, we believe that it is much more effective to have a manager create and post on the system his or her goals for the year. Then, that manager's staff can view those goals and adapt them for their own goal set. In other words, the staff itself determines what they must do to support their manager's objectives. Now, the manager can spend his or her time interacting and helping the staff members to refine and adjust their goals, instead of laboriously developing the entire goal set for each direct report. This has worked very well at Revcor, helping buy-in and getting everyone to pull in the same direction.

Self-assigned goals that are later reviewed and discussed with the manager have a whole host of benefits, which could probably be a session in itself. Let's just say that I'd rather have an employee who has thought through my goals and objectives and come up with solutions and supporting goals of his or her own, instead of dictating a set of goals that may never be thought through with any level of detail or commitment. Again, we're empowering people to be creative and set their own direction, but with

guidance from their manager after he or she has listened, rather than dictating.

The goal assignment process assures the top down alignment and translation of strategic, boss-initiated goals, to lower-level tactics and operatives. This translation process is critical to the achievement of understanding and buy-in. It is based upon translating your vision and strategies into attainable "line-of-sight" goals for all employees including metrics, leadership competencies, and MBO goals.

"The power of employees who are in support of company objectives is the catalyst sparking genuine improvement." (Beiersdorf, Inc., *IndustryWeek* winner)

Performance alignment eliminates most obstacles that prevent an organization from achieving its goals. Empowered employees focus efforts on achieving their concisely defined goals, knowing the basis on which their stakeholders will hold them accountable. I should give you the Revcor definition of performance alignment before I go any further. (See **Figure 2**.)

Performance alignment, in simple terms, is the execution of an organization's business plan. The plan is used to allocate the necessary resources. Goals are translated from the plan and aligned with the resources, and accountability for these goals is assigned to each employee. Results are closely monitored to identify opportunities for organizational development. The assessed results drive the ongoing cycle of realignment, reallocation of resources, and revised goals.

So far, I've talked about Revcor's alignment process and the assignment of goals. Now we need to discuss accountability and assessment at Revcor, to cover all aspects of the performance alignment definition.

Through our goal assignment process, everyone takes on responsibility for his or her share of the overall company strategy. The vision becomes a part of the very fabric of our organization. Everyone knows his or her roles and responsibilities and is held accountable. And at Revcor, they are held accountable by their stakeholders, not just their manager or team leader.

How does that work? Well, you recall that we used our software tool to set up reciprocally confirmed interdependencies or working relationships. That mechanism is also used to share and understand one another's goals. Part of that dialogue is devoted to understanding how the interdependencies affect achievement of one another's goals. We learn how we impact one another.

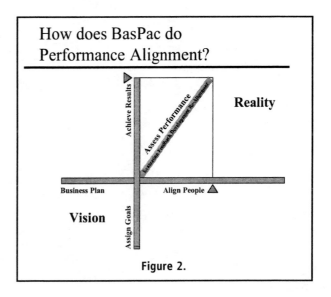

Figure 2.

Because we have fully defined our interdependencies, we have fully identified all stakeholders. In other words, we at Revcor can hold everyone accountable for their piece of our strategic vision, because we have identified who is affected by our execution or lack of execution. We have identified stakeholders, and we have given them the ability to provide feedback to everyone in our organization with whom they share a material business relationship.

In the pursuit of performance alignment, Revcor has bridged the gap between leadership development and performance management by expanding on the concept of multi-rater feedback. We systematically linked employees with their providers, customers, teammates, boss, and staff, and gave them the tools to provide feedback. And it's not just feedback on developmental issues, but feedback on how they've executed their goals related to the company's strategic vision.

Feedback comes from stakeholders, who are dependent upon the recipient of that feedback to accomplish their own goals. It couldn't be a more meaningful measurement of how well your organization is executing its vision. It has helped Revcor to truly understand for the first time why a goal wasn't met, and where we went wrong. We can diagnose our developmental opportunities for specific employees and groups and across the entire organization.

Revcor has actually been developing and refining our concept of performance alignment over the last 10 years. We implemented a semi-automated version of it in 1996, and have since evolved it into an in-house developed software tool. Revcor's strides towards alignment in that timeframe have helped take it from number three to number one in the HVAC air impeller market. Profitability has grown at a rate far surpassing the rate of sales growth.

About the Author

John Reichwein, CFPIM, is CEO of Revcor, a leading manufacturer of air moving solutions to the HVAC market for over 50 years.

Under his leadership, Revcor has moved from the fourth position to number one, with a 650 percent increase in sales, while improving inventory turns five-fold.

Revcor's success is attributed to performance alignment, a process Revcor created for communicating and aligning company, department, team, and individual goals—linking strategic, tactical, and operational goals throughout the organization.

Reprinted from the Production and Inventory Management Journal, *Second Quarter, 1996.*

Agile Manufacturing: Beyond Lean?

Chester W. Richards, Ph.D.

Somewhere around 400 b.c., Sun Tzu [33] wrote: "According to my assessment, even if you have many more troops than others, how can that help you win?"

What is he talking about? If size and strength are not the keys to victory, what is? Down through the years, agility has evolved as one answer to that question. The modern usage of the word dates back to attempts in the early 1950s to understand what made a fighter aircraft superior in air-to-air combat. The first concepts defined fighter performance in terms of the ability to change altitude, airspeed, or direction, and energy-maneuverability (EM) plots were generated showing where one competitor or the other had an advantage. Although EM gave a pilot useful insights, there were some disturbing exceptions. In Korea, for example, the American F-86 won handily over the Soviet MiG-15, even though the MiG had an advantage in turn and climb performance in certain flight regimes. After the war, when we had the opportunity to examine MiGs first hand, it was discovered that although the Soviet aircraft could sometimes turn tighter than the F-86, it was very sluggish and had a canopy that restricted the pilot's view. The American jet had a bubble canopy, which provided better visibility, and boosted hydraulic controls-power steering for fighters-which meant that the MiG rarely had an opportunity to use its theoretically better maneuverability.

To explain this phenomenon, Air Force strategists coined the term *agility*, defined as the ability to change maneuver state, or, put another way, as the time derivative of maneuverability. Maneuverability referred to maximum turn rate, for example seven gs, that is, seven times the acceleration of gravity. Agility, however, indicated how fast an aircraft could go from pulling, say, six gs in one direction to six in another. Such abrupt changes of maneuver are typical of how pilots actually fight in combat. Pilots reported that a more agile aircraft seemed to flit around the sky and rarely presented a good target.

Up to this point, agility might seem like something useful only for fighters and soccer players. But military philosophers quickly took the concept further. One of the principle authors of EM theory, USAF Col. John R. Boyd, noted that the true effects of agility were on the opponent's mind. A pilot in the less agile (although perhaps more maneuverable) fighter soon became frustrated and disoriented. This presented the more agile pilot with fleeting but exploitable firing opportunities. Boyd, a keen student of military history, made the connection between fighter agility and victory in other forms of combat. Japanese samurai, for instance, had known that by operating at a faster and more irregular mental tempo, they could cause gaps, *suki*, in their opponents' attention [20]. Several hundred years later, Rommel employed a similar strategy, believing that his rapid operating tempos and the superior training of his troops would allow him to create and exploit opportunities on the battlefield [7, 28]. By 1978, Boyd was interpreting these observations in terms of decision cycles. Opponents in a conflict can be viewed as cycling through four distinctive but indistinct stages: *observation,* absorbing information from the environment by all possible means, and where the F-86's canopy gave it an advantage; *orientation,* placing this information in context; *decision,* selecting a subsequent course of action; and *action,* attempting to carry it out [2, 23, 27]. Note that the performance of the hardware only affects the first and last items, while mental processes, sparked by observation, are involved in all four. After studying battles from Sun Tzu to Vietnam, and in particular the German blitzkrieg and its later Israeli refinements, Boyd observed that:

Observe, Orient, Decide, and Act (OODA) more inconspicuously, more quickly, and with more irregularity ... permits one to: Generate uncertainty, confusion, disorder, panic, chaos, ..., to shatter cohesion, produce paralysis, and bring about collapse [2].

This is how small armies beat big ones, and it broadened the concept of agility from air-to-air combat to any form of conflict. In Bosnia, U.S. pilots are finding the OODA loop concept as useful today as it proved in the Gulf [18]. And indeed, it is now generally accepted as a primary principle of strategy by the military services: "Agility is the ability of friendly forces to react faster than the enemy and is a prerequisite for seizing and holding the initiative [34]."

Is Agility Only for Warriors?

Business is conflict, but it is not war, despite all the nonsense that has recently been written on the subject. The primary difference, from the standpoint of strategy, is the customer. Competitors in business do not fight each other; they compete for the attention (and money) of the customer. You can use Sun Tzu all you want, but if your customer buys a competitor's product anyway, you lose. Oddly enough, however, the notion of agility applies to business with as much impact as it does to war. There is considerable evidence, cited in [15, 23, 26, 27, 30, 32], that the more agile company, in the Boyd sense of streamlined decision cycles, enjoys a decisive competitive advantage. But again, this was a concept well-known to the Japanese. In the famous H-Y War, Honda turned back a challenge by motorcycle rival Yamaha not by matching that company's manufacturing expansion but by introducing three times as many new models in the ensuing 18 months [32]. Honda's strategy built on a long tradition in Japan. The notion of agility was raised to a high degree of perfection in *The Book of Five Rings,* by the 17th century samurai, Miyamoto Musashi [19, 20]: "In the path of victory, taking the initiative at all costs is the most important thing.... If you consciously try to thwart opponents, you are already late.... Use an advantageous rhythm to arrest the powerful determination of the adversary's motivation." (Compare to OODA loops.)

Like Boyd, Musashi emphasized that the physical aspects of conflict, while important, are secondary to the mental. And of course, the Japanese are well-known for continually shortening their development and manufacturing cycles.

Agility and Manufacturing

So what would agile manufacturing be? The term apparently comes from the Agile Manufacturing Enterprise Forum (AMEF) at Lehigh University, formed to continue (with $5 million of DoD funding) the efforts of a 1991 Iacocca Institute study [31]. Their definition of agility is reasonable, although the use of the word "respond" suggests an overly passive orientation [26]:

Agility is the ability of an enterprise to thrive in a competitive environment of continuous and unanticipated change. To respond quickly to rapidly changing markets driven by customer valuing of products and services [13].

Certainly no competent strategist would argue against any enterprise, manufacturing or otherwise, becoming more agile. However, the AMEF has had less success in distinguishing agile manufacturing from the admittedly related forms of flexible, virtual, and lean, leading some to question whether there is anything to be gained by yet one more buzzword.

Is Flexible the Same as Agile?

There is such a thing as flexible manufacturing, which refers to the ability to produce different products on the same production line, although some definitions restrict the meaning to products within the same general family [35]. In this sense, *agility* might be the ability to switch rapidly among the various product lines, a concept also referred to as *mobility* [35]. Flexible manufacturing in its various forms is well understood in some industries; and, in fact, once a system achieves a level of flexibility it often becomes possible to extend the concept, allowing products to be designed, as well as built, in a lot size of one. Some manufacturers have created direct links to customers so that orders and even designs for products can be transmitted electronically. This is becoming commonplace in the garment industry, and is beginning to spread to the automotive sector, where Toyota and Saturn have goals of delivering a car built with a customer's options in less than a week.

There are caveats. Originally, *flexible* meant robots, on the presumption that one needed automated, programmable devices in order to manufacture different types of product on the same line. One might expect that once the process of automation is complete, the system would automatically demonstrate the virtues of flexibility, if not agility, but this has not proven to be the case. Data have indicated that automated lines tend to be less flexible in terms of product mix, perhaps reflecting the cost and time needed to acquire, modify, and program the machines [12, 35]. Perversely, such lines can become highly "agile" within a very narrow product range.

While technology does play a role, it is generally recognized today that the best way to become flexible is to begin by reducing certain nonessential activities, setup times in particular, so that the system can produce very small lot sizes of different (but often related) products

and still maintain competitive prices [10, 17]. One of the most agile automobile manufacturers, Toyota, installed only about one-third the industry average of automation in its latest plant [1].

All of this suggests that if implemented properly, an enterprise can achieve the flexibility to compete in the marketplace and, because it is not performing unnecessary activities, can switch between products rapidly enough to be considered agile, at least from the standpoint of the production floor. Conversely, just automating what we have today is unlikely to produce either flexibility or agility, and the infrastructure and internal focus that often accompany large automation projects can bog down decision cycles and slow the enterprise's play in the marketplace, as General Motors' $30-billion exercise demonstrated so conclusively in the 1980s [12].

Is Virtual the Same as Agile?

Generally, a virtual company is a true company in that it carries out all the functions necessary to exploit a particular set of business opportunities [3, 4, 8]. It is *virtual* in the sense that large pieces, such as marketing, design, manufacturing, legal, accounting, etc. are carried out by legally distinct units that have come together just for this opportunity, and will probably go their separate ways once it is over. The classic example is motion picture production. The core company may be as small as the producer him/herself, a secretary and perhaps a few administrative assistants. Everybody else on the set is likely to be an independent contractor or work for any of a number of specialized companies. Yet, for the duration of the picture, they form a real company. Can all business be done, and done better, by virtual organizations? The concept is new, so evidence is anecdotal, but a sizable crowd of management gurus appears to be heading in that direction [3, 4, 5, 8, 24, 25].

The reason given by business theorists to go virtual is, simply, to become agile. *Business Week*, for example, began its cover story on virtual companies with "Big companies can't react fast enough [3]." In this sense, virtual is a modular technique that a company might use to increase its agility. It should be noted, however, that there are highly agile companies that do not seem particularly virtual, although one might argue that they could become even more agile by becoming more virtual. The virtual concept is not a panacea for manufacturers, however, since it is hard to imagine how a fat virtual company would have much of a competitive advantage (i.e., what is gained by having useless functions performed by a legally distinct entity?).

As an aside, a virtual company should not be confused with virtual manufacturing, which refers to simulation of the manufacturing process so that decisions can be made before incurring the cost and risk of altering the factory floor. Virtual manufacturing defined in this way is classic simulation, and is neither virtual nor manufacturing. Of course, one could invent a meaning of "virtual manufacturing" that is both virtual, like virtual machines and virtual memory in computer science—or like a virtual company—and which can also manufacture products. But it is probably too late for that now.

What About Lean Production and Reengineering?

These two concepts are closely related and are frequently associated with agility [16]. One of the things that keeps companies from executing rapid OODA loops is waste, in particular, performing functions that do not need to be performed. Reengineering is a process for identifying and eliminating such functions [9, 10, 14]. Thus the fashionable term "business process reengineering" is a little misleading, since the focus of reengineering is on simplifying the overall company system by eliminating processes, not improving them [10]. The term "reengineering" was popularized, perhaps invented, by Michael Hammer in what is still the greatest title in modern management literature: "Reengineering Work: Don't Automate, Obliterate [9]." Eliminating inventory, undoubtedly the best known illustration, is a prerequisite for converting to a Just-in-Time production system, which experience suggests is required for agility [6, 21, 29].

But reengineering can do more than eliminate unnecessary activities from the current system. It can attack and simplify the company's underlying structure. Many companies have accumulated strong hierarchies of non programmatic functions, such as engineering, manufacturing, materiel, finance, and marketing. If decisions must go up and down these stovepipes, you will have slower OODA loops than a more streamlined competitor. This will be true regardless of how much you have simplified and improved your manufacturing processes. For this reason, every known case of successful reengineering has, at some point, stripped away several layers of management and taken the bulk of decision making away from functional hierarchies, The late Mike Walsh, when he began the spectacular turnaround at Union Pacific, eliminated six layers of management [22]. And, as Jack Welch, CEO of GE, put it in his 1993 Annual Report: "With the drag and nonsense of boundaries, management layers, bureaucracy, and formality cleared, the organization automatically accelerates."

Thus we can say that reengineering is a technique for improving the overall health of a system, and decision cycle time-agility—is one of the primary ways to measure it [30]. Cost structure and quality are two others, and a successful reengineering effort will improve them all. The end result is usually called a lean enterprise or lean production [36]. Examples abound: Chrysler today is enjoying a resurgence because it has drastically reduced its design and production cycles and is introducing one new model after another, a strategy also recently adopted by Chevrolet. In 1994, *Consumer Reports* selected the Dodge Intrepid as tops in its class, the first time in recent memory the magazine had so rated a domestic design.

Some of the proponents of agile manufacturing appear to overlook the corresponding goals of lean production. For example, *Industry Week* ran an article entitled "Agile Manufacturing: Stepping Beyond Lean Production [31]." They noted that "lean production is regarded by many as simply an enhancement of mass-production methods." Flexibility, they claim, will inevitably suffer under lean production. Perhaps, but it "will not be because the advocates of lean production have ignored that possibility:

The lean producer combines the advantages of craft and mass production, while avoiding the high cost of the former and the rigidity of the latter. . . . Lean producers (in contrast to mass producers) set their sights explicitly on perfection: continually declining costs, zero defects, zero inventories, and *endless product variety* [36]. (emphasis added)

And in fact, the leanest modern producers, companies like Toyota and Motorola, are among the most flexible.

So, What is Agile Manufacturing?

It probably would have been better to call the Toyota Production System agile manufacturing rather than lean production from the beginning. At this stage it is proving difficult to find anything in the AMEF usage that is not included in a more complete understanding of lean production. It is also becoming hard to see any payoff in continuing doctrinal debates on the concepts discussed in this article.

But let's be honest: The practitioners of lean production, reengineering, flexible manufacturing or whatever sometimes concentrate on the mechanics of the factory floor and lose sight of customers and competitors [1]. The canonical work on lean production, *The Machine That Changed The World* [36], does have a chapter on dealing with customers, but it merely suggests how to run a lean showroom.

In fact, it is worse than that. Trying to become lean without an equal emphasis on improving interaction with the world outside can be dangerous. This was the point of the canopy on the F-86 and why strategists emphasize observation and other mental aspects of competition. The principle applies to manufacturing as well. The fact is that the value or quality of a process cannot be determined purely by examining it within the context of the organization itself. The term "value added" should be used with great caution. Ultimately, only the customer, not manufacturing engineers, determine whether any value was added during production. How much "value," for example is added during lean production of excess inventory that must be unloaded at a loss?

As an aside, this is a special case of a general principle of strategy: You cannot determine the character or nature of a system within itself, and attempts to do so will generate confusion and disorder [2]. For some reason, and this is as true in business as in war, organizations confronted by more agile competitors often exhibit this same confusion and disorder. Stalk & Hout [32] observe that the less agile competitor often fails to understand the nature of the attack or even that one is taking place.

Consider the case of an aspiring karate enthusiast who, although working hard and doing all the right exercises, is so befuddled that he or she cannot ever quite decide in time what to do next. Our warrior may have all the physical equipment for agility, and be as fast and limber as any black belt, but the result is predictable: getting the stuffing beat out of him or her on a regular basis. In just this way, a focus on agile manufacturing misses the point. Your production processes may be agile in any sense you like, but if your enterprise is not creating products and services that customers want to buy, more than they want to buy those of the competition, you will soon be stockpiling inventory quicker and more efficiently than anybody else, If you are truly into Just-in-Time, you'll soon build nothing at all. Some agility.

Recall back to our opening discussion that military strategists designed their concept of agility, with its emphasis on observation and orientation, to avoid exactly this sort of problem. Why not take advantage of 25 centuries of success? So perhaps there is a useful concept of an agile manufacturer, something like:

A lean producer that has extended the concept to improve its ability to function as an open system (observe), change its worldview accordingly (orient), and make timely and effective decisions.

Or, put another way,

An agile manufacturer is an agile organization in the competitive, OODA loop sense, who also happens to be a manufacturer.

Similarly, we should broaden the idea of waste beyond its internal sense of cost to anything that interferes with

OODA loops, which, for manufacturers, implies providing value, as the customer and only the customer determines it, more quickly than the competition.

Epilogue

Which brings us back to Sun Tzu. He insisted in our opening quote that one does not guarantee victory through brute strength. So what did he like? The answer is agility, of course, as in the following quote [33] (to which I have made only one slight change, from military force to competitive manufacturer):

The condition of a competitive manufacturer is that its essential factor is speed, taking advantage of others' failure to catch up, going by routes they do not expect, attacking where they are not on guard.

References

1. Bartholomew, D., and B. Caldwell. "New Priorities." *Informationweek* (March 20, 1995): 14-15.
2. Boyd, J. R. *A Discourse on Winning and Losing.* Unpublished briefing, various editions 1976-1986.
3, Byrne, J. A., R. Brandt, and O. Port. "The Virtual Corporation." *Business Week* (February 8, 1993): 37ff.
4. Davidow, W. H., and M. S. Malone. *The Virtual Corporation: Structuring and Revitalizing the Corporation for the 21st Century.* New York: Harper Business, 1993.
5. Davis, D. "The Age of Decentralization?" *Manufacturing Systems* (January 1995): 6.
6. Deleersnyder, J.-L., et at. "Kanban Controlled Pull Systems: An Analytic Approach," *Management Science* 35, no. 9 (September 1989): 1079-1091.
7. Fraser, D. *Knight's Cross, A Life of Field Marshal Erwin Rommel.* London: Harper Collins, 1993.
8, Goldman, S. L., R. N. Nagel, and K. Preiss. *Agile Competitors and Virtual Organizations: Strategies for Enriching the Customer.* New York: Van Nostrand Reinhold, 1994,
9. Hammer, M. "Reengineering Work: Don't Automate, Obliterate." *Harvard Business Review* (July-August 1990): 104-112.
10.——, and J. Champy. *Reengineering the Corporation.* New York: Harper Collins, 1993,
11. "The Kindergarten that Will Change the World." *The Economist* (March 4, 1995): 63-64,
12.Krafcek, J. "Triumph of the Lean Production System." *Sloan Management Review* (Fall 1988): 41-52.
13.Lengyel, A. "New Thinking in Manufacturing for the 21st Century." *Proceedings of the 1994 Aerospace and Defense Symposium,* APICS (June 1994): 1-8.
14.Meadows, R. A., L. P. Beckerman, and C. W. Richards, "Systems Engineering for TQM." *Journal of Defense Systems Management College* (January/February 1990): 3-6.
15.Meyer, C. *Fast Cycle Time,* New York: The Free Press, 1993.
16.Miller, G. "Reengineering the Business System." *Proceedings of the 1994 Aerospace and Defence Symposium,* APICS (June 1994): 63-69.
17.Monden, Y, *Toyota Production System.* Norcross, GA: Institute of Industrial Engineers, 1993.
18.Moore, D. E., Jr. "Bosnia, Tanks, and 'From the Sea,'" *Proceedings of the U.S. Naval Institute* (December 1994): 42-45.
19.Musastii, M. *The Book of Five Rings.* Translated by Thomas Cleary, Boston: Shambhala, 1993.
20.——. *The Book of Five Rings.* Translated by Nihon Services Corp. New York: Bantam, 1982.
21.Ohno, T. *Toyota Production System.* Translated by Productivity Press. Portland, OR: Productivity Press, *1988.*
22.Peters, T. *Crazy Times Call for Crazy Organizations.* New York: Vintage, 1994.
23.——. "Garbage Gathering, OODA Loops, Control Conundrums, and Other Management Tools it the '90s," Palo Alto, CA: *Tom Peters Group, undated.*
24.——. *Liberation Management.* New York: Knopf, 1992.
25.Reich, R. B, *The Work of Nations.* New York: Vintage, 1992.
26.Richards, C. W. "Riding the Tiger: What You Really Do With OODA Loops." *Handbook of Business Strategy 1995.* New York: Faulkner & Cray, 1994.
27.Romm, J. J. *Lean and Clean Management.* New York: Kodansha International, 1994.
28.Rommel, E. *Attacks.* Translated by J. R. Driscoll. Provo, UT: Athena, Press, 1979.
29.Schmenner, R. W. "The Merit of Making Things Fast." *Sloan Management Review* (Fall 1988): 11-18.
30.Schonberger, R. J. *World Class Manufacturing.* New York: The Free Press, 1986.
31.Sheridan, J. S. "Agile Manufacturing: Stepping Beyond Lean Production." *Industry Week* (April 19, 1993): 30ff.
32.Stalk, G., and T. Hout. *Competing Against Time.* New York: The Free Press, 1990.
33.Sun Tzu, *The Art of* War. Translated by Thomas Cleary. Boston: Shambhala, 1988.
34.United States Amy. *Operations.* Field Manual 100-5. Washington, D.C.: GPO, 1993.
35.Upton, D. M. "What Really Makes Factories Flexible?" *Harvard Business Review* (July-August 1995): 74-86.
36.Womack, J. P., D. T. Jones, and D. Roos. *The Machine That Changed the World.* New York: Harper Collins, 1991.

About the Author

Chester W. Richards, Ph.D., is a business strategist at Lockheed Martin Aeronautical Systems, Marietta, Georgia. He has also built computer war-game simulations for the Office of the Secretary of Defense, the Royal Saudi Air Force, and Northrop, and led one of Lockheed's earliest successful reengineering efforts. He holds a Ph.D. in mathematics from the University of Mississippi.

Reprinted from the Production and Inventory Management Journal, *Fourth Quarter, 2000.*

Aligning Competitive Strategies, Manufacturing Technology, and Shop Floor Skills

Dean M. Schroeder, Ph.D., and Steven W. Congden, Ph.D.

Much has been written about using advanced manufacturing technologies for competitive advantage, but even as we become more dependent on these technologies, more questions remain than have been answered. For example, alignment of strategy with technology is said to be very important. But should technology be adopted to support strategy as is most often argued, or might it make more sense to adjust strategy to the technology in use [3, 4]? Also, although the key advantage of computer-controlled machines is said to be flexibility, many firms fail to use the technology for that purpose [1]. Worse yet, firms specifically combining these technologies with flexible product strategies, in many instances show no improvement in their performance [1]. Could having the appropriate complementary technologies be the key to success [5], or is combining technology with proper skill levels a more important issue? If so, will "smart" machines require "smart" workers [2, 7, 9], or will smart machines replace the need for smart workers [8]? Is it the technology that dictates the skills needed, or can management choose the skills needed to support the company's competitive strategy?

This article focuses on those questions by examining the alignment of competitive strategies, production technologies, and shop floor worker skills. It draws on the results of an extensive two-part research project involving in-depth studies of 20 small- to medium-sized manufacturers and survey results from 399 additional similar manufacturers. The findings provide insights for managers on matching skills and technologies with strategic requirements.

Research Methods

Our study focuses on contract manufacturers in the metal machining industry. This industry was selected because its highly competitive environment intensifies the importance of a firm's strategy/technology/skills alignment. Furthermore, the large number of firms within the industry allows for a good sample size, and the modest size of the firms helps to keep the data "cleaner" and to make the linkages between measures more evident.

The sample of 20 firms studied in depth was selected to include successful and less successful firms, and firms with varying mixes of conventional and advanced technologies. Extensive interviews conducted by two researchers (both with experience in manufacturing industries), plant tours, questionnaires, and the evaluation of secondary documents were used to gather data.

Firms for the large sample survey were selected from among members of the National Tooling and Machining Association. After firms that were either too small (fewer than 15 employees) or that did not fit the desired profile were eliminated from the list, detailed questionnaires were mailed to 1,577 firms. Forty-three percent (679) responded, an exceptionally good response rate for this type of research. Initial analysis reduced our sample to 399 firms by eliminating companies that derived less than 80% of their sales from metal-cutting activities. This step was taken to ensure a comparable sample.

The questionnaire was carefully developed to capture the actual strategies followed by firms in the industry so that identified strategies would not have to be force-fit into preconceived generic categories. The survey included 29 strategy measures that had been identified as critical, both in theory and by previous studies, and that were subsequently verified by a panel of industry experts as being used in practice. Principal factor analysis was used to analyze responses to the 29 measures, and eight underlying core strategic dimensions were identified. The eight dimensions were then cluster analyzed using Ward's method into six discrete and identifiable strategies. The steps followed and the various dimensions identified are illustrated in **figure 1**. Our panel of industry experts reviewed the resulting strategies, which are described in **table 1**, and verified that they represent the different competitive profiles of firms within the industry.

Sixteen technology measures were also identified through theory and practice. A principal factor analysis of the responses to these measures identified four technology dimensions that provided good theoretical and practical interpretation. Here again, the process is illustrated in figure 1 and the descriptions of the technology dimensions provided in table 1. Skill measures were more directly interpretable. Sixteen measures were used to identify the levels of training, experience, and skills breadth.

Findings

The qualitative data were used to build case profiles for each company; they focused on strategy, technology, and human and related elements. Open coding techniques were employed to identify key measures. High inter-rater reliability measures indicated consistent measure coding accuracy. These measures were then plotted in matrices to identify key patterns and themes. The results were reconfirmed directly with the original data from each firm.

The quantitative data were subjected to a variety of rigorous statistical techniques, including correlation analysis, moderated regression, and a variety of significance tests. The findings from the large sample were compared with those of the case studies for verification and interpretation. In this way, the cases provided a rich understanding, and the large sample helped to ensure more rigorous

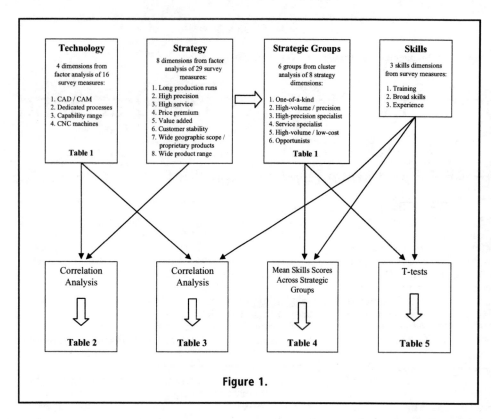

Figure 1.

Finding 2: A Specific Technology Can Support Different Strategies Depending on How It Is Used and Integrated

Although it seems to contradict our first finding, the same advanced manufacturing equipment can support more than one strategy. This finding proved true in both the case studies and the large sample. For example, identical models of a specific Japanese manufacturer's CNC machining centers were successfully used in two shops that had very different strategies. The first company used the technology to provide an advantage in long production runs of components for standard commercial products. The advantage was in low labor costs and rapid production cycles. The second company produced extremely precise jet fighter components for the defense industry. Here technology provided its advantage; it allowed the company to hold tolerances at half the already tight specifications, and thus pass the performance test much easier than its competitors, and it automatically captured process data for quality assurance tracking.

The large sample study reinforced that finding. Perhaps the best way to demonstrate how an advanced manufacturing technology can support more than one strategy is to look at how technology aligns with the core strategic dimensions that underlay the various strategies. **Table 2** shows the same technology aligning with several strategic dimensions. For example, the use of CNC equipment supported both long production runs and high-precision strategic dimensions. Computer aided design (CAD) supported high precision, value added, proprietary products, and wide product variety.

Two elements explain this seeming contradiction to the first finding. First, today's smart manufacturing equipment can be highly flexible with multiple capabilities. As a manager in one of our firms stated: "The Japanese [manufacturer] put bells and whistles on this equipment [a CNC machining center] that we never ring or blow.... We use maybe ten or fifteen percent of the machine's capabilities." A firm with a different strategy may use a different 10% or 15%. Consequently, the way a specific piece of equipment is used can produce different advantages.

Second, no single piece of production equipment operates in isolation—it is part of a system involving a blend of technologies. Although different strategies often use the same specific technology, how various technologies are "bundled" differs between firms with different strategies. Here again, we can observe in table 2 that both long production runs and high precision use CNC machining—but long production runs complement CNC technology with more dedicated automation technology, whereas high precision complements CNC technology with CAD and technologies with a wider range of capabilities.

and widely applicable results. Selected results of both are integrated into the following five findings.

Finding 1: Aligning Technology and Strategy Is Critical

Both the case studies and the large sample analyses show the importance of aligning production technologies with the competitive strategy. Case studies revealed that firms with strategies involving long production runs and/or a focus on very high precision work tended to perform better when CNC (computer numerically controlled) equipment was used. Firms following the same strategies, but without this technology, did not perform as well. Likewise, firms using the same type of equipment with strategies involving shorter production runs and without high-precision requirements did not perform as well. In several of these latter cases, firms invested heavily in expensive advanced technology equipment only to find that the new equipment provided little competitive advantage. In one case the equipment was sold. In two other cases the companies attempted to change their strategies to utilize the new technology's potential advantages.

The large sample survey reinforced the finding that a close strategy-technology alignment is needed. A moderated regression model including strategies, technologies, and profitability found that companies with different competitive strategies reported significantly different technology profiles. Furthermore, the tighter the alignment between the firm's strategy and technology, the better the firm performed financially. A tight strategy-technology alignment explained a higher percentage of profitability differences between firms than did the direct effects of strategy and technology combined. Stated differently, a good alignment between a firm's strategy and technology is more important to its profits than the choice of competitive strategy and technology taken separately.

process controls, and state-of-the-art quality-testing technologies and procedures.

Finding 3: Skills on the Shop Floor Must Align with the Strategy—Not Just the Technology

Do computerized technologies on the shop floor displace the need for skills, or do they require enhanced skills? We observed both situations in the case studies. One shop in the study employed very highly skilled and highly paid expert machinists, while another using a similar machining center employed a workforce that was largely unskilled and earning relatively low wages. The survey results from the large sample explain the reason for this seeming contradiction. **Table 3** correlates the four technology categories with training, broad skills, and worker experience. Whereas CAD is significantly correlated with higher skill levels, CNC equipment technology is correlated with lower skill levels. Although this is intuitively reasonable, it does not explain how the same technology can require different skill levels in different situations. This is where competitive strategy comes into play. Firms following different strategies employ workers with significantly different levels of skills (see **table 4**). Those with one-of-a-kind and high-precision strategies employed much more highly skilled machinists than did firms following high-volume-related strategies. Consistent with this behavior, companies with strategies involving high volume (high volume/precision, and high volume/low cost) also tended to use technology to replace worker skills, while firms following one-of-a-kind, high precision specialist, and high service specialist strategies do not (see **table 5**). In summary, strategies involving highly repetitive actions can replace human skills with computerized equipment. However, strategies requiring more flexibility and judgment will continue to require greater human skills. These differences hold even when the same computerized technologies are used. A firm's strategy along with its technology, not the technology alone, determines the skills required for success.

Finding 4: Timing the Acquisition of New Technology Is Critical

Technology is a moving target. As a technology develops it becomes less expensive, easier to use, and more capable and the supporting technologies that make it more effective are developed. We found that an emerging technology that made no sense for a company at one point in time was required a few years later. Companies that adopted too early found themselves investing excessive time and resources in an effort to make the technology work effectively within their operation. As one manager said about his experiences with early adoption: "You can always tell the pioneers (early adopters of technology); they're the one's with arrows in their backs!" Another shop owner reported that he would never adopt early again. When purchasing a new piece of sophisticated computer controlled equipment, his people, with some help from the supplier, were required to invest a great deal of development effort. The manager was quite upset to later discover the supplier selling the same equipment to competitors, along with the upgrades largely developed by his people.

Adopting too early can cause problems, but adopting too late or not adopting at all can be devastating. One manager/owner who said he could not understand how his competitors could afford the latest technology was waiting for the related high overhead to drive them out of business. He had "run the numbers" on upgrading and

---

TABLE 1: Strategic Groups and Technology Dimensions

Strategic Groups Descriptions

One-of-a-kind
 Machine shops with this strategy have stable customers, but a wide variety of low-volume, unique work. They tend to provide value-added services, particularly in design work. They are primarily die and mold makers.

High-volume/precision
 Machine shops with this strategy focus on the very highest batch sizes and repeat orders. Their customer base is fairly stable (often government defense work), precision is very high, but price competition is intense. Firms in this group are generally larger and are very efficient.

High-precision specialist
 Machine shops with this strategy typically produce smaller batch sizes of high-precision work—often prototypes—and provide significant value added from assembly. They also have low customer stability.

Service specialist
 Machine shops with this strategy provide very high levels of service with average product stability. This includes very short lead times, dependable deliveries (often on a Just-in-Time basis), and verifiable quality assurance (ship-to-stock). They accommodate fluctuations in orders and command significant price premiums.

High-volume/low-cost
 Machine shops with this strategy have moderately large and repeatable batches of relatively low-precision work. Low cost is the primary focus. No value-added services are offered. Their product stability is average.

Opportunist
 Machine shops with this strategy tend to focus on very local markets, offer value-added assembly, and produce low-precision work. They tend to have low customer stability. The primary element separating them from the high-precision strategy is their low precision and local focus.

Technology Dimensions

CAD/CAM
 This technology group may include stand-alone computer aided design (CAD), integrated CAD/CAM (computer-aided manufacturing), and direct numeric control network (DNC).

Dedicated processes
 This technology group may include dedicated material handling, automatic parts changing, product-specific machine layouts, secondary capabilities, custom machine tools, and multispindle machine tools.

Capability range
 This technology group may include machine tools with extra capabilities, a broad size range of capabilities, and multiaxis machine tools.

CNC machines
 This technology group may include computer numerical control (CNC) machine tools, automatic tool changers on CNC, and CNC code programming computers.

In addition to showing that technologies were bundled to support a strategy, the in-depth case studies showed that organizational structures, production procedures, and information systems were customized to support specific strategies. For example, one firm whose strategy involved competing with low costs on medium to long production runs of fairly standard commercial products had an exceptional cost accounting system, but a minimal support staff and relatively low-skilled machine operators. Another firm using the same technology to support a strategy involving complexity, high-precision, small-lot aerospace components had extensive support, testing, and information systems. The company employed highly skilled machinists, a large support staff, rigorous

TABLE 2:   Correlation of Strategy and Technology Dimensions

	CAD/CAM	Dedicated Automation	Capability Range	CNC Machines
Long production runs	−	+		+
High precision	+		+	+
High service				
Price premium				
Value added	+	+	+	
Customer stability		−	−	
Wide geographic scope/ proprietary products	+	+		−
Wide product range	+	−	+	

+ Positively correlated at or better than a 95% confidence level
− Negatively correlated at or better than a 95% confidence level

determined that purchasing used equipment cast off by other shops was the best value. At the same time, he kept complaining about how the margins in his business were constantly tightening and that he no longer made a profit every year. Not long after we interviewed this manager, his business was closed.

Careful timing of the adoption of new equipment can provide a competitive advantage—but it is usually short lived. Managers reported that purchasing new technology equipment provided advantages in cost, precision, capabilities, and cycle time reduction that customers quickly began to expect. As one manager said, "Because of competition, customers are the only real long-term beneficiaries of our adopting new technology." We did find one case, a tool and die shop doing very sophisticated work, where a sustainable advantage from new technology was observed. This company had extremely creative and capable people and followed a technology strategy that provided a sustained advantage through creating ongoing short-term advantages by constantly upgrading its technologies and pushing down the learning curve to exploit advantages rapidly. For example, on one bid the company was able to bid 20% lower than its nearest competitor. The customer, concerned about creating problems for a valued supplier, shared this information and asked if the company wanted to rebid the contract. Rather than increasing the bid as expected, the company actually lowered it by another 2%, and still made a higher than normal profit margin on the job. The company was able to do so because it was applying technologies its competitors lacked.

Finding 5: In the Alignment Process, Technology Follows Strategy, and Strategy Follows Technology, but Skills Follow Both

Should new technology be purchased to support an existing strategy, or should strategy be adjusted to exploit a new technology? While examples of both were observed, a mutual alignment process involving incremental adjustments in both was most common. Often the new technology made new strategies possible, but employee skills—even those of managers—required adjustments along the way.

One firm provides a good example of technology following strategy. The company sold the tooling portion of its business and shifted its strategy to focus on contract machined parts. After consistently losing competitive bids by as much as 20%, management discovered that competitors were using more advanced computerized technologies. Once similar equipment was acquired, the company found its highly skilled workers, who were needed for the specialized tooling area they recently left, were overpaid, overskilled, and underchallenged by the new work. The company outplaced these workers into companies that were thrilled to have their skills. The company began hiring less skilled people and training them to operate the new CNC equipment. Soon the company was again very competitive and growing.

A specialty metal cutting tool manufacturer in our study illustrates a case of strategy following technology. The company purchased an expensive German computerized grinding system to replace 16 conventional surface grinders. After a number of technical problems in

TABLE 3:   Correlation of Skills and Technology Dimensions

	CAD/CAM	Dedicated Automation	Capability Range	CNC Machines
Training	+	−	+ +	− −
Broad skills	+ +		+ +	−
Experience	+ +	−	+ +	− −

+ + Positively correlated at or better than a 99% confidence level
 + Positively correlated at or better than a 95% confidence level
− − Negatively correlated at or better than a 99% confidence level
 − Negatively correlated at or better than a 95% confidence level

©2001 APICS—The Educational Society for Resource Management

TABLE 4: Standardized Skill Means by Strategies

(Mean = 0)							Significance of difference between groups
	Strategic Group						
Skill Dimension	One-of-a-Kind	High-Volume/ Precision	High-Precision Specialist	Service Specialist	High-Volume Low-Cost	Opportunist	% Confidence Level
Training	.345	−.148	.207	.069	−.461	.095	99.9
Broad skills	.247	−.370	.083	.155	−.162	.041	95.0
Experience	.349	−.232	.175	−.039	−.420	.272	99.9

Data are standardized to clearly identify relative skill level differences between firms following different strategies.
Standardized data express all results in terms of the number of standard deviations away from a sample mean value of zero.

getting the technology operating, some personnel adjustments were required. Management initially assigned the most experienced and skilled machinist to the new equipment, but had to replace him with a worker who could learn and adapt more quickly. The result was that one machinist operating the computerized grinder two hours per day replaced four machinists operating 16 machines (4 each) eight hours per day. But this was only the beginning of the alignment process. As impressive as that improvement was, the real advantage gained from using the technology turned out to be in other changes throughout the firm. The new technology eliminated the need for several preceding operations, required one less heat treatment, facilitated an 80% cut in work-in-process inventory, and helped to reduce total product production cycle time from 16 weeks to 4. Those changes, along with the flexibility of the new technology, allowed the company to significantly change its strategy and move into higher-margin customized cutting tools. The biggest challenge, as reported by the plant manager, was to "unlearn everything I knew about making tools and learn entirely new rules." In this way, strategy changes followed technology changes. Changes in people skills—including management knowledge and thinking—proved critical.

Lessons for Production Managers

What do those results teach us? This section addresses four lessons derived from the research that we believe are important to production managers.

Lesson 1: Align the System—Not Just Strategy and Technology

Clearly, it is vital to ensure that the production technology used is able to deliver what the company's competitive strategy needs to succeed. But a specific piece of technology (equipment) is only one part of a larger technology system including other equipment and technologies—all of which must be aligned. More important, people's skills and other subsystems and processes must also be aligned with the technology. Doing so does not always require having the most highly skilled people, rather it requires having people with the most appropriate skill sets. The firm's competitive strategy must also be considered. Matching skills with technology alone is misguided. The same technology can be used to support several distinct strategies, but the way the technology is staffed, bundled with additional technologies, and supported by other operating systems and procedures provides the real competitive advantage. Misalignment anywhere in the system is costly! This point leads to our second lesson.

TABLE 5: Skills Impact of Computerized Technology by Strategic Group

	Strategic Group					
Skill Dimension	One-of-a-Kind	High-Volume/ Precision	High-Precision Specialist	Service Specialist	High-Volume/ Low-Cost	Opportunist
Training, Conventional	5.72	*5.35!*	5.64	5.33	*5.11**	*5.68**
Training, Computerized	5.71	*4.96*	5.63	5.24	*4.55*	*5.07*
Broad Skills, Conventional	5.11	4.07	*4.86!*	4.89	4.52	4.45
Broad Skills, Computerized	4.74	4.00	*4.21*	4.60	4.18	4.44
Experience, Conventional	5.69	*5.39**	5.43	5.42	*5.23***	5.64
Experience, Computerized	5.55	*4.67*	5.50	5.12	*4.69*	5.37

Mean scores of each skill measure for each strategic group are on a 7-point scale with 7 being the highest skill level.
Significant differences between conventional technology and computerized technology within strategic groups are indicated in italicized, bold numbers.
Significance levels are as follows: ! = > 90%, * = > 95%, ** = > 99%
Overall, across groups differences were significant for all three skill dimensions.

Lesson 2: Focus the System—Don't Try to Do Everything the Technology Can Do

We found that computerized production technologies were highly flexible and provided a wide variety of advantages. However companies should not try to use the equipment to pursue too wide a range of those advantages. Because a specific technology is a single part of a larger system, care must be taken to use the technology in support of the entire system. Focus is critical. Only those capabilities that are aligned with the rest of the system should be exploited.

Choosing a focus is often a balancing act. New technologies offer new capabilities and new strategic options. A company should exploit those capabilities that make strategic sense and that can be supported by the entire system. To do so often means making incremental changes and adjustments throughout the organization. This point, along with the changing nature of technology, leads to our third lesson.

Lesson 3: New Technology Is a Moving Target—Plan and Time Your Moves

Along with death and taxes, changing technology is a certainty today. We found that when new technology equipment should be adopted may be a more important decision than if it should be adopted. Timing the acquisition of new technology depends on a number of things: (1) the extent of the competitive advantage provided, (2) level of development of the technology, (3) ability of the company to deal with the challenges and uncertainty of early adoption, (4) fit with the company's current systems and competitive strategy, and (5) competitive pressure to adopt. Overall, hitting the moving target of new technology involves careful planning, monitoring, and preparatory adjustments. Appropriate emerging technologies should be identified, and their development carefully monitored well in advance of adoption. Trade shows, industry journals, and technology suppliers can facilitate this process. As a technology begins to hold promise for your operation, monitoring may include benchmarking visits to users and preparatory steps to begin realigning your skills and systems to accept the new technology. Once the new technology is acquired, lesson 4 becomes important.

Lesson 4: Learning Is Vital—The Ability to Learn Rapidly Is the Only Sustainable Competitive Advantage

Learning, organizationwide, is an important part of adapting to any newly acquired technology (see Schroeder and Congden [6] for a more complete discussion of technology and organizational learning). Realigning the entire organization to fully exploit the capabilities of a new technology is critical. It is part of a continuous improvement process that includes an ongoing planned effort involving upgrading technologies, modifying competitive strategies to exploit advantages offered by the new technologies, developing the required human skills, and constantly adjusting systems and procedures to ensure alignment. A company's ability to learn faster than its competitors has become the only sustainable competitive advantage it can develop.

References

1. Dean, J.W., and S. Snell. "The Strategic Use of Integrated Manufacturing: An Empirical Examination." *Strategic Management Journal* 17 (1996): 459-480.
2. Haskel, J., and Y. Heden. "Computers and the demand for skilled labour: Industry- and establishment-level panel evidence for the U.K." *The Economic Journal* 109, no. 454 (1999): C68-C79.
3. Hayes, R.H. "Strategic Planning: Forward in Reverse." *Harvard Business Review* 63, no. 6 (1985): 111-119.
4. Parthasarthy, R., and S.P. Sethi. "The Impact of Flexible Automation on Business Strategy and Organizational Structure." *Academy of Management Review* 17, no. 1 (1992): 86-1111.
5. Schroeder, D., S. Congden, and C. Gopinath. "Linking Competitive Strategy and Manufacturing Process Technology." *Journal of Management Studies* 32, no. 2 (1995): 163-189.
6. Schroeder, D., and S. Congden, "Integrating Manufacturing Innovation Through Organizational Learning." *Production and Inventory Management Journal* 36, no. 3, (1995): 55-60.
7. Siegal, D.S., D.A. Waldman, and W.E. Youngdahl. "The Adoption of Advanced Manufacturing Technologies: Human Resource Management Implications." *IEEE Transactions on Engineering Management* 44, no. 3 (1997) 288-298.
8. Shaiken, H. *Work Transformed*. New York: Holt, Rhinehart & Winston, 1984.
9. Zuboff, S. *In the Age of the Smart Machine*. New York: Basic Books, 1988.

About the Authors

Dean M. Schroeder, Ph.D., is currently the Herbert and Agnes Schulz Professor of Management at Valparaiso University where he teaches strategic management, the management of technology and change, and high-performing organizations. Dr. Schroeder holds a mechanical/industrial engineering degree from the University of Minnesota and an MBA from the University of Montana. Before receiving his Ph.D. in strategic management from the University of Minnesota, Dr. Schroeder managed several different plants and was president of his own firm. He has served for five years on the Board of Examiners of the Malcolm Baldrige National Quality Award, has written more than 50 articles and papers, and is an experienced consultant with clients in North America, Europe, and Latin America.

Steven W. Congden, Ph.D., holds a BS in chemical engineering and an MBA from Clarkson University. After six years of operations experience in the petrochemical industry in Houston, Texas, he received a Ph.D. in strategic management from the University of Massachusetts. His research interests focus on the strategic uses of technology and the effects of technological change. He has published in journals such as the Journal of Management Studies, Production and Inventory Management Journal, and the Journal of Small Business Management. Dr. Congden currently teaches strategic management and technology and innovation management at the University of Hartford.

Reprinted from the 1992 APICS International Conference Proceedings.

Managing Technology to Improve Customer Response

David R. Schuchts, CFPIM

The objective of this presentation is to show how we can respond quickly and well to our customers' requirements by managing technology effectively. We will examine two very profitable applications of technology, EDI (Electronic Data Interchange) and bar coding. EDI and bar coding are enabling manufacturers and distributors to react quickly to changing sales demand, and to manage material flow efficiently throughout the supply chain. Thus they can respond effectively to their customers' needs.

EDI communicates vital information quickly and accurately throughout the supply chain. Bar codes speed the flow of goods through the chain, greatly reducing errors and handling time. We will follow the information chain (via EDI) from the retail point of sale through the supply pipeline and back. We will also trace the physical flow through the pipeline (with bar codes used to control the flow) from the raw material supplier, through several manufacturing and distribution levels, to the consumer.

What Is EDI?

Electronic Data Interchange is the process of transmitting data, computer-to-computer, from one location to another, in some mutually agreed and understood format. It implies the use of a standard format (the ANSI X.12 U.S. standard, the EDIFACT world-wide standard, the UCS format used by the grocery industry, the TDCC standard for transportation, or one of several other industry-specific EDI standards) and usually involves the transmission of specifically defined business documents (Purchase Orders, Invoices, Shipping Notices, Sales Activity Summaries, Inventory Advices, etc.). EDI is also sometimes referred to as Electronic Document Interchange. However, in its broadest sense, EDI includes transmission of data between or within organizations, from one location to another. It is used to inform others quickly of an important event and to provide data in computer-processable form that can be used to act at once upon the information.

For purposes of this presentation, EDI will denote the exchange of information between a pair of companies doing business with each other (in a supplier/customer "trading partnership" relationship). Our focus will be on rapid communication of key business information between a company and its suppliers and customers, often using a third-party "mail box" service as intermediary.

Why Use EDI?

Many companies begin using EDI because their customers demand it. Others perceive that they can save clerical costs of paper handling and re-transcription by feeding the EDI data into their systems. Most companies eventually recognize that EDI can greatly improve their responsiveness to their customers if they use it well, and that it can help to increase their sales. But EDI can only become fully effective when integrated into the business, and effectively managed. This is the essence of the "Quick Response" movement.

Using EDI to send orders at electronic speed to a supplier can cut several days from the mailing time. But faxing these orders can accomplish nearly the same thing unless the EDI data is used in the supplier's integrated computer systems for fast processing and quick response to the order. Likewise, simply sending the customer's invoice data via EDI is of little use unless the customer uses the information for efficient processing and to eliminate redundant clerical handling. Full integration of the information flow between the customer's systems and supplier's systems is what provides the payoff. And we're not just talking about *computer* systems here, although they are involved. Quick Response requires the integration of EDI, bar coding and other cost-effective technologies and techniques into a company's organization, often changing the company's mode of operation in a fundamental way.

The "trading partnership" between a customer and supplier is consummated by the linkage of key elements of

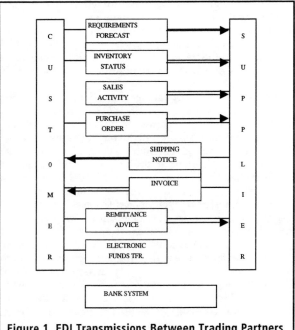

Figure 1. EDI Transmissions Between Trading Partners

their businesses. EDI is the basic communication medium for this linkage. **Figure 1** shows a typical set of EDI transactions between the two. The first step may be the customer's transmission of its Inventory Status and a Sales Forecast to a key supplier, followed by data on Sales as they occur. Thus the supplier can plan inventories to support the customer's projected requirements. A Purchase Order would follow as the customer decides to replenish the inventories (or the supplier could initiate a Recommended Order if they have agreed to this approach). A Shipping Notice from the supplier details the items shipped so the customer can plan receiving schedules and can process the receipts quickly and accurately (reconciling orders to receipts and eliminating clerical time and inaccuracies). An Invoice from the supplier could be quickly processed against the prior-reconciled documents, triggering a Remittance Advice to the supplier, and an Electronic Funds Transfer from customer's to supplier's bank. Paperwork in this kind of environment is greatly reduced, along with the time, cost, and inaccuracies of handling and filing it. Often more importantly, both of the companies gain from the clear, unambiguous, and fast communication of vital information between and within their organizations. It's a definite Win/Win situation.

What Is Bar Coding? Why Use It?

Bar codes have been used for years to mark items with a machine-readable identification to track movement, record inventories, or just recognize a particular item from among others. Railroad cars, animals, vehicles, and other objects have been marked with a variety of bar code schemes using alternating dark and light stripes. The marked objects are then "read" by scanning across the bar patterns, decoding the bar code, and storing, processing or printing the results.

Bar codes are used by many manufacturers to record the receipt of materials, record usage and production, track in-process material movement, post finished goods production, and control their shipment to the proper customers. A number of bar code patterns are used for these purposes, including Code 3 of 9, Interleaved 2 of 5, and Code 128. Industry groups have standardized the use of one or another of these codes on items moving between customers and their suppliers, making the bar codes more effective. Recent cooperative efforts by major retailers, their suppliers and the transportation companies serving them, have made Code 128 the most popular choice for marking shipments of goods.

Once the goods arrive at the retailer, with shipping-container labels bar coded to identify their contents (even more effective when used in conjunction with an EDI Advance Shipping Notice transaction), the bar codes speed receiving, put-away, subsequent invoice-reconciliation processes and posting of the items to the inventory. UPC (Universal Product Code) bar codes on each item are then scanned at the point of sale to record item sales transactions, price the transaction, and post inventory reductions. The retailer can use the point-of-sale data to determine timing and quantity of inventory replenishment (sending a Purchase Order to the supplier) or can send the raw sales data directly to a supplier for his use in determining replenishment timing. The result, once again, is a reduction in paperwork and in the time, cost and inaccuracies of handling the materials moving through the supply chain—another Win/Win situation, especially when EDI and bar codes are employed together in a well-integrated system that serves all parties well.

1. Improve responsiveness to the consumers' demands: move information and materials through the supply chain as fast and as efficiently as possible, to meet the demands of the consumer while achieving profit objectives.

2. Develop mutually beneficial, value-added trading partnerships throughout the supply chain as the primary means to improving the effectiveness of the chain.

3. Improve the processes employed by each of the trading partners in the chain to raise quality levels, reduce waste, reduce costs, and provide for maximum flexibility with efficiency and cost-effectiveness.

4. Induce internal changes at all levels of the supply chain, linking technology with business functions and procedures and integrating the QR philosophy into all business functions (manufacturing, sales, finance, administration and clerical, etc.)

Table 1. Quick Response Objectives

The Quick Response Movement

The Quick Response (QR) movement developed out of the efforts of a number of major retailers and their key suppliers who recognized the need and the advantages of working together much more cooperatively. Their initial efforts were aimed at improving the interchange of vital information to reduce costly, redundant steps in the handling of materials through the supply chain and speed replenishment of the goods sold. These efforts resulted in the formation of the Voluntary Inter-industry Communications Standards organization (VICS) to identify and encourage the use of the strategic technologies required to support Quick Response. Two foundational technologies were singled out bar coding (extended beyond its use in capturing Point-of-Sale data, to help control flow of merchandise and materials throughout the pipeline), and EDI (as the mechanism for rapid, accurate information exchange).

Four annual Quick Response conferences have served to solidify and expand the movement. QR practitioners now agree that EDI and bar coding are just tools to be used to accomplish the real objectives (see **Table 1**). You will note a great similarity between the QR and JIT concepts and objectives. The Just-in-Time philosophy was one of the cornerstones of the QR movement, and its principles continue to influence the development.

The Quick Response movement takes the ideal of Business Trading Partnerships (from JIT) and extends it in several ways. The use of standardized EDI and bar coding as basic communications and movement-control media is an important cement for the Trading Partnerships.

Managing Technology, Profitably

Why the big deal about managing technology? Why is it any different from management of people and operations? The fundamental difference is in the ever-accelerating pace of technology-based change today. We are in a state of perpetual change. Our understanding of change and

©2001 APICS—The Educational Society for Resource Management

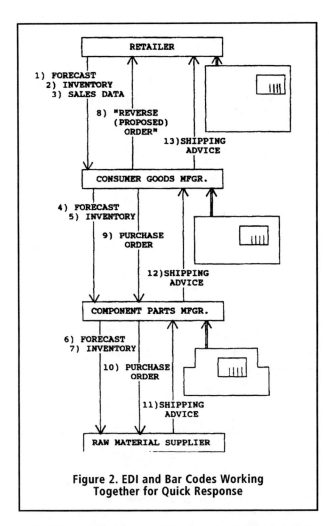

Figure 2. EDI and Bar Codes Working Together for Quick Response

Putting It All Together

Figure 2 illustrates the combined use of EDI and bar codes to move materials quickly through the supplier pipeline so that they will be on the shelf, available for the consumer to buy. By exchanging key information about plans and status, trading partners at all stages of the supply chain keep each other well informed. Thus the entire chain is prepared to respond quickly to consumer demand. Forecasts, inventory status, and sales activity data are passed along from one level to the next quickly and accurately via EDI.

The consumer goods manufacturer (per a prior agreement with the retailer) recognizes the need to replenish the retailer's stock of an item, and transmits an EDI "Reverse Order" (P.O. "Acknowledgment"), issues a Purchase Order to its parts supplier, and so forth along the chain. Each of the suppliers should be ready to ship their order quickly, apply a bar coded shipping label to each container shipped, and transmit an EDI Shipping Notice detailing the contents of each container. Thus Quick Response becomes an effective reality.

Conclusion

EDI and bar coding cut miscommunication and time from the replenishment process—shifting demand patterns are recognized early; suppliers can take action quickly to meet the change cost-effectively. This application of an appropriate set of technologies plays a major role in making trading partnerships truly effective, offering each of the partners an opportunity to increase sales and cut costs. Good communication is the key to a good trading partnership.

Managing technology well enables us to take a proactive role to improve our relationships with our customers. We can initiate programs to build mutually beneficial trading partnerships, knowing that we have developed the capability to follow through. We will be ready and able to provide true Quick Response service. True Quick Response is far more than a catchy motto. True Quick Response is delivering the right (quality) product to the right place at the right time, as promised, every time. If you manage technology well, you will greatly improve your response to your customers, very profitably.

About the Author

David R. Schuchts, CFPIM, has 30 years of experience in the field of production and inventory management, ranging from inventory control clerk to educator, consultant and manager. Dave has designed, implemented and used many P&IC systems in diverse industry environments. He is Director of Information Services for the O. Ames Company, manufacturers of lawn, garden and industrial tools since 1974.

Dave is active on the speaking circuit for APICS and other professional associations. He is the Director of Membership Services for APICS Region III, is a Past President and current Board member of the Parkersburg Chapter, and is certified by APICS at the Fellow level. He is also President of the Mid-Ohio Valley Chapter of Software Valley and serves on the Software Valley Corporation Board and Executive Committee.

our ability to integrate rapidly changing technology into our business environment will determine the extent of our success (or failure).

As Larry R. Pugh, CEO of VF Corporation, stated in March of 1991, "We must use our new technology to streamline our day to day operations. Change is essential. What we're talking about here is literally changing the way we are running our businesses. The technology exists to support [this]. What's lacking is a common vision. I envision an entirely new way of sharing and using information to improve the business opportunities for retailers, manufacturers and suppliers." VF's vision set goals of 40% reduction in cycle time, 30% reduction in overall inventories, and 20% reduction in cost.

The key to managing technology effectively, and thus profitably, is to discard the old view that "If it isn't broken, don't fix it!" Daniel Burris, a leading science and technology forecaster, warns "If it works today, it's obsolete, and you'd better have your sights set on what you'll replace it with!" Look for better ways, including new technologies, to take you beyond your present capabilities. EDI is only a stopgap along the path to excellent inter- and intra-company communications. Bar coding is the forerunner of new and better automatic identification methods. Use these two technologies today, with your eyes open for their successors.

Reprinted from the 1996 APICS International Conference Proceedings.

Accounting and the Theory of Constraints
Charlene W. Spoede, Ph.D., CPA, CMA

Until recently, Theory of Constraints proponents have paid far more attention to criticizing cost accounting than to encouraging its adaptation to support TOC decisions. At best, practitioners were told to "forget costs" and to concentrate on throughput. However, no firm can afford to ignore costs. And most of our performance measures reinforce the importance of costs. Fortunately, there is a way that cost accounting can be adapted to generate information that focuses on throughput as well as costs.

This paper will try to reconcile cost accounting and the Theory of Constraints. The first section will review a bit of the history of cost accounting, so that we know how we arrived where we are today and why our traditional cost systems no longer provide the information we need. To validate this section and to clarify your own cost accounting beliefs, you should take the Accounting True/False Test included in Appendix 1 to this paper.

The second section of this paper will discuss "throughput" accounting as it is being used today, and how it might be integrated with activity-based accounting. This section also reviews a model for presenting the income statement in a segmented format. Segments might be defined as products, business lines, geographic areas, customers, or any other cost object of interest.

The subject of the final section is using appropriate costs in decision making. Capacity availability and utilization are critical pieces of necessary decision information. This section includes suggestions for identifying relevant items and some simple examples of relevant items for some common decisions.

Traditional Cost Accounting

Assumptions Upon Which Cost Accounting Was Built

Cost accounting was originally designed to give decision makers relevant information to make informed decisions regarding adding additional products, automating operations, making or buying component parts, increasing capacity and many other decisions we still make today. The assumptions underlying the system as it was developed reflected the reality of that time period. The assumptions were that direct materials were a purely variable cost; direct labor, which was paid on a piece-work basis, was a purely variable cost; and overhead existed primarily to support direct laborers and was a small portion (less than 10%) of total product cost.

With these assumptions and some reordering of record keeping, F. Donaldson Brown, in the early part of this century, was able to develop a system for DuPont and later General Motors that gave them a tremendous advantage over competitors.[1] Overhead was firmly established as a function of direct labor, and total production costs were carried down to the unit level. At some point, we became enamored of "cost per unit" and forgot the basic assumptions upon which it was built.

A basic truth about cost allocation is that the relative total of whatever base is used to allocate a total cost, over time, will decrease. All that is required for this "truth" to hold is that people are rational. That is, once people know that they will be "charged" for their use of the base, they will try to decrease their consumption of the base. Because the original base was direct labor, there was tremendous incentive for all parties (engineers, operating managers, etc.) to reduce the quantity of direct labor in all operations. Hence, automation almost was assured once the base was chosen.

Also, because overhead was spread over all users and no one decision-making manager was directly responsible for all overhead items, there was every incentive not to expend considerable effort to control or reduce overhead spending. Thus, we might logically have predicted the occurrence of the current situation of greatly decreased direct labor and tremendously increased overhead.

Violation of Basic Assumptions

Today, labor is not a significant part of total product cost (on average, about 10 percent of total product cost and falling), and generally workers are paid by the hour or week, not by each piece produced. Overhead, rather than being a small portion of total product cost, now is a major cost item representing about 50-60 percent of total product cost. Two of the three major assumptions upon which our traditional cost systems were built currently are invalid, yet we remain in love with the unit product costs resulting from this flawed system.

To see how entrenched this system has become, answer the 15 true/false questions in Appendix 1 to this paper. While all of the questions have some truth in them, the general answer to each one is "false."

Current Accounting Axioms that Frequently Are Violated

In a working paper case study (1995), Eric Noreen has summarized some basic cost axioms that seem entirely reasonable and acceptable:

1. The sum of product costs should equal total (manufacturing) costs. [The sum of the parts is equal to the whole.]
2. No cost should be assigned more than once. [There should be no double-counting of costs.]
3. Given a fixed production technology and the prices of inputs, the cost of a product is a constant. [There is a true and immutable cost for every product or service.]
4. If fabrication of a product consumes a costly resource and the amount that is consumed is known, then a portion of the cost of that resource should be assigned to the product. [All production costs should be assigned somewhere.]

While these four axioms seem entirely reasonable, they routinely are violated by all traditional cost systems. The first axiom justifies our concentration on total manufacturing, as opposed to total costs of getting our product or service into our customers' hands and fulfilling all warranties. The second axiom implies that once actual costs have been covered, we cease the allocation process. Of course, we do not discontinue allocations, we merely end the period in an "overapplied" status. The third axiom assures us that there is a true product cost and all we have to do is find it. Unfortunately, this "truth" is entirely governed by our assumptions, which we can change at will. Finally, the fourth axiom states that all production costs must be assigned, not that they must be assigned in a way that is defensible to all parties. There is no axiom relating to the assignment/allocation of selling and administrative expenses because we generally have ignored these things when we design our cost systems.

In spite of the fact that the foundations of our traditional cost systems have crumbled, our managers use the results of their systems as if they reflected reality. The real problem is not that the wrong overhead base was selected, or that we should have switched bases at some past point in time. The real problems are the assumptions that (1) there is a cause-effect relationship between the base and the cost to be allocated, and (2) that cost behavior can be ignored. The theory of constraints addresses these two issues.

Theory of Constraints Accounting

Throughput Accounting

The theory of constraints, as well as just-in-time and total quality management concepts, emphasizes the revenue or "throughput" side of the net income equation. Throughput is generally defined by the people who developed the theory of constraints as revenues minus the costs paid to people outside the firm such as vendors, subcontractors, etc. Because materials and subcontracting work are variable costs, it is a small step to enlarge the definition of throughput to revenues minus all variable costs. This definition also fits the broader philosophy that "cost" should include whatever it takes to deliver a product or service to a customer since it would include items such as sales commissions determined on a percentage of sales (or, more uncommonly, gross margin or contribution margin) basis.

Once we have modified the definition of throughput to revenues minus variable costs, the result, called contribution margin, is widely recognized by accountants and business school graduates. This contribution margin format forms the basis for direct or variable costing income statements, now referred to as "throughput accounting," as well as the basic structure for cost-volume profit (break-even) analysis.

Direct (Variable) Costing or Throughput Income Statements Versus Traditional Income Statements

Throughput accounting, like direct or variable costing accounting, focuses on the behavior of costs. All costs must be divided into their fixed and variable components. However, this process need not be precise—if a cost is mostly variable or mostly fixed, it can be treated according to its more heavily weighted behavior.[2]

An example of a variable costing (throughput) income statement and a traditional (absorption costing) income statement is shown below for a company that has no beginning inventories of work-in-process or finished goods, produces 20,000 units, and sells 15,000 units for $20 each. There is no ending work-in-process inventory. Costs are shown in **Figure 1**.

The traditional (absorption costing) income statement shows $97,500 - $82,500 = $15,000 greater income than the variable costing (throughput) statement. This is because the traditional statement has deferred to another period a portion of the fixed manufacturing overhead costs assigned to the units produced but not sold. The variable costing statement has expensed all fixed manufacturing overhead costs in the current period.

When inventories are increasing, the traditional income statement always will show greater income.[3] Since the example company increased its inventory by

Cost Item	Details	Total	Per Unit
Direct materials	40,000 units @ $2	$ 80,000	$4.00
Direct labor	2,500 hours @ $8	20,000	1.00
Variable manufacturing overhead	4,000 mach. hrs. @ $10	40,000	2.00
Fixed manufacturing overhead	4,000 mach. hrs. @ $15	60,000	3.00
Variable selling and administrative		22,500	1.50
Fixed selling and administrative		30,000	2.00
Total costs incurred		$250,000	

Variable Costing (Throughput) Inc. Stmt.

Revenues (15,000 units)		$300,000
Variable costs		
Direct materials	$60,000	
Direct labor	15,000	
Variable mfg. OH	30,000	
Var. sell. & ad.	22,500	
Total variable costs		127,500
Contribution margin		$172,500
Fixed costs		
Manufacturing	$60,000	
Sell. and admin.	30,000	
Total fixed costs		90,000
Net operating income		$ 82,500

Traditional (Absorption Costing) Inc. Stmt.

Revenues (15,000 units)		$300,000
Cost of goods sold		
Beg. Fin. Goods	0	
Cost of goods manufactured	$200,000	
Less end. Fin. Gds.	50,000	
Cost of goods sold		150,000
Gross profit (margin)		$150,000
Sell. and admin. expenses		
Variable	$ 22,500	
Fixed	30,000	
Total sell. and ad. exp.		52,500
Net operating income		$ 97,500

Figure 1. Costs

	Killen Company		
	Product 1	Product 2	Product 3
Revenue	$150	$120	$ 90
Variable costs	60	40	45
Contribution margin	$ 90	$ 80	$ 45
Constraint time	20 min.	20 min.	5 min.
CM per constraint time	$4.50/min.	$4/min.	$9/min.

Figure 2. Killen Company

	Killen Company			
	Product 1	Product 2	Product 3	Total
Revenues	$13,500	$1,200	$7,200	$21,900
Variable costs	5,400	400	3,600	9,400
Contribution margin	$ 8,100	$ 800	$3,600	$12,500
Traceable fixed costs:	2,600	500	1,900	5,000
Segment margin	$ 5,500	$ 300	$1,700	$7,500
Common fixed costs				7,000
Operating income				$ 500

Figure 3. Segment Margins Statements

5,000 units, the traditional income will be 5,000 units x $3 fixed manufacturing overhead cost per unit = $15,000 greater than the variable costing statement. If inventories decrease, the opposite effect occurs: variable costing operating income is higher than traditional operating income.

Note that total selling and administrative expenses, while shown on different parts of the two statements, are identical in total amount. Also, note that variable selling and administrative expenses vary with sales, not production.

Importance of Capacity Information

Throughput accounting requires information on capacity availability and capacity utilization as well as contribution margin, to make appropriate decisions. Assume the Killen Company has an internal physical production constraint and three products with contribution margins of $90 for Product 1, $80 for Product 2, and $45 for Product 3. Products 1 and 2 require 20 minutes of time on the constraint to produce each finished unit; Product 3 requires 5 minutes. Even though it has the lowest contribution margin, the firm's best product in this situation is Product 3. Product 3 is the "best" product, because its contribution margin per constraining factor is $9 per minute, versus $4.50 for Product 1 and $4 for Product 2 (See **Figure 2**).

Therefore, Killen Company should concentrate on producing and selling Product 3 until it exhausts its demand in the marketplace. Then it should concentrate on Product 1 until its demand has been entirely filled. Finally, any remaining processing time should be devoted to Product 2.

Notice that total processing time on all resources is not a required piece of information once a constraint has been identified.[4] While individual resource processing times might be used by an activity-based accounting system to assign costs to products, these costs usually are not relevant for decisions. (The last section of this paper will discuss relevant items.)

Selecting the appropriate product mix, using the concept of contribution margin per constraining factor, is a central piece of the logistics portion of the theory of constraints. However, the idea of contribution margin per constraining factor has appeared in management accounting textbooks (usually in an abbreviated treatment) for over two decades.

Segment Margin Income Statements

The two income statements shown above are aggregated for the entire firm. If detailed information on product lines, areas, or customers is desired, the fixed costs can be treated in a better way. Rather than grouping all fixed costs together, they can be separated into traceable fixed costs that can rationally be linked to the cost object of interest—and therefore easily assigned—and common fixed costs that only can be assigned on some arbitrary basis and are best kept together and not assigned or allocated.

For example, a traceable fixed cost is a cost for an item either used exclusively by the cost object (such as an inspection device used for only one product) or is a joint cost, where several cost objects have pooled their resources to provide more efficient, effective service (such as a centralized purchasing department or a centralized graphics lab). The definition of the cost object, what fixed costs are "traceable," and what fixed costs are "common" to all units must be decided by each company. A tracking system such as activity-based costing would provide the information for determining traceable fixed costs. This process can result in segment margins statements such as the following one for the Killen Company in **Figure 3**.

The advantage of showing traceable fixed costs is that it clarifies how past decisions have impacted current profitability. Thus, to the extent possible, managers are encouraged to control[5] traceable fixed costs and find ways they can be used more effectively.

While the segment margin describes each product's contribution to cover common fixed costs and operating income, it does not in any way define the "best" product. This is because most of the traceable fixed costs may be sunk, meaning that even if the product goes away, the cost will not. Therefore, this statement format can be used only to compare actual results with expectations for the period and to make product (segment) managers aware of the fixed costs for which they are responsible.

The use of costs in decision making requires that we first identify which costs are relevant to a particular decision. The final section of this paper addresses relevant items.

Using Costs in Decision Making

The Danger of Arbitrary Allocations

There is a fundamental truth about cost accounting. The moment the company begins arbitrarily assigning costs to areas or segments, it causes people to begin to focus on the wrong thing(s) for decision-making purposes. As we saw in the Killen Company example, even nonarbitrary assignments of fixed costs can cause us to come to erroneous conclusions.[6] The key to making good decisions is the ability to recognize what is relevant to a particular decision.

Items That Are Relevant for Decisions

A relevant item is easy to define, but hard to practice. A relevant item (revenue or cost) is one that will occur in the future and will be different for the alternatives under consideration. Relevant items are those things that make a difference in a decision. For example, if revenues will be the same no matter which equipment is purchased, revenues are irrelevant to the equipment purchase decision. Likewise, expenditures that occurred in the past are sunk costs, and book values are irrelevant. However, if a

	Units Demanded	Killen Company Time required on each resource for each unit produced[7]				
		A	B	C	D	Total
Product 1	90	10	20	5	10	45
Product 2	50	5	20	5	5	35
Product 3	80	15	5	10	10	40

Total Time Required on Resources (in minutes):

	A	B	C	D
Product 1	900	1,800	450	900
Product 2	250	1,000	250	250
Product 3	1,200	400	800	800
Tot. Min. Needed	2,350	3,200	1,500	1,950
Total Min. Avail. (Capacity)	2,400	2,400	2,400	2,400
Resource Load	98%	133%	63%	81%

Figure 4. Killen Company

previously purchased item has a current market value, that amount is relevant to a replacement decision.

In throughput accounting, most decisions can be made by checking the impact on three critical measures: throughput, inventory, and operating expense. The idea is to increase throughput, decrease inventory (to shorten manufacturing lead time and increase future sales), and decrease operating expense. Of course, all three desirable movements do not have to happen for each decision. In fact, inventory or operating expense may increase if they are more than offset by an increase in throughput.

In the Killen Company example in the previous section, individual resource capacity availability and utilization were necessary in order to know if an internal constraint existed. Assume that Killen Company has determined that the market will buy a maximum of 90 units of Product 1, 50 units of Product 2, and 80 units of Product 3. A complete schematic of the Killen Company's production process, showing flows, times, capacities, costs, sales prices, and market demand, is included in Appendix 2 to this paper.

The Killen Company accumulated the data in **Figure 4** in order to identify a constraint.

Even if Resource A had been loaded more than 100%, but less than 133%, resource B would still be the most binding constraint. Therefore, the theory of constraints suggests a type of step-wise optimization algorithm. Companies can focus on the "worst" constraint until it no longer is a problem, then go to next constraint.

Most companies, however, would identify an internal constraint using logic and intuition (cause-and-effect analysis from the theory of constraints thought process), not analytic data. The primary reasons why analytic data cannot be used to identify a constraint are that our data are notoriously corrupt, and our processes are so complex and changing that by the time we establish a computer program to precisely calculate resource loads, the entire environment is likely to have changed. It is possible, however, for a company to decide what markets they will serve or what products they will produce, and not be subject to the whims of every customer that comes to the door.

Once a constraint is identified, the time required on the constraint (not the time required on all resources) is needed in order to compute the contribution margin per constraining factor. Using this information for the Killen Company, Product 3 was determined to be the best product, Product 1 next best, and Product 2 the third best product.

Therefore, relevant information for the Killen Company product-mix decision is (1) contribution margin per constraining factor (resource B), and (2) market demand. Given the current resource base, the product mix of 80 units of Product 3, 90 units of Product 1, and 10 units of Product 2 permits Killen to earn the highest weekly operating income possible. This plan also determines exactly how much inventory is required (sufficient to only cover items produced). Excess inventory in the system almost surely will guarantee that the preferred mix will not be produced because of worker confusion regarding what they should work on next when they have too many choices.

In a make-or-buy decision, the relevant cost to make a component are the costs that go away if we buy. Generally, these costs include direct materials and little else. However, if the component we are considering outsourcing requires time on an internal constraint, the additional contribution margin the company could generate if additional time on the constraint were available is an opportunity cost of continuing to make the component (or, alternatively, an "opportunity revenue" of purchasing, which reduces total purchase cost).

Looking for opportunity costs and opportunity revenues can be accomplished by maintaining a logical cause-effect-cause orientation to potential changes. This process does not require a genius, it merely takes someone familiar with the operation who is willing to spend some time thinking about the implications of changes. Theory of constraints training provides this ability.

Accountants generally are not good at identifying opportunity costs and revenues because they are too far removed from actual operations. Managers close to the process must communicate these opportunities to accountants if accountants prepare decision analyses. Alternatively, operating managers must learn how to structure a decision analysis.

Other short-term decisions such as deciding to sell as-is or process further, setting priorities for quality improvement projects, and scrapping or reworking defective units, follow the same general pattern. Prioritizing quality improvements is particularly difficult because we are in the habit of looking at quantities of defects, rather than the "cost" of defects. The total cost of defects, of course, includes time lost on a constraint (that is lost forever) and not total time on all resources because most resources have excess capacity and are idle a good part of each day.

The only relevant costs (or revenues) are those that will be different for the various alternatives being considered and that are future costs. Also, opportunity costs (or opportunity revenues) are relevant pieces of information that must be included in the analysis.

Long-Term Decisions

In addition to short-term decisions, long-term capital budgeting decisions also must include relevant costs and revenues. To appropriately do this, the impact on the entire system must be considered, not merely what an individual resource might accomplish if it were independent of all other resources. Most resources are part of a chain of dependent operations. Unless the entire chain is strengthened, any improvement or additional investment is wasted.

Our present capital budgeting techniques, such as net present value and internal rate of return, apparently work well when all relevant items are included in the analysis. However, the procedure is difficult for some employees to understand.

The theory of constraints people recently have developed a new long-term decision technique called Flush that calculates the point not only when all cash will be returned (as payback models do), but also when all the days of cash investment have been matched by an equal number of days of cash inflows. This is an intriguing technique, but, because of space limitations, it will not be pursued in this paper.[8]

Conclusion

One thing that activity-based cost accounting and activity-based management ideas have done for the accounting profession is to make clear to accountants and nonaccountants that cost accounting systems not only must be changed, they can be changed. A "standard" financial reporting system will not provide the information managers require.

The solution is not as easy as adding nonfinancial measures to our reports. Developing and implementing management reporting systems that help our managers, rather than put them on the defensive each month or each quarter, certainly is within our capabilities.

To do this, however, we must be willing to question all the assumptions that underlie our reports. We also must be much more system oriented and less "locally" oriented.

Consider the Following Question

Rather than focusing our attention on a more detailed reallocation of costs, would we be better off concentrating on the efficient use of our current resources?

Appendix 1

Accounting True/False Test

1. You need to know the fully absorbed unit cost of your product before you can prepare a bid or decide whether to accept a price offered by the customer.
2. A company can measure its company-wide efficiency by measuring the efficiency of each individual worker and/or machine.
3. Worker processing time on a component must be tracked 100% of the time to have accurate measures for standards, for cost allocations, and for efficiency calculations.

4. The only negative effect of carrying excessive work in process inventory is that it ties up working capital.
5. If each area of the company does its best, the entire company will do its best.
6. Measuring an employee's achievement of actual amounts to budgeted amounts is a good way to evaluate performance.
7. Detailed direct labor reporting enables a company to accurately summarize the total direct labor costs of each job.
8. The largest opportunities for improvement for a manufacturing firm are on the plant floor.
9. Just-in-Time and Total Quality Management and Theory of Constraints concepts are applicable only to physical product flows.
10. Direct materials and direct labor are variable costs.
11. A company can earn satisfactory profits if it makes sure that each price proposal that it offers customers covers fully absorbed unit cost plus an adequate margin.
12. The only legitimate concern about capacity is that, on average, it be almost completely (fully) utilized.
13. There is a true and immutable cost for every product or service.
14. Service organizations do not have work in process.
15. Service organizations generally do not need to be concerned about logistics and scheduling.

Notes

1. See F. Donaldson Brown, *Some Reminiscences of an Industrialist*, (Easton, PA: Hive Publishing, 1977, reprint of 1958 ed.). Also see an evaluation of Brown in Peter F. Drucker, *Adventures of a Bystander*, (New York: Harper & Row, 1978), 263-266.
2. There are fairly simple ways to do this ranging from "best guess" to regression analysis.
3. This frequently serves as an incentive for many managers to increase inventories at the end of a period, despite ongoing inventory reduction programs.
4. Be aware that an organization's real constraint is not likely to be in production but rather in order entry, engineering, sales procurement, or some other area.
5. In today's environment, "control" means reduce.
6. Product 1 is not the "best" product even though it has the largest segment margin. With the company's current resource base, Product 3 is the "best" product.
7. See the times required for each operation in Appendix 2.
8. The A. Y. Goldratt Institute's Project Management course includes a detailed explanation of *Flush*.

Reprinted from the 1992 APICS International Conference Proceedings.

The ABCs of Activity-Based Costing
James D. Tarr, CPIM

The increase in global competition makes it increasingly important that every organization understands its true product costs. Yet most companies are using, virtually unchanged, a cost system that was developed almost 70 years ago under substantially different business conditions. The purpose of this paper is to discuss the problems created by this archaic cost system and to introduce a different costing model which more closely simulates the way costs are actually incurred in business today.

Background

The traditional cost system focuses on capturing direct material and direct labor costs, while summarizing all other costs as a percentage of direct labor hours or dollars. This volume based overhead allocation system has become institutionalized as a part of Generally Accepted Accounting Principles (GAAP) as a consistent, although not necessarily accurate, method of inventory valuation. However, it no longer serves to provide accurate or adequate cost information for management decision making for the following reasons:

- The homogeneous product lines of the 1920s have given way to widely varied products and product lines produced in the same facility.
- The overhead activities of logistics, planning, quality and product development have expanded dramatically while automation, CADICAM, CNC and robotics have reduced direct labor content.
- Sales, distribution and other "below the line" costs have increased dramatically and can vary substantially from product to product.
- Data collection, sortation, and reporting technology has improved substantially, allowing far more analysis of overhead data. While the collection of data has become more detailed, primarily smaller increments to a greater number of decimal places, it still gets summarized into one or more overhead rates by function. No attempt is made to sort overhead costs by product.

Current System Deficiencies

As a result of these changes in the business environment volume based costing currently has these deficiencies:

- A significant portion of product cost, that is, overhead, goes virtually unanalyzed.
- Overhead rates of 400, 500, 600 percent, even into quad digits are common. In many cases, the largest portion of this cost cannot be traced directly to the product at all.
- Significant cost in the value chain, marketing and distribution cannot be identified and analyzed by product at all.

- No information is provided to allow for analysis of various product mix profitabilities.

Key Problems

Among the key problems created by volume based costing are the following:

- High volume, standard products are allocated a share of overhead disproportionately higher than they actually incur (overcosting). Gross margins are reported as lower than they actually are, creating the potential for incorrect pricing decisions. In the extreme, management can decide to stop making perceived "low margin" products that actually are very profitable.
- Low volume, custom products are, conversely, undercosted. This leads to high perceived gross margins on produces that may actually be money losers. Management decisions to emphasize this type of business over traditional "bread and butter" products can increase true cost and complexity of a business to the detriment of actual profit.
- The application of large overhead rates to direct labor biases cost reduction efforts in favor of labor cost reduction over material cost reduction. For example, at a 400% overhead rate, a $1 direct labor reduction created by a $3 increase in material would yield a perceived cost reduction of $2. Actually overhead cost probably wouldn't change (after all, who is going to reduce their budget as a result of this direct labor reduction and material increase? Certainly not purchasing! Thus, the true cost change would be a $2 increase, not a reduction.
- Make or buy decisions are similarly affected. As products are purchased rather than being manufactured, overhead does no reduce proportionally. Since the overhead is spread over a lower volume of direct labor, the overhead rate goes up, causing additional products to appear uneconomical to manufacture. In the extreme this can lead to the decision to shut a plant down entirely.
- Product mix decisions are distorted in favor of low volume, custom work and against high volume, standard work because of misleading and incorrect "high" margins for the former and "low" margins for the latter.

Changes Needed

It is clear that the volume based costing system is inadequate and needs substantial modification. A new framework should fulfill the following requirements.

- Simulate the actual application of costs as closely as possible.

- Create measures of performance for overhead cost elements that help management evaluate cost for performance as it applies to individual products.
- Provide a basis of projecting realistic costs for existing products, new products and various product mixes.
- Provide adequate information for correctly evaluating make or buy and cost reduction decisions. Traditionally, although we talk about overhead as "fixed" and "variable," in reality all overhead is fixed in the short run and variable in the long run. As we view overhead costs over increasing periods of time, the proportion of overhead that is variable increases in a continuum as the time horizon gets longer.

The current overhead allocation system makes the assumption the all overhead varies with direct labor volume, but in actual fact this is not often the case, especially where direct labor has become a minor part of the total product cost. Inspection may accrue in direct proportion for a given product, but it can be substantially different for different products. Setup and production planning costs accrue on a per order basis. Engineering changes, bill of material development and shop order development accrue on a per product basis.

Developing Overhead Element Costs

Several activities must take place in order to match overhead costs to products. First, the activities performed by various elements of the overhead pool must be isolated. Next, you must determine the total cost of that activity over a given time period.

Third, the determination must be made if the cost varies with volume or is fixed. A truly fixed cost would not change no matter what volume or mix of work was flowing thought the factory. Thus, the budget of this department, except for inflation, would remain unchanged year after year. If a function is identified as fixed and has an increasing budget, it is either variable or has waste.

If it is variable, a determination must be made as to the cause of variation. This is called the "cost driver" and it can be a variety of activities. Among common cost drivers are number and hours of setups, number of shop and customer orders, number of receipts and shipments, number of stock picks, number of inspections, number of moves and number of engineering change orders. From product to product some of these may be major elements of cost and some may be small enough to lump together.

Next, the quantity of cost driver activities performed by the overhead element must be determined. This number is then divided into the total cost of the element to determine the cost per unit cost driver. For example:

Total Annual Purchasing Department Cost: $450,000
Annual Number of Purchase Orders (cost driver): 2000
Cost per Purchase Order: $225

Obviously, this is a simple example. There may be more functions and cost drivers to Purchasing Department costs. For example, researching and selecting new vendors may be a significant cost driver for some product lines and not others. Further analysis may be called for in many situations.

Each overhead element that can be so identified is treated as a "little business" providing services to the overall organization at a given price. Their costs are then "absorbed" by user departments for services provided. Budgeting, reporting, measurement and control in these departments are no longer just a matter of comparison to abstract budgets set as a percentage increase over last year

with no relationship to amount of service provided. Managers of overhead departments would receive "Profit and Loss statements" for their departments based on costs absorbed by user departments and would be expected to manage their department costs to yield breakeven or profit over the long run.

As with any "vendor" performance measurement system, the cost per unit performance cannot be the only measure of the overhead department. Quality of services measures must be an integral part of any comprehensive measurement system. However, further discussion of these issues is beyond the scope of this paper.

Applying Cost Drivers to Products

Once cost per unit cost driver is established, products must be analyzed to determine their degree of use of each cost driver. First, each product must be analyzed through its entire bill of material structure and summarized by cost driver. First, each product must be analyzed through its entire bill of material structure and summarized by cost driver. Cost drivers generally fall into four categories and are often summarized as shown below.

- **Factory sustaining activities** represent fixed and variable expenses that are undifferentiable by product. They are applied to the product on the basis of value added rather than direct labor and represent a much smaller percentage than the traditional overhead pool. Among other things they consist of:
  - Plant management.
  - Building and grounds.
  - Heat and light.
- **Product sustaining activities** are activities that develop and update product and manufacturing information. They are amortized over the expected product life cycle. They include:
  - Process engineering.
  - Product engineering and specs.
  - Routings, standards and bills of material.
  - Engineering change notices.
  - Product and process enhancements.
- **Batch level activities** are balancing transactions that match the supply of materials, labor and capacity with demand. They are allocated to product cost by dividing batch costs by average batch size. Batch level activity costs include:
  - Purchasing.
  - Setups and material movement.
  - Inspection.
  - Materials planning.
  - Production control.
  - Material movement.
  - Receiving, picking, packing, shipping.
- **Unit level activities** are costs traditionally associated with individual production units plus other costs that can be measured on a unit by unit basis. They include:
  - Material and direct labor.
  - Expendable tooling.
  - Identifiable machine and energy costs.

A useful approach is to create a matrix multiplying each product by its expected quantity production and summing over each cost driver to determine if the total cost bears a relationship to the actual total cost of the overhead department. Wide discrepancies indicate either 1) problems with the cost driver model or 2) an indication that an overhead department is over or under budgeted.

As with any predictive model, it is also useful to test it against historical data. This is useful in 1) further analyzing the two discrepancies mentioned above, 2) verifying that the model accurately summarizes product costs into total cost and 3) developing a measure of accuracy of the costing model.

An Example

A simple example will clarify how perceived costs are affected by this method of analysis. The XYZ Company makes two products. Product A is a standard, high volume, "bread and butter" product, while Product B is a semi custom, low volume product which sells at a "premium price." Traditional costing is a follows:

Unit Cost	A	B
Mat'l	$20.00	$20.00
Dir Labor	4.00	4.00
O/H @ 545%	21.80	21.80
Total Cost	$45.80	$45.80
Selling Price	55.00	85.00
Gross Margin	16.7%	46.1%

Activity Based Cost analysis yields the following information per time period:

	Product A	Product B
Units	100,000	100,000
Orders		
• Shop	1,000	1,000
• Customer	10,000	1,000
P.O.s	3,000	6,000
ECOs	200	1,800

Department Costs

Factory Overhead	$200,000
Prod. Control	500,000
Purch/Receiv	500,000
Order/Shipping	600,000
Engineering	600,000
Total O/H	$1,200,000

Unit Cost Driver Cost
Factory Overhead

Factory Overhead/Total Direct Cost
$200,000/$2,640,000 – 7.6%
Unit Direct Cost x Factory Overhead Rate
$24 x 7.6% = $ 1.82

Production Control

Total PC Cost / Shop Orders
$ 500,000 / 2000 = $ 250/Order

Purchasing/Receiving

Total P/R Cost / P.O.s
$ 500,000 / 9000 = $ 55.60

Customer Orders

Total Cust Cost / Orders
$ 600,000 / 6000 = $ 100

Engineering

Total Engineering / ECOs
$ 600,000 / 2000 = $ 300

Total Cost, Unit Cost and Margin, Product A

Mat'l	$20 x 100,000 = $2,000,000
Dir Labor	4 x 100,000 = 400,000
Fact OH	1.82 x 100,000 = 182,000
Prod Cont	250 x 1,000 = 250,000
Purch/Recv	55.60 x 3,000 = 166,800
Order/Ship	100 x 5,000 = 500,000
Engineer	300 x 200 = 60,000

Total Cost $3,558,800
Unit Cost (divide by 100,000) $35.59
Gross Margin (@ %55 sell) 35.3%

Total Cost, Unit Cost and Margin, Product B

Mat'l	$20 x 10,00 = $200,000
Dir Labor	4 x 10,00 = 40,000
Fact OH	1.82 x 10,00 = 8,200
Prod Cont	250 x 1,000 = 250,000
Purch/Recv	55.60 x 6,000 = 333,600
Order/Ship	100 x 1,000 = 100,000
Engineer	300 x 1,800 = 540,000

Total Cost $1,481,800
Unit Cost (divide by 10,000) $148.18
Gross Margin (@ $85 sell) (74.3%)

Distortions of this magnitude caused by the traditional volume based cost system are not unusual. It is not hard to find cases where the Pareto Principle applies to product profitability, that is, 20% of the product line is very profitable while the other 80% is made up of money losers.

Benefits

The benefit of Activity Based Costing for a high overhead, mixed product company are obvious.
- Calculated costs reflect more accurately the way costs actually accrue. This leads to better management decision making.
- Overhead element analysis measured against quantity and quality of service provided creates a better analytical and measurement tool for this most rapidly growing manufacturing cost category.

Until organizations revise their cost systems to reflect the way in which cost truly accrue, poor decisions made on incorrect information and lack of control of a major portion of manufacturing cost will continue to be the result.

About the Author

James D. Tarr is President of J.D. Tarr Associates, an education and consulting firm focusing on JIT, TQM and the relationship of measurement systems on management decision making and performance. Formerly, he held positions as Executive Vice President in a Manufacturing company and Senior Management Consultant for a "Big Six" public accounting firm. He also teaches coursed in JIT and Production Management at California State University Dominguez Hills. Tarr holds a B.S. from Case Western University, an MBA from California State University Long Beach and is currently pursuing a PhD. At the Peter F. Drucker Management Center of The Claremont Graduate School. Within APICS Tarr is a Past President of the Los Angeles Chapter; former Region VII Director and Past Chairman of the Society Award Committee.

The Real Key to Creating Wealth

Shawn Tully

What if you could look at almost any business operation and see immediately whether it was becoming more valuable or less? What if you as a manager could use this measure to make sure your operation—however large or small—was increasing in value? What if you as an investor could use it to spot stocks that were far likelier than most to rise high? What if using this measure would give you a marked competitive advantage, since most managers and investors aren't using it?

There is such a measure—but you'll have to move fast to seize your competitive advantage, because it is catching on quick. It goes by several names, depending on which user or consulting firm you talk to; McKinsey and others do a lively trade teaching it. The preeminent popularizer of the concept is Stern Stewart & Co. of New York City, which calls it economic value added, or EVA. It is today's hottest financial idea and getting hotter.

Seeing why is easy. Managers who run their businesses according to the precepts of EVA have hugely increased the value of their companies. Investors who know about EVA, and know which companies are employing it, have grown rich. Little wonder that highly regarded major corporations—Coca-Cola, AT&T, Quaker Oats, Briggs & Stratton, CSX, and many others—are flocking to the concept. "EVA played a significant role" in AT&T's recent decision to buy McCaw Cellular for $12.6 billion, says William H. Kurtz, an AT&T financial executive. AT&T this year will make EVA the *primary* measure of business units' and managers' performance. Explains Quaker CEO William Smithburg: "EVA makes managers act like shareholders. It's the true corporate faith for the 1990s."

So what is it? Simply stated, EVA is just a way of measuring an operation's real profitability. What makes it so revealing is that it takes into account a factor no conventional measure includes: the total cost of the operation's capital. The capital is all the money tied up in such things as heavy equipment, real estate, computers, and other stuff that's expected to be productive for a while after it has been purchased, plus so-called working capital, mainly cash, inventories, and receivables. EVA is simply after-tax operating profit, a widely used measure, minus the total annual cost of capital.

Here's how Coca-Cola CEO Roberto Goizueta, a champion wealth creator, explains it: "We raise capital to make concentrate, and sell it at an operating profit. Then we pay the cost of that capital. Shareholders pocket the difference." This turns out to be profound. Incredibly, most corporate groups, divisions, and departments have no idea how much capital they tie up or what it costs. True, the cost of borrowed capital shows up in a company's interest expense. But the cost of equity capital, which the

shareholders have contributed, typically appears nowhere in any financial statements—and equity is extraordinarily expensive capital. Until managers figure all this out, they can't know whether they're covering *all* their costs and value to a company.

Understand that while EVA is easily today's leading idea in corporate finance and one of the most talked about in business, it is far from the newest. On the contrary: Earning more than the cost of capital is about the oldest idea in enterprise. But just a Greece's glories were forgotten in the Dark Ages, to be rediscovered in the Renaissance, so the idea behind EVA has often been lost in ever darker muddles of accounting. Managers and investors who come upon it act as if they have seen a revelation.

You'd act that way too if you had been at CSX for the past five years. "EVA is anything but theoretical," says CEO John Snow, who introduced the concept at his company in 1988. "How we use capital determines market value." Snow has lots of capital to worry about, a mammoth fleet of locomotives, containers, and railcars. His stiffest challenge came in the fast-growing but low-margin CSX Intermodal business, where trains speed freight to waiting trucks or cargo ships. Figuring in all its capital costs, Intermodal lost $70 million in 1988. In other words, its EVA was negative $70 million. Snow issued an ultimatum: Get that EVA up to breakeven by 1993 or be sold.

Freight volume has since swelled 25%, yet the number of containers and trailers—representing a lot of capital—has dropped from 18,000 to 14,000. They used to sit in terminals for two weeks between runs, but once CSX managers started seeing them as expensive, idle capital, they figured out ways to return them to the rails in five days. This is hardly rocket science. But before EVA, no one had done it; no one had had enough incentive to do it.

The company is also making do with a locomotive fleet of 100 instead of 150, a $70 million reduction in capital. How? On the route from New Orleans to Jacksonville, Florida, four locomotives used to power trains at 28 mph. But the trains arrived at midnight, long before they were unloaded onto trucks or freighters. Spurred by the EVA imperative, CSX decided to run the trains at 25 mph with only three locomotives and arrive three hours later, still in plenty of time to be unloaded at 4 or 5 a.m. The three locomotives also use some 25% less fuel than four. Slower trains and surging productivity met Snow's challenge. Intermodal's EVA was $10 million last year and is on track to triple in 1993. Wall Street had noticed: CSX stock was at $28 when Snow introduced the EVA program and was recently at $75.

It's a similar story in another capital-intensive business, making gasoline engines. Before introducing EVA in 1990,

©2001 APICS—The Educational Society for Resource Management

Briggs & Stratton was a rigid hierarchy. The company had no profit centers in the engine business below the corporate level—like most companies, it had no idea of each divisions EVA—and took macho pride in making almost all components in-house.

Today headquarters grants a wide berth to five divisions that make engines for lawn mowers, pumps, and other products. Each knows its EVA, and that knowledge has led to big savings from outsourcing. The company is phasing out production of the largest engines for pumps and generators, freeing the capital that had been unprofitably tied up in making them. Says John Shiely, the executive in charge of engineering: "EVA's discipline caused us to make the right decision." Now it buys premium engines, at a lower cost, from Mitsubishi. Molded plastics and other components, once made in small batches in-house, flow from suppliers that produce huge quantities.

Briggs & Stratton struggled with a miserable 7.7% return on capital in 1990, way below the capital's 12% cost. By focusing on that hurdle, the company has just cleared it, and the stock market is applauding: The share price has jumped from $20 in 1990 to $80 recently.

One of EVA's most powerful properties is its strong link to stock prices. The two numbers show a remarkable tendency to move up and down together. Says James Meenan, chief financial officer of AT&T's long-distance business: "We calculated our EVA back to 1984 and found an almost perfect correlation with stock price." Stock prices track EVA far more closely than they track such popular measures as earnings per share or operating margins or return on equity. That's because EVA shows what investors really care about—the net cash turn on their capital—rather than some other type of performance viewed through the often distorting lens of accounting rules. For example, IBM's cash flow per share and book value per share increased smartly between 1984 and 1989. But anyone looking at the company's EVA in that period (see chart) had a far better idea what was happening.

For this reason, investors understandably favor companies committed to increasing EVA. Eugene Vesell, senior vice president of Oppenheimer Capital, which manages $26 billion, says, "We like to invest in companies that use EVA and similar measures. Making higher returns than the cost of capital is how we look at the world." Oppenheimer has earned 17% annually on average over the past decade, well above the S&P 500.

EVA is not just for industrial companies. In general, it works fine in service businesses as well. A few types of companies require special adaptations of basic EVA analysis. Examples: natural resource and land companies and others with assets that appreciate rather than depreciate.

At AT&T, Chief Executive Robert Allen is breaking the ultimate corporate monolith into lean operating units. The driving tool is EVA. Until recently AT&T provided balance sheets for only a half-dozen huge groups, such as long-distance services and telephone equipment. But dozens of units sold products and services ranging from telephone sets to toll-free 800 numbers. The capital used by each of the myriad long-distance services was lumped together at the group level. Since no individual service knew how much capital it used, none had any idea if it was beating its cost of capital and thus adding value to AT&T.

Allen's solution: Starting last year he encouraged managers to divide their businesses into profit centers resembling independent companies. The long-distance group now consists of 40 units selling such services as 800 numbers, telemarketing, and public telephone calls. All the capital each one uses, from switching equipment to new-product

development, goes on its balance sheet. "The effect is staggering," says Meenan. "'Good' is no longer positive operating earnings. It's only when you beat the cost of capital." Some businesses found they had been posting negative EVAs for years. Now they're on a tough timetable to make the hurdle.

One of America's most enthusiastic proponents of EVA is Coca-Cola's Goizueta, who extolled return on capital long before formally introducing EVA companywide in 1987. "I'm a great returns man." Says Goizueta, seated in his antique-filled Atlanta office sipping steaming espresso from a red Coca-Cola cup. He has included a clear and persuasive description of EVA in Coke's latest annual report. On weekends Goizueta scours other companies' annual reports for impressive rates of return, reclining on pillows embroidered with a favorite slogan. *THE ONE WITH THE BIGGEST CASH FLOW WINS.* He uses simple metaphors to distill EVA: "When I played golf regularly, my average score was 90, so every hole was par 5. I look at EVA like I look at breaking par. At Coca-Cola, we are way under par and adding a lot of value."

To get there, Goizueta used a double strategy. First he concentrated capital in the hugely profitable soft drink business: "As Willy Sutton used to say about banks, that's where the money is." He dumped a motley of businesses that made pasta, instant tea, plastic cutlery, desalinization equipment, and wine. All posted returns on investment of 7% or 8%, far below their cost of capital. Soft drinks earn much, much more, so that Coke last year earned 29.4% on capital, almost 2 times its cost.

Second, Goizueta focused on raising returns far faster than the bill for capital. One tool is leverage. In the early 1980s Coke was practically debt-free. To Coke's costly equity—it was much costlier in those high inflation days—Goizueta added less expensive borrowings, lowering the average cost of capital from 16% to 12%.

At the same time, he coaxed the business into doing more with the capital it had—or with less. The company produces more concentrate with 40 plants now that it produced with 52 in 1982. "We've even replaced expensive metal containers for concentrate with inexpensive plastic ones," says Coke CFO Jack Stahl, another gung ho EVA advocate.

Result of all this: Coke's EVA has surged an average of 27% annually for the past five years. Coke stock is up form $3 to $43 since Goizueta took over 12 years ago.

To see how EVA can change a company's attitude and behavior from top to bottom, look at Quaker Oats. Until Quaker adopted the concept in 1991, its businesses had one overriding goal—increasing quarterly earnings. To do it, they guzzled capital. They offered sharp price discounts at the end of each quarter, so plants ran overtime turning out huge shipments of Gatorade, Rice-A-Roni, 100% Natural Cereal, and other products. Managers led the late rush, since their bonuses depended on raising operating profits each quarter.

This is the pernicious practice known as trade loading (because it loads up the trade, or retailers, with product), and many consumer products companies are finally admitting it damages long-term returns. An important reason is that it demands so much capital. Pumping up sales requires many warehouses (capital) to hold vast temporary inventories (more capital). But who cared? Quaker's operating businesses paid no charge for capital in internal accounting, so they barely noticed. It took EVA to spotlight the problem.

The evangelist is William Smithburg. A smooth extrovert who sports striped suspenders and flamboyant ties. Smithburg, 55, became Quakers's CEO in 1981 at age 43.

He is a physical-fitness buff and fierce competitor who plays handball and pumps iron.

Smithburg is using EVA to pursue a lofty goal: transforming Quaker from a journeyman into one of the food industry's most profitable companies alongside Kellogg and General Mills. Says he: "Our biggest problem was using too much capital."

Quaker employs a version of EVA it calls controllable earnings, which is yielding big savings at a sprawling plant in Danville, Illinois, that makes breakfast cereals and snacks. Until last year the plant operated at a slack pace early in each quarter and planned purchases, production, and deliveries for the big bulge at the quarter's end. Near the start of each quarter the plant would start filling warehouses with two-to three-month supplies of boxes and plastic wrappers as well as ingredients like granola and chocolate chips. It needed huge stocks because it turned out most of its products in a six-week surge. As products rolled out, Quaker packed 15 warehouses with finished goods. Corporate headquarters absorbed the costs of those inventories and encouraged managers to keep big, comfortable stocks. Says Steven Brunner, the strapping, mustachiod plant manager: "I used to treat inventories like they were free."

To smooth out the bumps—and save capital—Quaker ended the trade-loading madness in the fiscal year ended June 30, 1992, canceling the usual year-end promotions. Predictably, the stock plunged—temporarily. Free from the quarterly scramble, the Danville plant is whittling away at working capital and pays a stiff capital charge in the internal accounts for stocks of raw materials and finished goods. Result: The plant has trimmed inventories from $15 million to $9 million, even though it is producing a much more, and Quaker has closed five of the 15 warehouses, saving $6 million a year in salaries and capital costs. Says Brunner: "Controllable earnings makes me act like an entrepreneur."

As Smithburg forecast, the long-term strategy is paying off. "We know the customers would come back," he says. "But when they did, our capital costs were much lower." Controllable earnings have flourished. Most important, the stock is up 30%, to a recent $65.

Since EVA measures value creation and can be figured at levels well down in the company, it is an ideal basis for many managers' compensation. It provides a startling new view of a familiar process.

Most companies determine bonuses by how an executive performs against a budget; the most common target is a percentage rise in operating earnings. But the budget benchmark has a glaring flaw: Managers have an incentive to negotiate a target that's easy to beat. "The negotiation process is long and difficult," says Derek Smith, executive vice president of Atlanta's Equifax, an information services company that now bases compensation on EVA. "Instead of reaching for the stars, managers have an incentive to aim low." Most plans also rein in managers by imposing caps. For example, Harnischfeger Industries of Brookfield, Wisconsin, limited bonuses to 40% of base pay for all but a half-dozen top executives. It's switching to an EVA compensation plan in November.

Such a plan typically consists of two familiar parts, a bonus and stock incentives, applied in new ways. Bonus targets are established automatically each year as a percentage gain in EVA, determined by averaging last year's target, say 10% with last year's result, say 20%. That would fix this year's goal at 15%. Bonuses have no limits. But what if a manger gets lucky, earning a handsome bonus because of a swing in the business cycle? Companies generally put some part of an exceptional bonus in a "bank" and pay it out over the following three years. The manager's "bank balance" shrinks if he or she fails to keep meeting targets.

Some EVA companies object to setting goals by formula. Coca-Cola and Quaker negotiate EVA targets with their mangers. "There are too many variables," says Philip Marineau, Quaker's president. "Some businesses, for example, are just starting out with heavy investments and need a special timetable to reach a positive EVA." Marineau, however, says that it's far easier to set challenging targets than under the old system: "The compensation system is driving managers to reach higher."

Pay component No. 2, a stock incentive program, is also unusual. Instead of receiving stock options, a no-lose arrangement by definition, managers risk real money. CSX's plan shows how the program works. In mid-1991, 160 managers accepted a company offer to sell them shares at the market price of $48.325. They paid 5% cash; the company lent them the balance at 7.9% interest. The program ends next July, when the managers can cash in their shares. If the price stands above $69, CSX will forgive the loans' interest and 25% of the principal. If it doesn't, they'll have to pay the interest on their loans; they could even lose money. But with the stock recently at $75, that looks unlikely. Shareholders won" complain.

EVA is powerful and widely applicable because in the end it doesn't prescribe doing anything. If it tried, it would inevitably run aground in certain unforeseen situations. Instead it is a method of seeing and understanding what is really happening to the performance of a business. Using it, many managers and investors see important facts for the first time. And in general, they validate EVA's basic premise: If you understand what's really happening, you'll know what to do.

Ways to Raise EVA

There's nothing fancy or complicated about how to make economic value added (EVA) go up. It is a fundamental measure of return on capital, and there are just three ways to increase it:

- Earn more profit without using more capital. You probably spend much of your time thinking of ways to do this; cost cutting is today's favorite method. Nothing wrong with that. But focusing on it often blinds companies to the other ways of raising EVA.
- Use less capital. In practice, this is often the method that companies adopting EVA find most effective. Coke uses plastic containers for concentrate instead of costlier metal ones. CSX figures out how to operate with 100 locomotives instead of 150. Quaker reschedules production to require fewer warehouses. What to do with the capital save? Companies can return it to the shareholders through higher dividends or stock buybacks, or can . . .
- Invest capital in high-return projects. This is what growth is all about. Just make sure you expect these projects to earn more than the *total* cost of the capital they require.

Reprinted from the 1996 APICS International Conference Proceedings.

How to Succeed with Activity-Based Costing

Peter B. B. Turney, Ph.D.

Activity-Based Costing (ABC) is a method of documenting, measuring, analyzing, and improving business performance. ABC has been around a long time, but came to prominence in the late nineteen eighties as a solution to the ills of cost accounting. ABC is closely linked to emerging management practices such as continuous improvement and design for manufacturability and has now achieved broad application beyond cost accounting.

There are several published examples of companies that have successfully implemented ABC and achieved results. These companies include Chrysler and a Printed Circuit Board manufacturer.[1] However, some companies have found the promised benefits of ABC hard to achieve.

Responding to this mixed implementation experience, the National Center for Manufacturing Sciences (NCMS) instituted a study in 1994 to find a way to successfully implement ABC. This study tested a new methodology for implementing ABC—called Workforce Activity-Based Management (WABM)—that was believed to alleviate the critical implementation difficulties associated with ABC.[2]

The NCMS research study covered the implementation of WABM at two manufacturing companies. The results were compiled in a research monograph that documented the value of WABM and the lessons for successful implementation.

This paper briefly describes the WABM methodology. It also lists seven ways that WABM can improve the chances of success with ABC. These seven ways to success are based on the NCMS study results and other WABM implementations.

Workforce Activity-Based Management

WABM integrates people, activity-based information, technology, and innovative management practices into a single system. This system includes teaming, communication and problem solving, organizational learning, continuous improvement, performance management, and costing. There are three primary WABM subsystems: Storyboarding, ABC, and Goal Alignment.

Storyboarding is a process in which work teams develop and apply activity-based information to improve and re-engineer their work. Teams are made up of people who work together and interact on a daily basis. All employees participate in teams and in the storyboarding process.

The storyboards allow the teams to take responsibility for improving the performance of work and the profitability of the company. Teams use the storyboards to develop priorities for improvement and to communicate with their customers and suppliers.

ABC is a method of reporting information about work, its performance, and its results. ABC reports the cost of products, services, and customers (the cost dimension).

ABC also includes information about the causes of work and the consequences of poorly defined processes (the process dimension).

ABC cost information is primarily used to support strategic decisions. It helps optimize product, service, and customer mix. It is also used to model alternative strategies, evaluate the impact of new technology, focus cost-improvement efforts, and generally improve the quality of management decisions.

ABC process information is used to monitor and improve work. It helps set priorities and is used in performance measurement, benchmarking, and budgeting. ABC performance measures include organization-wide measures of cost, lead times, and quality for each activity and process.

In addition to its benefits in decision making, ABC is also a communication tool. ABC terminology (enhanced via the visual dimension to the information on the storyboards) is the common language of communication within the WABM system. It is used as a medium of communication within teams, across functions, and between organizations.

Goal alignment is a method of linking everyone to the goals of the organization. Linkage is reinforced through activity-based budgets, responsibility statements, and other aligning mechanisms.

Goal alignment integrates people and organizational units to the strategic plan of the organization. It helps focus and refocus attention on rapidly changing plans and competitive circumstances. Everyone understands their role in creating an agile and profitable organization.

Seven Ways to Achieve Results with WABM

1. Involve the Workforce. Lesson one from WABM is involve the workforce in all phases of the implementation. All workers and managers should participate in the development of the ABC information as well as in its application for planning and decision making.

Workforce involvement creates widespread understanding and ownership of ABC. This understanding and ownership translates directly into action, with improved performance and enhanced communication visible from the earliest stages of implementation.

2. Treat ABC as a Management Change Initiative. ABC should be treated as a major change initiative that requires proper attention to leadership, communications, and management involvement. ABC information can be threatening since it is revealing of performance deficiencies and can lead, in some cases, to the removal of resources from processes. So it is important that management champion the initiative and communicate this support to the workforce.

Proper attention to change management places ABC in a central role for operations. Ownership by operations, rather than accounting, significantly increases the likelihood of successful application and results. A Total Quality Management (TQM) or continuous improvement program is treated as a change management program, so why not ABC?

3. Use a Process-Based Architecture. ABC is too often treated as an accounting allocation process. This leads to limited understanding by nonaccountants, limited application and utility, and a general perception that ABC is owned by accounting.

ABC information created using an allocation approach may yield accurate product costs. But is it not useful as process documentation for continuous improvement, quality, and ISO 9000 applications. A separate set of documentation using a different approach is required for these other initiatives.

In contrast, WABM has a process-based architecture for ABC that utilizes information from business processes to build the ABC model. This process-based information documents process flow and performance as well as cost hierarchy. It is easily understood by everyone, including those without an accounting background, and therefore widely used in decision making.

4. Implement Information Exchange. An important lesson from WABM implementation is that ABC information must be available to everyone. Cost information is no different from quality information in its potential to empower the organization.

In many ABC implementations, however, information is extracted from the organization using interview or other top-down techniques. These techniques are threatening and may diminish both the quality of the resulting information and its acceptance by the organization. In contrast, WABM creates an effective exchange of information in a participative team environment.

If cost information is only available to a small number of managers and accountants, then its impact is necessarily restricted. In contrast, if all workers and managers have full access to cost information, all members of the organization can take ownership of cost and be collectively responsible for improving the organization's profit performance.

Information exchange requires that ABC information be in a form that is easily accessible by workers and managers. WABM uses storyboards, visual communication and problem solving tools, to create and display activities, performance measures and other ABC information. These tools are non-intimidating and easily used by people at all levels of the organization.

5. Integrate ABC with Other Management Initiatives. ABC must be integrated with other management initiatives. Integration reduces wasteful overlap and enhances initiative application and effectiveness.

For example, ABC provides vital process understanding and measurement for Business Process Reengineering (BPR). Separate information gathering and measurement for ABC and BPR is wasteful of company resources and may result in organizational stress and diminished learning.

In addition to integrating well with other process-based initiatives, WABM uses work teams as the primary implementation. This helps ABC work successfully with TQM and other team-based processes leading to better decision focus, worker empowerment, and team communication.

6. Tie ABC to Performance Measurement and Compensation. ABC is a set of measurements that, if applied properly, can have a significant impact on company performance. Cost, time, and quality are measured by ABC at each level of responsibility. This provides a significant opportunity to focus the organization around the goals of profitability, customer service, and product quality.

It is important to turn off existing measures because they may be inaccurate, invalid, and contradictory to ABC. They should be replaced with ABC measurements that are clear, understandable, and provide proper decision focus.

The next step is to tie ABC measures to compensation and other rewards. Only when this is done will ABC answer the vital involvement and ownership question, "What's in it for me?"

7. Take a Long-Term Perspective. Improvements occur quickly in most WABM implementations. But even the most successful WABM implementation cannot change organizational culture and behavior overnight. And learning to use the new ABC information takes time.

It is therefore important to maintain a long-term perspective for ABC. Significant and pervasive change may take years to accomplish. For example, the Printed Circuit Board Company took three years from initial implementation of ABC to world-class performance. Other companies that have not used WABM, such as Dayton Technologies, have taken longer to achieve results with ABC.[3]

Conclusion

Activity-Based Costing (ABC) is a method of documenting, measuring, analyzing, and improving business performance. It is unique in its ability to identify and exploit hidden opportunities to improve profit performance.

For many companies, however, the promise of ABC has been difficult to achieve. Simple in concept, ABC is hard to implement successfully.

This paper describes an approach to implementing ABC—called Workforce Activity-Based Management (WABM)—that directly addresses the key difficulties associated with ABC. WABM is an organizational approach to ABC that involves work teams in both the development and application of ABC information.

The paper provides seven lessons from WABM that are vital to implementing ABC successfully and achieving improved performance:
- Involve the workforce
- Treat ABC as a management change initiative
- Use a process-based architecture
- Implement information exchange
- Integrate ABC with other management initiatives
- Tie ABC to performance measurement and compensation
- Take a long-term perspective
- If these lessons are followed, the chances of turning the promise of ABC to reality are greatly increased.

References

1. Joseph A. Ness and Thomas G. Cucuzza, "Tapping the Full Potential of ABC," *Harvard Business Review*, July-August 1995, and Peter B.B. Turney, *Common Cents: The ABC Performance Breakthrough* (Beaverton: Cost Technology), 1992.
2. Peter B.B. Turney, *Workforce Activity-Based Management*, (Beaverton: Cost Technology), 1995.
3. Neal R. Pemberton, Loan Arumgam, and Nabil Hasson, "From Obstacles to Opportunities," *Management Accounting*, March 1996.

About the Author

Dr. Peter B.B. Turney is president and CEO of Cost Technology, Inc., a consulting firm that provides project leadership and the technical expertise required to implement activity-based cost systems successfully.

Reprinted from the Production and Inventory Management Journal, *Fourth Quarter, 1992.*

Benchmarking: A Reality Check for Strategy and Performance Objectives

Robert Venetucci, CPIM

The ancient wisdom of an old Chinese warlord, Sun Tzu [I], expressed some 2,500 years ago, still rings true in today's highly competitive business environment.

If you know the enemy and know yourself you need not fear the result of one hundred battles. If you know yourself, but not the enemy, for every victory gained you will also suffer a defeat. If you know neither the enemy nor yourself you will succumb in every battle.

If you do not know the strategic and operational strengths and weaknesses of your business—and those of your competitors—you will surely forfeit market share and profits. But, unfortunately, as businesses grow, they tend to become more and more internally focused, thereby losing touch with the realities of the marketplace. Attitudes, strategies, and processes become molded by history, past experience, and introspective evaluations that are insulated from the outside world. Finally, when the economy softens or when competition increases, the inaccuracy of these perceptions becomes painfully obvious. Customers discovering that others are better able to understand and satisfy their needs, and long-time leaders finding that they have been outmaneuvered by their competition, are typical manifestations of the problems that result.

Head-to-Head Marketplace Comparisons Test the Potential Effectiveness of Strategic Plans and Reengineering Initiatives

One way to remain sensitive to the environment and avoid this fatal error is to evaluate company strategy and operating performance against existing competition and best-in-class performers. *Best-in-class* performers are those companies generally recognized for exemplary performance in a particular process. One technique for accomplishing this evaluation is benchmarking—a well-established method for comparing the performance aspects of competing products and services (e.g., computer hardware and software, automobile acceleration, meantime between failure). Using this technique to critically evaluate strategy and business processes can help identify flaws in new or existing strategies and tactics as well as highlight operational areas that might require re-engineering to increase their value in supporting the business.

In any case, benchmarking, when properly executed, results in decisions and actions that improve the competitive position of the company.

Strategic Benchmarking

Developing a successful business strategy depends heavily upon a sound understanding of the driving forces (i.e., potential entrants, suppliers, customers, substitutes, industry competition) that influence the industry. Using market research techniques, information about these forces is collected and analyzed and responses formulated, yielding a strategy.

Strategic benchmarking, however, is an appraisal rather than a planning activity. Although it deals with the same market dimensions as strategic planning (e.g., brand identification, channel selection, pricing policy, technological leadership, service), the objective of the benchmark is to compare the strategies of two or more competing or noncompeting performers to determine their relative strengths and weaknesses. In this way, possible flaws and shortcomings are identified *before* the strategy is implemented. Armed with this information, actions can be taken to revise the strategy or to launch corrective operational initiatives, thereby strengthening those areas found to be deficient.

This type of comparative analysis can assist management in defining critical success factors and identifying shifting trends that may have been overlooked in the original planning effort. Results may point to the need for new or special capabilities to be developed, while shifting customer demographics may indicate a need to develop an alternate distribution channel. It may prove useful, for example, to track a non-competing business that is an early barometer of future events. As trends first appearing on the West Coast may eventually reach the East Coast, it would behoove a regional competitor in the East to keep an eye on these bellwethers for major differences or changes in strategy and tactics. Differences in strategy can signal shifts in the industry cost drivers that may favor one competitor over another. Economies gained by one competitor through a vertical integration strategy may generate opportunities for another through a more flexible subcontracting strategy. All of this could have a dramatic impact on your business's strategy and operations. If the comparative analysis is not performed, many opportunities could be missed.

But identifying differences is not the primary value of benchmarking. Once these differences are discovered, it is important to understand their significance and to identify the opportunities or threats they pose. This information, coupled with a meaningful analysis, will enable decisions to be made to modify strategy and tactics, thereby strengthening your competitive position.

Process Benchmarking

Process benchmarking seeks to measure the relative effectiveness of two or more businesses in performing a specific process by comparing both the cost to perform the process and the level of success with which it is executed

(e.g., inventory turns, order fill rates, MIS expense). This type of benchmarking serves two basic purposes:
- Identifies performance weaknesses
- Sets performance goals for re-engineering activities.

By examining the relative costs and activities necessary to perform a process, conclusions can be drawn regarding its efficiency and the value that it contributes to the manufacture and delivery of products and services. Those processes that are found to be out of line with either competitors or best-in-class performers are candidates for re-engineering.

Benchmarking as a process reengineering tool not only helps to guide the setting of performance objectives, but also acts as a catalyst to spark the innovative thinking (breaking the mold) that is necessary to achieve dramatic performance improvements. The external market view afforded by a benchmarking initiative can stimulate the discovery of creative solutions to business problems that would never have been considered otherwise. Many of the most successful productivity innovations have resulted from applying variations of existing processes or adapting existing technology from one industry to another.

Because *process* benchmarking is a more detailed activity than strategic benchmarking, accurate data collection is admittedly more difficult. But even if data is not readily available, the analysis and rationalization of each activity within a given process will, in and of itself, provide insight into how to improve operating performance and yield benefits.

Planning and Conducting a Benchmark

Two questions are fundamental to the benchmark:
- "What strategies or processes should be compared?"
- "Against whom or what should they be compared?"

A strategic benchmark may cover the entire gamut of market dimensions or it may be limited to just a few (e.g., channels of distribution, pricing policy).

An internal assessment may be needed initially for an operational benchmark to identify baseline performance metrics for the business processes. The results of this assessment can then be used to select specific functions or processes for comparison (e.g., engineering, customer service, order fulfillment).

While it may be appropriate to benchmark strategy only against competitors, process benchmarking may prove valuable against any company considered to have a best-in-class process. For example, there might be little benefit for a computer manufacturer to benchmark its strategy against L.L. Bean, but it may make sense for that same computer manufacturer to benchmark its parts distribution process against L.L. Bean's order fulfillment processes.

Conducting a benchmark analysis requires that a significant amount of data be collected from both printed and field interview sources. The more specific the subject of the benchmark, the more heavily data collection will need to rely on field interviews. To avoid being overwhelmed, it is recommended that a clear statement of objectives and a strategy for collecting, analyzing, and presenting the information gathered be developed before data collection begins. The plan should present a *top-down* approach, starting with a general view and "drilling down" to finer levels of detail. By enabling an overall sense of the source data and its limits, needs can be identified in sufficient detail and clarified accordingly.

Information for a benchmark is available from several sources. Printed information can be found in publications such as newspaper articles, trade journals, financial analyst reports, government filings (e.g., tax returns, patent filings), etc. Field data can be obtained from interviews with the sales force, distribution channel, suppliers, personnel in the employ of the target companies, professional and trade association meetings and conventions, etc. Another source of data for a process benchmark in large corporations may be sister divisions. This approach has the benefit of being able to provide the most detailed and accurate information, but it may not yield a very objective comparison with the real world since the data source is subject to the same cultural influences as the division doing the benchmarking.

Access to the information will depend upon your relationship with the comparison companies. It is unlikely that a competitor will voluntarily offer information that could later prove to be detrimental to itself. But many times, noncompeting companies are willing to share information if there is some potential benefit for them.

Case Study

The following case will demonstrate the use of benchmarking in defining a process strategy and setting management's expectations for operational improvements. In the following example, benchmarking was only one step in the overall process re-engineering effort. Other steps included:
- Definition of customer requirements
- Development of a business vision
- Re-engineering of the process environment.

Background

Faced with increasing competitive pressures and an erosion in business and profitability, a major electronic controls manufacturer set out to identify the root causes of its problems and define a turnaround strategy. The company's product line covered a wide spectrum, from highly specialized electronic assemblies requiring engineering and technical support in defining configurations, to off-the-shelf customer-installed upgrades and maintenance items.

To conduct an investigation into the root causes of the problem, a consultant was engaged to facilitate discussions with company executives, sales and marketing, and a select panel of customers. The objective was to collect facts regarding the types and characteristics of each business segment and the critical success factors surrounding each of them.

It became clear that customer specifications of the engineered products and the replacement component products segments differed significantly. For example, timing was less important in the engineered segment than it was in the replacement segment. In fact, the component business segment had relatively simple requirements—responsiveness, ease of doing business, correctness, and cost.

As the results of the survey were reviewed and validated, a vision was formed of how the business needed to respond to meet customer expectations.

Defining the Benchmark Objectives

Having crystallized a vision of the desired environment, the company saw that a strategy needed to be developed to implement the vision. It was decided that a best-in-class benchmark could provide considerable insight into how the vision should be implemented. The benchmark focused on the following areas:
- Order fulfillment processes
- Information technology support

- Organization
- Cost.

The benchmark project was structured into two key initiatives. The first involved baselining the existing processes and costs, while the second focused on collecting field data from the best-in-class target companies. A project team was assigned to each initiative.

The baseline team went about developing an activity based costing (ABC) profile of the existing operations focusing on the component business. In addition, a high-level overview was developed of the current processes and information systems deployed to support the existing order fulfillment process. This information would be used later to perform a gap analysis and to identify potential process candidates for re-engineering.

The field data team identified a sample of companies that, in the minds of management, represented the best-in-class for each of the functions necessary to support order fulfillment for the component business segment. This list included companies within the same industry as well as companies outside the industry that were believed to have similar order fulfillment process characteristics. The list was then screened by management in order to select the final group of benchmark target companies.

With use of existing company contacts, phone interviews were conducted with most of these companies. Following the phone interviews, site visits were arranged with a select group of companies. This enabled the discussion to cover a wider range of topics and to probe more deeply into areas of particular interest.

Analysis of the benchmark results revealed a number of common process characteristics across the benchmarked companies despite their inherent product and industry differences.

- **Customer-Driven Process.** Knowing the cycles of service is critical. The processes developed were specifically geared to supporting the needs of the customer.
- **Executive Commitment and Support.** The executive's role is to set direction and establish commitment. Without the top-down commitment of executives, it is difficult to redirect the momentum of the organization.
- **Major Reengineering of Order Fulfillment Process.** In most instances, the benchmark companies had gone through similar self-evaluation and rethinking exercises to improve the effectiveness and responsiveness of their order fulfillment processes. In many cases, this rethinking did not occur until competition had eroded their business franchise.
- **Segmented Order Stream.** Different processes are needed for different order types. Processes were segmented along markets (domestic vs. international), along product type and distribution channel (new business vs. repair), or on the basis of customer need.
- **Process Ownership.** Ownership of the process establishes accountability and focuses improvement activities. Many of the benchmarked companies have centralized order service centers overseeing the complete order fulfillment cycle.
- **Order Ownership.** Full-stream responsibility over the entire order cycle from order entry through customer receipt provides one focal point of coordination and ensures satisfactory completion.
- **Up-Front Planning.** Extensive pre-sale activity avoids rework later on. Clearly defined order cycles ensure proper handoffs. A network of communication among materials, manufacturing, sales, etc. ensures that customer needs can be met.

- **Order Change Management.** Situations occur that necessitate changes to orders, product, price, schedule, etc. Formal processes and internal deadlines prevent the process from getting bogged down. The process ensures that changes are authorized and communicated.
- **Multifunctional Coordination.** Today's business is highly complex, with several disciplines involved in satisfying an order. Coordination and teamwork are part of the culture from pre-sale through billing, preventing "fall downs" in the process.
- **Product Standardization.** Standard product options improve quality by allowing for a reduced number of stocking units, thereby shortening response intervals.
- **Integrated Information Systems Architecture.** Information support is the key to providing exemplary customer service. Availability, accuracy, and timeliness are the results of focused information systems driven by business needs.
- **Focused, Customer-Driven Metrics.** Metrics drive behavior. If you want to improve the process, metrics need to be structured to produce the desired result.
- **Quality Improvement Teams.** Competitive performance is a constantly moving target. Front-line quality improvement teams reporting to the process "owner" continually evaluate and improve the process. Process performance metrics are tracked and improvement goals set.

Summary

The benchmark contributed to the re-engineering of the order fulfillment process by:
- Identifying best practices that should be incorporated into the re-engineered process
- Indicating the level and type of information technology currently in use
- Establishing management expectations regarding the customer service and cost performance levels necessary to be competitive in the market.

Since a number of the companies surveyed had also gone through the process of benchmarking and re-engineering their processes, it was possible to set an expectation vis-à-vis the resources and time frames required to complete the re-engineering of the fulfillment process.

Vis-à-vis with a design intent based upon the business vision and benchmark inputs, detailed process requirements were defined for implementation across the organization. An implementation plan was also developed that called for a pilot process to be operational within six to nine months and the entire material planning and order fulfillment processes to be re-engineered over a two-year period.

The pilot operation would include a limited number of accounts to test out the new concepts within the vision. If these proved to be effective, the pilot would be deployed to a wider range of accounts and products. In a parallel effort, a separate group of process teams would re-engineer the technology platforms to reflect the desired process improvements confirmed by the pilot.

Final Words

Keep in mind that it is not necessary, nor is it recommended, that every aspect of the business undergo a benchmark. Initial efforts should be directed at identifying the critical strategic and operational success factors in the business or industry. Once these are identified, specific benchmarking objectives can be defined. Whatever the benchmark subject, the results should be actionable. *If information obtained during the benchmark cannot be translated into an initiative to strengthen strategy or improve performance, it is of little value.* In addition, the information must be reviewed in the context of an overall outcome. There may be conflicting objectives that need to be weighed and trade-offs made that maximize the overall benefits. The classic example of this is the production planner who must balance the conflicting objectives of finance—inventory turns; customer service—product availability; and operations—production efficiency. Like successful Just-in-Time implementations, it is not the efficiency of a single activity that determines overall success, but, rather, the effectiveness of the entire process.

References

1. Tzu, Sun. *The Art of War.* New York: Delta, 1988.
2. Porter, Michael E. *Competitive Advantage.* New York: Free Press, 1985.

About the Author

Robert Venetucci, CPIM, is a senior management consultant with M.F. Smith & Associates, Inc., a professional consulting and business services firm located in Bernardsville, N.J. His experience as a management consultant, operations executive, and designer and developer of management information systems spans machine tools, electronics, consumer products, health care, financial services, and communications. Mr. Venetucci is a graduate of Cornell University with a B.S. degree in industrial engineering and operations research. He has completed graduate work in marketing at the University of Rochester.

Reprinted from the 1988 JIT Seminar Proceedings.

Changing Performance Measurement Systems

Thomas E. Vollmann

Manufacturing companies are increasingly concerned with how best to evaluate performance in the light of new competitive challenges, the need to roll out more new products faster, the steady decrease in direct labor as a source of value added, and the impact of new manufacturing technologies, such as Just-in-Time, Computer Aided Manufacturing – International (CAMI), other groups, and individual researchers have been working on improved manufacturing performance measures to meet these challenges. [1] However, the bulk of this work either attempts to retain a great deal of classical cost accounting (in that cost accounting functions such as individual product costing are preserved), or attempts to provide some monolithic replacement for cost accounting (i.e., the same new measures will be used by most if not all firms).

I believe that both of these approaches are futile, and that they are keeping us from properly attacking the manufacturing performance measurement problem. It has been said that one gets what one measures: measuring costs may well be the tail wagging the dog. Costs and other financial measures increasingly need to be viewed as a result or "follower" rather than a cause or "driver" of good or bad manufacturing decisions. Taking this point of view focuses attention on manufacturing strategy as the key element in determining appropriate performance measures. Moreover, this view leads to a contingency model for performance measurement: One needs to measure things that are congruent with the *present* set of perceived strategic objectives. The measurement of performance can and should evolve as strategy evolves. In fact, not changing manufacturing performance measures to support strategy is the *cause* of many present problems of American competitiveness.

Shortcomings of Traditional Cost Accounting Systems

The Boston University Manufacturing Roundtable has been investigating manufacturing performance measurement for several years.

Included in this investigation are the annual surveys of manufacturing companies in North America, Europe, and Japan. These surveys examine current practices in manufacturing with regard to perceived manufacturing concerns, priorities, action programs to improve effectiveness, and performance. Also collected are data on cost structures and expected changes in these structures. Several key observations come from the surveys and from follow-up discussions with manufacturing executives.

What we see from the Manufacturing Futures Project and from discussions with manufacturing executives is growing frustration with traditional cost-based measures.

As quality and time become more important for company survival, measures that are driven by quarterly earnings reports and investment decisions based solely on "cost savings" are ever less relevant to long-term company health.

The attainment of corporate objectives is increasingly less determined by the traditional activities of direct laborers working on the shop floor. The factory must routinely execute schedules with high quality and low cost. This is the ante to play in the game. Winning requires more. The routine things need to be done routinely, with more knowledge work done by all employees, both "direct" and indirect" workers. It is critical to devote more efforts to rolling out new products faster, to higher quality, and to responding to the vagaries of the market place. Achieving these objectives, and having more knowledge work done by everyone in the organization, requires a new set of performance measures [2]

Many war stories could be told here based on specific company examples, but space constraints do not permit it. The key points are:

- Managers are frustrated with traditional cost-based measurement systems.
- There is a growing irrelevance of "cost" to the newer strategic objectives in manufacturing.
- Cost is an accounting convention subject to wide latitude.
- Cost is best seen as a follower not a driver.
- Managers who put cost and short-term financial measures as drivers may be hindering the achievement of long-run company health.

Let us now turn to a three-phase framework that describes how companies are changing their performance measurement systems.

Phase One—Tinkering with Cost Systems

The first phase of development in changing measures of performance in manufacturing is to tinker with or adapt present cost-based systems to better reflect reality. The classic response is to attempt new methods for overhead allocation. We have seen several firms decide that since a growing proportion of their product cost is from purchased materials, they should allocate all overhead costs associated with purchases to these items. While this at first seems like a laudatory idea, it has some basic flaws. If, for example, overhead is allocated on the basis of purchasing dollars, that might seem "reasonable." But what about two product lines, one mature and the other new with many engineering changes? Do they both require the same degree of attention from purchasing managers? From engineers? From quality control?

It is useful to identify three separate activities performed by accounting systems.[3] The first is financial reporting with the objective of reporting financial health of the enterprise, on a consistent basis with other firms, to outside interests such as shareholders and taxing authorities. The second activity performed by cost accounting systems can be called "cost modeling." Included are studies for pricing, analysis of product line "profitability," study of one-time decisions, and make-buy analysis. The third activity performed by cost accounting systems is feedback and control. This has usually been accomplished with variance reporting and similar approaches.

Separation of accounting into these three categories leads to some useful observations. There will always be a need for category one, and the present methods for reporting to outside interests are probably as good as any (they are not broken, so let's not fix them). It is categories two and three where the problems occur. In both cases the present cost-accounting-based systems can easily lead to poor decision making. Moreover, tinkering with existing approaches simply will not do the job. As long as the requirement exists that the results of cost accounting will aggregate into the financial reporting (category one), the results will be lacking. Why should a firm consistently perform either cost modeling or feedback/control?

Cost modeling should be done on whatever basis makes the most sense for that problem. There are many long-term decisions, such as investments in new technology, that simply should not be based on cost. The real question is what will happen if the firm *does not* make the investment? Similarly, there are short-horizon and one-time decisions that are situation dependent.

Feedback and control, the third activity performed by cost-accounting-based systems, are even less well fulfilled. For most firms, by the time accounting based variances are determined, it is far too late to do anything about the problems. Moreover, the "cure" may not match the disease. Most accounting measures for feedback and control are a misnomer. They are followers rather than drivers.

We have seen far too many situations where drivers and followers get mixed up to the overall detriment of the company. Examples include building unneeded inventories to utilize capacity and "improve" manufacturing variance measures, restricting capital expenditures to make accounting statements look better, and forgoing important maintenance projects.

The right feedback drivers in many cases have to be in real time and in fine detail. For example, quality control has to be very current, and specific, to particular processes. The idea of waiting until a week after month end to determine overall performance is ridiculous for most critical manufacturing variables. It is these variables that need to be controlled. Moreover, if they are held in tight control, the financial variables should work out. If they do *not*, the fault may well be in the financial analysis, not in what is truly important for the company.

Phase Two—Cutting the Gordian Knot

At some point, a few firms have concluded that there is simply no way that a cost accounting system can nor should be used for all three activities. It will always be necessary to report to outside interests on a basis consistent with that of other firms. But there is no reason for consistency in either cost modeling or feedback/control. In both of these activities, the firm should base its actions on whatever best matches its set of strategic objectives.

Saying this and doing it are two different things. Many people will agree with the basic conclusion but will they make the change? Will they cut the Gordian knot that ties short term financial accounting to decision making in manufacturing? Will they not only adopt new performance measurements, but discard those that are no longer appropriate? What sort of change process needs to occur in a company for this to happen?

One telecommunications firm recently gave up absorption costing for all internal reporting. It was felt that this step would create a new awareness of what was truly important in manufacturing. Accompanying this change in accounting was the participative development of a well defined manufacturing strategy for the company. This strategy clearly defined fundamental objectives for manufacturing in terms of revenue growth, overhead growth, inventory (material velocity) quality, and new product introductions. The strategic objectives led to a definition of what was important to measure, and the abandonment of absorption costing provided a way to unshackle the old measurement constraints.

Another Gordian knot cutting is a growing tendency among high tech companies to abandon the concept of "direct labor." These firms increasingly view their employees as an asset to be managed and enhanced. They employ people, not direct and indirect. There is work to do, and there will be continual redefinition of who is to do what. The objective is to evolve as quickly as possible (i.e., to *learn*). Employees to continually increase their skill base and take on new challenges.

The abandonment of direct labor means that accounting necessarily needs to change the basis for many kinds of calculations. Costs of products clearly cannot be determined in the same way. This forces people to think less about "cost" and more about the nature of decisions. For example, the focus might shift from some parochial view or product cost to a better understanding of where the knowledge workers of the company are being deployed and whether this is the best use of their time.

A key issue in Gordian knot cutting is who is going to lead the change process. Our experience indicates that it is critical for the financial function to buy in. Manufacturing can not do it alone, and financial people need to understand that they have to be a part of the solution instead of only being a part of the problem. Without this commitment, the expectations are that the company will not get beyond the "grousing" stage. In the United States, the financial function has significant power in most companies. They can provide the necessary clout to make changes, or they can block the changes.

A sense of the need for change in manufacturing performance measures exists in a large number of firms, but there seems to be some lack of understanding of the pervasiveness of the problem and the extent to which existing measurements are impeding progress toward important enterprise objectives. One technique that we have found helpful, whether or not the knot has been cut, is a questionnaire we have designated for assessing performance measurement conflicts.

The questionnaire is typically administered at several levels in a company, and is divided into three sections. The first section asks each respondent to assess the long-run importance of about two dozen improvement areas that the firm might undertake to improve effectiveness. A follow-on question asks the extent to which present performance measures either inhibit or support improvement in each of the improvement areas. The second section of the questionnaire provides a set of about 40 performance factors, which are again assessed in terms of long run importance to the company, and the extent to which they are or are not being measured in the company. The third section of the questionnaire asks the respondent to pick the performance measures from the prior list which he or she feels are used to evaluate his or her own performance on daily, weekly, monthly, quarterly, and annual basis.

By administering the questionnaire at several levels in the company, it is possible to assess the extent of congruence on several key performance measurement issues. Congruence can be assessed within manufacturing as well as across functional boundaries. In one firm we surveyed people at three levels of authority in manufacturing as well as people in staff areas of manufacturing and other functions. The results provided a diagnosis of the gaps between important improvements and current measurement support, and the congruence (or lack thereof) of important areas for improvement. For example, in one case we found a great deal of disparity about both the importance and measurement support for computer-integrated manufacturing (CIM). This company had not done its homework on defining where CIM fits into their needs. Another common result is for an individual to rate far too many things as being of greatest importance. If everything is equally important, then there is not an overriding sense of priority for coordinating improvement efforts.

Phase Three—Embracing Change

The final phase of development in changing manufacturing performance measures is to consider the process of performance measurement as an integral facet of manufacturing strategy. That is, if strategic goals are to be developed and reached, it is critical to develop performance measures that are supportive of these objectives, and to get rid of any measures that are counterproductive. Moreover, as goals are achieved and new one formulated, performance measurement should similarly evolve. In fact, an interesting chicken-and-egg question arises from this line of discussion. Perhaps the *first* thing one should do to implement a change in strategic direction is to consider what changes in performance measures might be most conducive to achieving the change.

Changes in performance measures need to be seen as both a top-down and bottom-up exercise. The top management strategy should determine the overall direction, but the ways in which those goals are to be achieved, and the best ways to support them in particular organizational units are situation dependent. A top-down objective to reduce the time to introduce new products might lead to quite different programs in particular parts of the company.

Elimination of performance measures can be useful as adding them. In this day of high-powered computers, it is tempting to add more and more measures, without discarding any. Thus, some people will suggest that traditional cost measures be kept and that new measures be added. A good lesson can be learned from the service industries. At the fast-food chains such as McDonald's, the primary measure is simple volume per time period expressed in dollars. The restaurants work with such a high material velocity that there is little point keeping track of any inventories. The output is, in essence, the input as well. As manufacturing firms move to JIT the same ideas are true. If quality can be guaranteed and high material velocity achieved, many standard measures can be eliminated. Manufacturing's job is to take any order and fill it in a lead time that appears as if the products were held in stock, when in fact little or not finished goods are held.

Phase three is called "embracing change" because the expectation is that performance measures should be continually improved. Manufacturing excellence is the objective, and the definition of excellence is clearly contingent upon what is *now* being achieved, the challenges from competitors, bench-marking against the best in any activity in any company – not just a competitor, new technologies and their associated opportunities, and new ideas for enhancing the products and services provided to our customers.

Concluding Remarks

In this paper I have tried to identify the role that is increasingly being played by performance measurement changes in the quest for manufacturing excellence. The importance of using knowledge workers more effectively and increasing the amount of knowledge work done by all workers is one aspect. Another is providing the right direction for JIT and related efforts. Still another is the growing importance of manufacturing strategy in attainment of enterprise objectives, particularly in the fact of global competition. It is imperative that the long-run competitive vitality becomes the driving force for selecting measurement objectives. Finally, I believe that firms need to adopt a new, more dynamic attitude toward changing objectives and measure—one that focuses on achieving even greater levels of excellence.

• Portions of this work have been supported by the Boston University Manufacturing Roundtable.

References

1. See for example, Kaplan, Robert, "Yesterday's Accounting Undermines Production," *Harvard Business Review*, July-August 1984; and Nanni, Alfred J. Jr., "Measuring Manufacturing Costs," Working Paper, Boston University Manufacturing Roundtable, 1987.
2. See Miller, J.G., and T.E. Vollmann, "The Hidden Factory," *Harvard Business Review*, September-October 1985, for a related discussion.
3. See also Nanni, A.J., J.G. Miller, and T.E. Vollmann, "What Shall We Account For?" *Management Accounting*, January 1988.

Reprinted from the 1999 APICS International Conference Proceedings.

Can Anyone Control a Project?
Roly White, CFPIM

Organizational change and systems and technology implementation projects typically are high-risk and return endeavors. They require the commitment of significant resources and have potentially high returns, but a large number of them produce disappointing results. This paper defines a methodology for controlling projects to maximize the likelihood of completing them on time and within budget. The methodology has been successfully applied to dozens of large and small projects. It is presented as a means of controlling a single project, but is equally appropriate for overall control of a group of related sub-projects. **Figure 1** summarizes the steps required to control a project.

Controlling a project seems so simple, yet few organizations do it effectively. Why? It is typically because they
- don't understand what is required
- don't have a methodology or the tools
- are focused on controlling the wrong things
- don't believe that it is worth the effort.

The methodology presented addresses all of these reasons, and each of these steps will be explored in more detail. It is important to apply a variation of Pareto's Law in each of the steps. Focus on the very important few, but don't let the important many cause unexpected and unpleasant surprises.

Successful control of a project begins with a sound definition of the critical assumptions and the expected outcomes. This definition must be written and agreed to by all parties. The project plan that defines the work that must be done to produce the desired outcomes is developed from the project definition. A project control system must be implemented before execution of the project plan begins. The execution of the plan is the step with the largest resource commitment and risk. The implementation of a control system to measure progress and report status during execution is critical to producing the desired outcomes. No project is complete until the lessons learned and suggestions for future project teams are captured and documented.

Define the Project

The project definition begins with a mission statement that identifies what is to be accomplished, the target for accomplishment, and the expected benefits. **Figure 2** presents a template for and an example of a mission statement. The expected benefits are the business reasons for undertaking the project. The organizational change or technology is the means to the benefits, not the benefits themselves. The benefits should be time-phased because they typically are not all realized upon completion of the project. Some of the benefits are realized after the project has been completed and the organization has had time to improve its operations using the capabilities delivered by the project.

The mission statement is then broken down into a set of objectives that are necessary and sufficient to achieve the project mission. This means that the mission cannot be met unless all the objectives are accomplished and that it will be met when all the objectives are accomplished. Too frequently, the mission statement will not be met by achieving the objectives, or objectives are included that are not necessary to achieve the mission of the project. The first case cannot be tolerated. The second case provides opportunity to recover from schedule slippage. Each objective must have a target date and a list of the expected benefits from accomplishing the objective. A project will typically have 5 to 20 objectives, and each objective will have a list

---

1. Define the Project

2. Plan the Project

3. Establish the Control System

4. Execute the Plan

5. Initiate Corrective Actions

6. Close the Project

Figure 1. Steps to Contral a Project

Template
The mission of this project is to
by
which will

Example
The mission of this project is to implement a tracking system for all production material from receipt of raw stock to loading the finished goods for shipment to the client by September 1, 1999, which will:
•Reduce the searching and expediting costs by 50%
•Improve on-time shipments by 25%
•Reduce rerun costs by 25%.

Project Mission Statement

Figure 2. Project Mission Statement

---

of deliverables associated with it. Each deliverable must be defined, bounded, and time-targeted. It is helpful if the deliverables can be categorized as:
- critical with widespread use
- critical with limited use
- necessary
- deferrable.

This categorization facilitates recovery planning when it becomes necessary. A valuable component of the project definition that is frequently overlooked is a concise summary description of each deliverable. Write a paragraph describing each deliverable in business terms and sequence them by expected availability date. Avoid the typical scope of work that can only be understood by the individual who wrote it.

The critical assumptions are the last component of the project definition. They should include:
- any firm deadlines
- resource constraints
- minimum performance levels
- regulatory or contractual requirements.

The project definition provides the first opportunity to manage expectations. The mission statement, objectives, deliverables, and target dates define the expectations for the project. The boundaries of the project scope, performance measures, target dates, and the timing of benefits characterize them. Test key stakeholders to ensure that there are no undocumented expectations.

The available options when you are handed an ill-defined project are to
- ignore the problem and gladly accept the assignment
- turn the offer down and pursue a different job
- create fear, uncertainty, and doubt about successful completion
- build the refinement of the definition into the project plan.

The last alternative is the only one that makes sense. It makes the problem visible and presents a reasoned way to address it without delays or unpleasant surprises.

Plan the Project

This step transforms the project definition into a plan that can be controlled by the project manager. The first activity in this step is to identify the work that must be done to accomplish each of the objectives and who is responsible for getting it done. Don't forget the activities of presenting information and making decisions. They typically take longer than planned because few organizations make decisions on the spot. The level of detail in the definition of the work to be done will vary by project and by the timing of the work. There should be a minimum of three to five activities leading to each deliverable. The near-term activities covering the first 25 to 30 percent of the schedule should be defined as precisely as is practical. The later activities can be refined as the project progresses and more information becomes available.

Once the work to be done has been identified, the duration of each activity must be estimated and the relationships among the activities must be defined. There has been a great deal of debate about whether duration, effort, or both should be estimated. The duration seems to be most critical in projects producing "soft" results and depending on part-time resources. It may be necessary to include estimates of effort for a few critical resources. It is important to include explicit management reserves in the plan so that the project manager can decide when to use that time. If the individual estimates are inflated to include a reserve, the activities will consume the time.

This rough project plan provides the first opportunity for testing the feasibility of the target dates and deliverables. The testing is similar to rough-cut capacity planning in that only critical resources and blocks of time are considered. If the project is not feasible, a combination of three types of project modification must be agreed upon:
- Resources can be added.
- The scope of work can be reduced.
- The target date can be changed.

This is why the objectives that were not necessary and the deliverables that were not critical were identified in the define-the-project step. They can be dropped from the plan or rescheduled beyond the original target date. This is recovery planning in the earliest stages of the project.

Once that it is determined that the work to be done is feasible in the time allotted with the available resources, a real project plan must be developed. The project network is the basis for all project controls. Gantt charts are fine for reporting upward and outward and for representing the project schedule. However, a project cannot be controlled unless the relationships among the activities are understood. The project network must realistically represent these relationships. It is tempting to combine the project network and schedule into a single diagram. This may have been necessary for manual project planning and control, but should be avoided to keep the level of effort for maintaining the project network reasonable. At this point, pure finish-to-start and start-to-start relationships should be used unless there is solid information on the degree of overlap. This somewhat overstates the duration, but this time can be used to recover from deviations from the plan. The completed project plan provides the second test of feasibility of the project. If the network indicates that targets can't be met, the previously defined alternatives must be evaluated.

There are many microcomputer-based project management systems that can assist in developing the network and maintaining the plan. They are also powerful enough to allow the project team to make professional-looking presentations on projects that are not understood or being controlled. Use these tools wisely to reduce the amount of routine work, but don't expect them to control the effort.

Establish the Control System

When the first two steps are executed properly, there is a well-defined project that can be controlled. The simplest control system that supports completion of the project on time and within budget is usually the best one because of the ease of understanding and time required. Some organizations attempt to control projects to budget rather than schedule. These attempts are typically unsuccessful because
- the control system becomes complex
- the time devoted to assigning effort to budget categories or accounts is not built into the plan
- many of the costs associated with a project are period costs that vary with time rather than effort.

If the project is controlled to schedule and the planned level of resources are employed, on-time delivery will ensure meeting the overall budget. The allocation of costs to specific budget categories or accounts can be done separately from the control system.

The project control system defines the guidelines for
- reporting activity status and problems
- measuring progress
- maintaining the project plan
- reporting project status.

The reporting of activity status and problems must occur at least weekly. A project of less than 90 days' duration may require more frequent reporting. The purpose of frequent reporting is to identify deviations from the plan before they become problems. The basic facts that should be reported are the activities that were scheduled to complete and those that were completed. Do not bother trying to estimate the percentage of an activity that has been completed. Too many people think that they are 20 to 30 percent done with any task soon after they start it and then take 50 percent of the planned time to completed the last 10 to 20 percent of the work.

Activities on or near the critical path require additional reporting because they are the very important few. Planned and actual starts as well as completions should be reported for these activities. A recovery plan should be presented for any of these activities that have actual or projected schedule slippage. Finally, any problems or issues that will impact meeting the schedule should be documented.

The project manager must take the activity status and problem reporting and measure progress to the plan. This includes updating the project plan and resolving any missing or inconsistent reporting. The project manager must also attempt to resolve any problems that were identified within the project team. These activities should not be underestimated. They are time consuming and time critical. The project plan cannot be maintained and status reports cannot be prepared until they are completed.

Maintaining the plan is also a time-consuming and time-critical activity. It must be done before the status reports are prepared and presented. The future activities and relationships between activities should be continually refined to reflect a better understanding of the work to be done and the passage of time. The activity reschedules and refined activity and relationship definitions must be reflected in the project plan and in the network. Any negative slack must be resolved or the problem must be raised in the status report. The project plan that is plotted in color on a 36" x 17' Mylar sheet and never touched is impressive, but it won't help deliver the results on time and within budget. The maintenance of a large project network may justify the investment in a large color plotter—cutting and taping dozens of 8-1/2" x 11" sheets of the project network that were printed on a laser printer is very time consuming and error prone.

The next component of the control system is status reporting. There are typically three different levels of reporting. The most detailed and time-critical reporting is to the project team. This report must be distributed within 24 hours of receipt of the activity and problem reports. It should identify key successes and problems that must be addressed. An e-mail note is typically appropriate for this level of reporting.

The next level of status reporting is to the project champion or the steering committee. This should be a formal written report and presentation delivered on a regular schedule. Weekly reporting is recommended, but some project managers have been successful reporting every other week. The written report must be distributed in advance of the presentation. There must be a set agenda and time limit for the presentation. **Figure 3** presents a representative status meeting agenda. Keep the meeting crisp and address only the topics that are appropriate for the audience, but be prepared for very detailed questions that are raised by the written report. This level of reporting typically includes a summary of activity starts and completions to plan, projection of completions for the next two reporting periods, recovery plans, and any issues requiring management attention.

The highest level of reporting is to the community of individuals and organizations that will be impacted by the project outcome. A written monthly report is typically adequate at this level. Make sure that it reports status and prospects in business terms rather than internal project terms and acronyms. Include the short description of capabilities that will be delivered in the next 30 to 90 days and the training plan for each.

Execute the Plan

When execution of the plan begins, the project manager's focus shifts from planning to understanding what is being accomplished and facilitating the resolution of problems.

All status reporting must be received by the predefined cutoff. This is necessary to allow time for updating the plan and preparing the status reports. Timely reporting is an indicator that the plan is being used to control the execution of the work to be done. Late or incomplete reporting is an indicator of potential problems waiting to explode or individuals who have not bought into controlling the project. Do not tolerate it!

Executing the plan includes refining the definition of the work to be done as time passes and as additional information becomes available. The refinements include decomposing activities into smaller units of work, revising estimates of duration, and refining the dependencies. The project manager must ensure that this gets the proper attention and update the project plan to reflect the latest information. This should be done as part of the weekly activity of maintaining the plan.

If the project manager demands timely reporting from the team members, he or she must meet every target for status reporting. It is tempting to shortchange or skip status reports in the heat of the battle, but this is a mistake because of the message it sends to everyone associated with the project. The project status reports are the communications link to the outside world and should be complete, truthful, and concise. Use them wisely to manage expectations and get the necessary support.

Initiate Corrective Actions

If a project goes exactly according to plan, the project manager withheld information while developing the plan or was unbelievably lucky. Therefore, deviations from the plan will occur and the response to them is another key to completing the project on time and within budget. The first decision that must be made is whether the activity or deviation is important enough to warrant a recovery plan. There must be a recovery plan for any slippage on or near the critical path. A second category of activities that must

---

- •Review of action items
- •Summary of status
- •Activities with negative slack
- •Recovery plans
- •Problems and issues
- •Action items

Figure 3. Status Meeting Agenda

---

have a recovery plan are those that are slipping because the definition of the work to be done is changing or required decisions are not being made. These are symptoms of creeping scope that must be stopped if the project is to be successful.

Objectives and deliverables that were not critical to the success of the project were identified in the project definition and planning steps. The activities leading to these objectives or the deliverables can be rescheduled out to compensate for the recovery plans for critical activities.

There are four questions that must be addressed as part of recovery planning:

- What are the feasible alternatives?
- What are the impacts of each alternative?
- Which alternative should be selected?
- Why should that alternative be selected?

Include the answers to these questions in the project status reports so that everyone understands the situation and the decision. They may not like the decision or its impacts, but they will understand how and why it was made. The guidelines in the APICS body of knowledge for recovery from production problems apply to projects as well:

- Don't work on a recovery plan for a task that is not needed because of other delays.
- Always attempt to recover as close to the problem as is practical.
- Don't overcommit the project resources.
- Changing the committed delivery date is the last resort, but if it must be done, tell the customer the truth.

Close the Project

No project is complete until the acquired knowledge is captured and organized in a way that can benefit future projects. If the organization has a format for the project close report, use it. Otherwise, create one and it is likely to become the de facto standard. Organize the report into lessons learned and suggestions for future projects. Within each of these sections, organize the information by project life cycle stage—the steps in the methodology. Most importantly, make the report accessible to future project teams because the purpose of the project close report is to save future teams from having to learn the same lessons on their own.

Summary

Anyone can control a project and increase the likelihood of completing it on time and within budget. It requires a structured approach and attention to details. The methodology presented is a common sense approach that can be adapted to both large and small projects. Apply Pareto's Law to each step to focus on the very important few while not getting unpleasantly surprised by the important many. **Figure 4** summarizes the steps in the methodology and the key components of each step. Use them wisely with a large dose of common sense to achieve the objectives of your projects.

About the Author

Roly White, CFPIM, is an independent provider of education and situation management services. His prior experience includes 24 years with IBM assisting customers and prospects in the selection, implementation, and use of IBM and complementary products. His industry experience has primarily been in manufacturing but also includes process, distribution, utilities, and insurance.

- Step 1 - Define the Project
  - Mission
  - Objectives and deliverables
  - Critical assumptions
- Step 2 - Plan the Project
  - Work to be done
  - Duration and dependencies
  - Construct the network and balance the plan
- Step 3 - Establish the Control System
  - Reporting activity status and problems
  - Measuring progress
  - Maintaining the project plan
  - Reporting project status

- Step 4 - Execute the Plan
- Step 5 - Initiate Corrective Actions
  - Identify feasible alternatives
  - Evaluate impacts
  - Select an alternative and document reasoning
- Step 6 - Close the Project
  - Capture lessons learned and suggestions
  - Conduct a debriefing
  - Make it available for future projects

Figure 4. The Methodology

Reprinted from the 1999 APICS International Conference Proceedings.

Aligning Performance Measurements with Organizational Strategies

Ann K. Willis, CFPIM, CIRM

To remain competitive in today's marketplace, companies must develop performance measurements that will reveal current baseline values, highlight opportunities for improvement, and drive operational strategies. This presentation will focus on understanding the need for performance measurements, identifying overall performance measurement targets, and applying sound measurements, which satisfy organizational objectives. Information will include the importance of aligning measurements with strategies, converting to new types of measurements, and utilizing specific measurements to achieve world-class goals.

Understanding the Need for Performance Measurements

Performance measures are not new. We have been aware for some time that you cannot effectively manage that which you cannot measure. What is new is the recognition that improved performance is necessary for the continued survival of many companies. Today's global competition mandates that manufacturing organizations strive for excellence through continuous improvement in order to remain competitive. Current trends of continuous improvement include viewing inventory as a liability that covers up underlying problems, changing to a more flexible workplace, considering rejects as unacceptable rather than inevitable, learning to respond immediately to customer demand changes, and elimination of all waste.

Why measure? Customer requirements are more stringent than ever, placing tremendous pressure on everyone within the organization. Higher quality, lower prices, rapid product development, and reliable service are changing the way we perform. Achieving best-of-class has become the focus for many of us, but how do we answer the question, "Are we there yet?"

Performance measurements are the yardsticks that tell us how we've done, where we are, and where we need to arrive. They help us make decisions on what to change, and on what to change to. They are a checkup on the vital signs of the organization, and serve as communication mechanisms for expectations downward, and results upward. Performance measures themselves cannot change an organization's culture, but can be a powerful catalyst for change, by promoting teamwork, establishing accountability, and making performance visible.

Performance measurements also motivate us to improve. If a company chooses to measure a process, it is placing priority on that activity, and people will concentrate on improving the process. It is foolish to assume we can continue to repeat the same activity, yet expect to get different results.

Taking measurements identifies and focuses attention on those areas that need improvement. Changing the mindset that uncovering problems is good, not bad, is the responsibility of management, but once this is achieved, the workforce should begin to support the idea of being measured. Everyone reacts to how they are measured, and relating a performance measure to an organizational goal helps people better understand the purpose of the measure and why it is important.

Another reason for establishing measurements is to ensure support of an objective. Performance measures are an excellent way to communicate a company's strategy throughout the organization. The first step in the process is to establish that goal or objective, then arrive at a strategy that drives the organization toward achieving the goal. Performance measures assure continuing progress toward that goal, encouraging actions that are consistent with the company's strategic direction, as well as identifying unnecessary activity that can be eliminated.

Whatever the impetus behind the measurement, the relationship between performance measures and the strategies they are intended to support should be clearly understood by all. How can performance be measured when only one or two individuals know the company's operational strategies? A formal system allows everyone to work toward a mutually understood goal.

Steps for Identifying Performance Measurement Targets

How does one build a set of performance measures that are consistent with the strategic goals of the firm and provide feedback on the activities critical to the business?

1. Determine what is needed to manage the business successfully. Focus should be on those activities that contribute to the success of the vision, and measurements of those activities should be consistent with, and support, those policies and practices that will achieve company objectives. Ask "why" five times to make sure the measurement is far enough into the process to facilitate improvement.
2. Decide on the source of information to be used, and the who, what, when, where, and why of collecting the data. Selecting measures that are easily attainable ensures that they can be started quickly, and continued without difficulty.
3. Clarify and simplify the measures. There should be a clear understanding of what is expected and agreement that the measure is meaningful. The process should be made as mistake-proof as possible, and the process of measuring made simple to ensure that results can be generated easily and consistently. A process that is not

well understood by everyone is difficult to measure and improve.

4. Involve or co-develop the measures with the people who participate in the activity being measured. Actual participants usually have the best feel for what activities would be improved by measuring. Managers should be made accountable and delegate resources and authority to those doing the measuring. The work force must take ownership and responsibility for the measurement.

5. Relate local, or functional, measures to global measures, to ensure the activity is consistent with strategic goals of the firm. The measures should be integrated throughout the company so various functional areas are working together for the good of the organization.

6. Establish performance goals that are out of reach, but not out of sight, both short-term and long-term. People respond to challenges, not impossibilities. Milestones should be set that demonstrate progress made toward the ultimate goal. Achieving milestones validates change and improvement.

7. Collect information for a trial period, and evaluate its effectiveness at both local and global levels. This ensures that data and collection procedures are available. If the information being collected is not meaningful, change it.

8. Examine every process and activity that is being measured. Ask the following questions: Does measuring contribute significantly to control of the process or improvement of the activity? What would happen if we discontinued this measure?

9. Celebrate achievements of every milestone and goal, resetting the goal to the next level. Successes should be rewarded, and failures coached for success in the future. Seeing progress toward a goal improves morale, garners support, and increases total participation in all improvement activities.

Evaluating Performance Measurement Effectiveness

Once the performance measurement system is in place, it should be audited to ensure its effectiveness. World-class organizations use the following characteristics to evaluate performance measurement systems.

- The cost of the measurement should not exceed the benefit derived.
- Measurements must be simple and easy to use, understand, and report.
- Those being measured should clearly understand the relationship between measurements and goals, and should be involved in the selection of the measures.
- Measurements must be accepted and trusted as valid by those who use them.
- Feedback should be provided in a timely manner to both operators and managers, in order for performance to be adjusted toward goals.
- The measurement should convey meaningful detail that can be used and understood at all levels of the organization.
- Measurements must be based on readily and continuously available data, and usable at all levels of the organization.
- Measurements should provide operational as well as financial measures.
- Measurements should be easy to change, as needs change.
- Measurements must focus on improvement and corrective action, rather than monitoring or control.

- Short- and long-term goals are established for each measurement.
- Measurements should always be expressed as a positive, such as yield of good product rather than reject rate. People are more motivated by upward trends.
- Accomplishments achieved should be visible, and recognition given for those accomplishments.

World-Class Values

World-class organizations are finding it necessary to change baseline values to determine appropriate, meaningful measurements. Examples of a few of these changes follow.

Quality

Quality measurements, coupled with a drive toward a decrease in the cost of quality, focus on a goal of continuous improvement. Monitoring quality improvement costs in conjunction with quality performance data gives a truer picture of the quality progress. Quality measures are also reflecting goals of perfection and customer delight, rather than status quo and just getting by.

Productivity

Today's trends reflect measuring total productivity, rather than drawing traditional lines between direct and indirect, salary and hourly. Measurements focus on getting the most output from current levels of input.

Inventory

Inventory makes up a large part of working capital, many times amounting to half to two-thirds of the total investment base. Measurements such as inventory turns are some of the best short-term measurements of utilization, as no credit is given for what is produced, only what is sold.

Time

Reduction of time elements, such as customer response time, manufacturing cycle time, process control feedback time, supplier reorder lead time, and transport time, enables an organization to be better able to respond to dynamic demands.

Innovation

Measures in innovation indicate the ability to achieve and maintain a competitive advantage by introducing more new products, faster, at lower cost and more reliably than competitors. Cheaper, better, faster is becoming the motto for the next century.

Customer Satisfaction

Customer satisfaction has emerged as a strategic goal for many organizations today. Indicators such as customer retention rates, referral rates, repurchase rates, market share trends, complaint rates, and satisfaction survey trends are being used to gauge satisfaction levels.

Converting from the Old to the New

Most performance measurements in the past were based on financial and costing information. These types of measurements usually represent outcomes of processes, but do not always provide the best information about what actually occurs behind the scenes. Today's performance measurements must reflect and encourage the new culture of people empowerment, the value of time, emphasis on continuous improvement, a quality mindset, and total people productivity. How we behave is dictated by how we are measured, and we cannot expect people to behave under the new culture if we continue to measure them under old standards.

Eliminating all of the old measurements, such as efficiency and utilization, may be too much change for some organizations and individuals. One alternative would be to change efficiency to labor effectiveness, by dividing standard hours earned by the total hours worked by both direct and indirect employees. Utilization can be changed to machine performance by simply dividing the run hours for scheduled production by the standard hours for scheduled production. This ensures that there is no incentive for producing more than the scheduled or needed quantity. The ideal number is one. When the ratio is less than one, it is an indicator of unplanned downtime. When it becomes greater than one, it took more hours than planned to accomplish the schedule.

Cultural changes may be necessary before an effective measurement system can be put into place. Fear of negative consequences to being measured may result in distortion of data and a reluctance to participate and take ownership of the measurement process. If there is a distrust of management to use measurements in order to find fault or punish, many problems will be omitted from the reporting.

Accountability is another cultural change for many organizations. People should only be held accountable for performance if they can control the outcome and have the authority to change the process. For example, an inventory control manager should not be held accountable for excess inventory created as a result of a poor forecast. In order to establish accountability for performance, each performance measure should have a sole owner who is responsible for the process and the measurement of that process.

Four specific activities are necessary when converting from one measurement system to another.
1. Changes must not only be published, but also communicated openly and discussed with all those who are involved or impacted by the changes.
2. Training is vital for people to feel comfortable with the new process and to alleviate the anxiety of not having the skill or knowledge to succeed in the new environment.
3. If people are to remain motivated during the change process, rewards should be given in return for services or accomplishments. These can be in forms other than monetary, such as additional responsibility, promotion, public recognition, or simply a letter from top management. The key is to have a reward system that includes various types and that contributes to the success of the overall process.
4. Benchmarking helps raise people's awareness of best practices, and helps organizations measure from an "as is" position to a "should be" position. It allows them to see that others have succeeded while going down the same path and proves that what seems to be impossible is possible.

Specific Measurements to Achieve World-Class Goals

New ways of doing business require new performance measurements. The following are but a few of the measures being used by world-class organizations to foster continuous improvement and achieve strategic goals.

Quality

- defects per million
- cost of quality (prevention, appraisal, internal and external failures)
- supplier certification or certified items
- reduction of supplier base
- hours of employee quality training
- hours of preventive maintenance
- mean time between failure
- certification of internal operations
- unscheduled machine downtime
- number of customer complaints, warranty claims, and recalls
- unscheduled service call
- percentage of lots rejected in error.

Cost

- reduction in data transactions
- materials shipped to point of use by supplier
- dollars of product output per employee
- throughput times from supplier to customer
- budgeting expense trends
- projects operating within budget.

Flexibility

- reduction in cycle time
- reduction in setup time
- reduction in lot/batch size
- increase in standard materials used per product
- number of parts and levels in bills of material
- degree of cross-training of production personnel.

Reliability

- increase in overall equipment effectiveness
- reduction in warranty costs
- reduction in engineering changes.

People Productivity and Development

- sales per person
- value added per person
- employee turnover ratios
- number of employees participating in improvement teams
- competitive compensation packages
- accident rates
- absentee rates
- training hours per employee
- employee grievances
- workdays lost due to accidents
- percentage of appraisals completed on time
- percentage of positions filled from within the organization
- percentage of employees with personal development plans
- number of recognition events and awards.

Inventory

- inventory turnover by product and group
- inventory days on hand

- inventory record accuracy
- items above/below target limits
- physical inventory variances
- number of adjustments to inventory records.

Lead Times

- delivery time to customers
- setup reduction trends
- in-house transit time
- supplier delivery performance
- throughput times
- work in process investment
- performance to MPS
- performance to FAS
- ratio of promised customer delivery lead time to cumulative production lead time
- administrative process times.

Responsive After-Market Service

- number of hours of field service training
- average response time to service calls
- time to repair
- availability of spare parts
- warranty expense
- overstocked field supplies.

Customer Satisfaction and Responsiveness

- average customer response time
- reduction in customer response time
- number of complete items delivered on time
- time from customer's recognition of need to delivery
- quoted lead time
- customer order processing time
- time from receipt of order to start of manufacturing
- number of customer promises met
- percentage of customer orders shipped on customer's request date
- customer returns, complaints
- backorder rate
- degree of satisfaction with complaint resolution
- number of customer partnerships established
- number of certifications received from customers
- enhanced customer value, via added product features or reduced costs.

Product and Process Design

- time from idea to market
- rate of new product introduction
- percentage first firm to market
- number of engineering changes after design
- reduction in new product introduction lead time
- new product sales revenue as a percent of total sale revenue
- project completion cycle times
- number of errors found during design review and evaluation.

Manufacturing Planning Process

- master schedule items achieved per week
- final assembly schedule items achieved per week
- material requirement plans achieved per week
- manufacturing orders released on time

- data accuracy of inventory, bills of materials, routings, and forecast
- material and tooling availability
- MPS on-time performance
- number and types of changes made to MPS.

Procurement Process

- average procurement cycle time
- on-time performance of deliveries
- reduction in purchasing lead time
- purchase orders released on time
- reduction of supplier lead times
- purchase order errors
- downtime due to shortages
- excess inventory
- percentage of parts from certified vendors.

Manufacturing Process

- reduction of manufacturing lead time
- percentage queue time in manufacturing lead time
- percentage value-added time in manufacturing lead time
- shop orders completed on time
- manufacturing cycle times
- unscheduled machine downtime
- number of past due operations
- yield and scrap rates
- transactions per person.

Management

- net income/number of employees
- total sales/number of employees
- net income/total direct labor payroll
- net income/total factory payroll
- total earned hours direct labor/total factory payroll.

Marketing/Sales and Customer Service

- total sales/number of employees
- average lead time in backlog
- lead time performance
- premium freight outbound/total freight outbound
- performance to sales plan
- accuracy of forecast assumptions
- number of incorrect order entries
- credit request processing time.

Delivery Performance

- timeliness and accuracy of supplier order placement and delivery
- accuracy of shop floor schedule to customer requirements
- ability to meet, but not exceed, MPS
- correct quality and quantity delivery to customer per customer requirements
- analysis of lost sales due to delivery deficiencies.

Information Services

- number of errors per line of code
- percentage of reports received on schedule
- number of rewrites
- number of test-case runs for successful completion.

Financial/Accounting

- amount of non-value-added activity (scrap, rework, excess queue and move time)
- total value of usable finished product produced per period per employee
- total cost and output value ratios
- time-based overhead usage
- performance to budget
- percentage of late payments
- time to respond to customer requests
- number of billing errors
- number of incorrect accounting entries
- number of payroll errors.

Whatever measures are used, one must remember that performance measurements in and of themselves do not add value. Attempts should be made to always focus measures on value-adding activities.

The most useful information derived from performance measurements is the trend of the results as opposed to the actual value of the measurement. We should be more concerned with relative performance over time than with absolute numbers. Small incremental improvements should be encouraged and celebrated as progress toward the goal. When dramatic changes do occur, these should also be acknowledged. It is often worthwhile to set targets that may at first seem completely unrealistic. But doing so forces us to view the process from a completely fresh perspective, perhaps to find an entirely new way to accomplish the objective.

To truly be beneficial, performance measures should be used for more than just keeping score. In addition to identifying opportunities and problems, and determining priorities and process improvement, they can be instrumental in changing or adjusting strategy, providing feedback to change behavior, and recognizing and rewarding accomplishments.

Summary

To thrive, or even simply survive, organizations must establish, review, and update comprehensive performance measurements. These measurements are the vehicle that drives a company to achievement of its operational goals. Due to the current trends in world-class organizations to develop and sustain customer satisfaction as well as achieve ongoing improvement, measurements should be designed to drive the improvement process and achieve customer delight.

Often the difficulty is to select measures that satisfy the criteria of meaningfulness, acceptance, reliability, ease of reporting, and consistency. Performance measurements must fit an organization's individual needs, not that of a competitor or another facility. The measurements must be meaningful to the organization using them to achieve strategic objectives.

It is important to remember that performance measurement systems must remain fluid and flexible, in order to change with the constantly changing needs of an organization. How a company measures itself can have significant impact on how well the company performs in the marketplace.

Once measurements are established, success can be measured by marking progress week to week. This progress, no matter how small, must be published internally, rewarded, and used to motivate everyone within the organization to strive for continuous improvement and achieve excellence.

References

Bogan, Christopher E., and Michael J. English. *Benchmarking for Best Practices*. McGraw-Hill, Inc., New York, NY, 1994.

Buker, Inc. *World Class Manufacturing Performance Measurements*. Antioch, IL.

Hronec, Steven M. *Vital Signs*. American Management Association, New York, 1993.

Kaydos, Will. *Operational Performance Measurement*. St. Lucie Press, New York, 1999.

Maskell, Brian H. *Performance Measurement for World Class Manufacturing*. Productivity Press, Portland OR, 1991.

Oliver Wight Publications. *The Oliver Wight ABCD Checklist for Operational Excellence*. Fourth Edition, Essex Junction VT, 1993.

About the Author

Ann K. Willis, CFPIM, CIRM, is resource and education manager for ObTech, Inc., a firm dedicated to providing integration services, resource management consulting, ERP implementations, and project management to organizations throughout North America, Asia, and Europe. Her 18 years of supply chain and manufacturing experience encompass all levels from material planning to management. She is responsible for implementation and training of manufacturing systems and has written several customized ERP courses. She has also been responsible for setting up customer-driven partnerships between organizations, and has assisted companies in developing and managing strategic methods of customer focus, integration, performance measurement, and people empowerment.

Ms. Willis has been a member of APICS for 15 years. She currently serves as chair of the CPIM program and is a past member of the MRP/CRP Curriculum Committee. She has held several chapter and region positions, including three years as chapter president. She was a member of the 1993 International Conference Committee and the 1993 and 1996 TEAM committees. She is a frequent speaker at chapter and regional meetings, and regional and international conferences. She teaches certification review courses, and is certified in both Train-the-Trainer and Learning Dynamics for Instructors.

Reprinted from the Production and Inventory Management Journal, *Third Quarter, 1991.*

Linking Firm Strategy to Operating Decisions through Performance Measurement

Joel D. Wisner, Ph.D., and Stanley E. Fawcett, Ph.D.

During the past 20 years, the world has witnessed the evolution of a globally integrated economic system. This globalization of economic activity is one of the most important changes in the business environment this century and has already had a tremendous impact on industrial competition. As this globalization continues, companies must re-evaluate their approach to international competition to meet competitive challenges.

One of the areas most affected by today's "new" industrial competition is performance measurement. As much of corporate America responds to intensified competitive pressure by attempting to develop a distinctive competitive advantage, the need to develop performance measurement systems that link firm strategy to operating decisions increases. Further, many American companies are integrating value-adding systems and adopting new manufacturing philosophies, such as Just-in-Time (JIT) and computer-integrated manufacturing (CIM), leaving traditional performance measurement systems incomplete since they do not provide all the necessary information for decision making in these new environments.

Performance criteria that are capable of guiding a firm's operating decisions so that strategic objectives are realized must be flexible, easy to implement, timely, clearly defined at all management levels, and derived from the firm's strategic objectives. Unfortunately, traditional performance criteria alone do not allow a firm to fully understand its competitive position and can lead many organizations to relegate manufacturing decisions to a nonstrategic level. By focusing on the short-term efficiency information produced by traditional measurement systems, opportunities to improve competitiveness are overlooked. For example, a typical response to increased competitive pressure is a directive to "cut costs," often resulting in decisions to reduce capital investment, minimize research and development, cut back on preventive maintenance, and lay off workers. Each of these decisions may reduce the firm's long-term competitiveness. Therefore, the development of an overall performance measurement system that directs the firm's productive resources to enhance its value-adding capabilities is needed.

Performance criteria must be designed to help a firm achieve its objectives along the lines of manufacturing's five competitive dimensions: quality, cost, flexibility, dependability, and innovation [9]. Companies considered "world-class" manufacturers already realize that a reliance on traditional financial and cost accounting measurements alone does not guarantee success. Rather, they emphasize the effectiveness and continual improvement of those value-adding activities associated with designing and producing high-quality, innovative products, which are then supported with the appropriate levels of customer service.

The purpose of this article is to (1) review the recent literature on performance measurement systems, (2) identify basic characteristics of world-class manufacturers, (3) discuss the lack of guidance traditional performance criteria provide the firm in its efforts to achieve manufacturing excellence, and (4) discuss approaches to the development of performance criteria that are both flexible and promote continual improvement in a firm's competitive position.

A Review of the Performance Measurement Literature

Numerous researchers note that aside from "trimming the fat" to increase productivity, American industry must develop performance systems that are consistent with a long-term competitive strategy for growth. Some authors suggest areas in need of effective measurement systems while others recommend actual criteria. Almost all emphasize the need for strategies that encourage high-quality and low-cost production, lead-time reduction, product and process innovation, and continuous improvement.

In an early study, Skinner [21] recognizes the emphasis placed on low costs and high efficiencies and warns that this shortsightedness can be counterproductive. He recommends steps leading to effective long-term policies. More recently, Skinner [22] notes little substantial improvement in many U.S. manufacturing efforts to increase competitiveness, and reiterates a need for less emphasis on "productivity improvements" through cost-cutting measures.

Globerson [6] suggests guidelines for developing an effective performance measurement system:

- Select criteria that are derived from firm strategy.
- Develop clearly defined criteria that are indeed measurable.
- Relate the criteria to competitive dimensions that are critical to the success of the firm.

Richardson and Gordon [19] argue for more comprehensive, adaptable performance criteria that follow the firm and its products through life-cycle, product, and strategy changes. They identify eight areas requiring performance measurement: facility output, productivity, cost, quality, delivery, flexibility, new product introduction, and new process introduction. Kaplan [12] lists the quality criterion as most important, followed by inventory, productivity, and new product introduction. He also discusses the importance of incentive systems relying on criteria consistent with the long-term health of the firm.

In their discussion of optimized production technology, Goldratt and Fox [7] describe as counterproductive traditional efficiency criteria that emphasize machine utilization. They recommend criteria that link the shop floor to bottom-line profits: throughput stated in terms of sales dollars, inventory stated in terms of material cost of for-sale items only, and operating expense stated as all expenses used in converting inventory to output. Ashton and Cook [1] recommend creating visual performance criteria: actual versus planned lead times and labor, and time between defect detection and correction.

Discussing performance criteria for JIT firms and firms involved in a transition from material requirements planning (MRP) to JIT, Rao and Sheraga [18] note that firms need to change individual efficiency criteria to group criteria when group technology layouts are used. Kim, Park, and Besser [13] and Lea and Parker [16] suggest that firms should pay less attention to traditional cost minimization, utilization, and efficiency criteria and concentrate more on efforts to track production setup and lead time, quality, and inventory levels. Flexibility, as an element of JIT, is considered strategically important and performance criteria that monitor and promote flexibility are suggested in Cox [3].

In addition to the literature that focuses on relating firm strategy to operating decisions through development of new performance criteria, much discussion is directed at managing and reducing overhead as a means for increasing competitiveness. In their discussion of allocating costs to products, Miller and Vollmann [17] describe transactions (logistical, balancing, quality, and change) as being responsible for high manufacturing overhead. They suggest these transactions could be minimized through JIT adoption, manufacturing stabilization, and automation. Johnson and Kaplan [11] and Kaplan [12] contend that traditional cost accounting systems are not relevant in a world-class manufacturing environment. Because direct labor is no longer a major part of product cost, it should not be used to allocate indirect and overhead costs. Several authors suggest using lead time to allocate these costs [16, 20] while Rao and Sheraga [18] suggest using total labor required to operate and support a workcenter. Cooper and Kaplan [2] present activity-based costing, arguing that all firm activities support products and should be considered product costs.

Another area in the performance measurement literature focuses on capital investment decisions. Johnson and Kaplan [22] and Haas [8] hold that capital investment decisions should be based on long-term economic value rather than on return on investment (ROI). Economic value includes tangible as well as intangible assets—innovation, flexibility, quality, and customer service. An over-reliance on performance criteria such as ROI can sacrifice the long-term health of the firm.

Characteristics of World-Class Manufacturers

World-class manufacturers recognize the importance of manufacturing as a strategic weapon and demonstrate an extremely strong commitment to manufacturing excellence. For these firms, the manufacturing function derives its importance from its central role in creating and sustaining customer satisfaction along the dimensions of quality, cost, flexibility, dependability, and innovation. World-class manufacturers view manufacturing excellence as critical to continued success and as a principal vehicle for improving a firm's competitive position.

An inspection of the management practices of world-class manufacturers reveals several characteristics that are common to manufacturing success. Although manufacturing practices often differ among successful firms, most pay close attention to the forces driving global competition—

quality and productivity. Other shared characteristics of world-class manufacturers are: [5]

1. Active pursuit of a systems-integrative approach to competition, emphasizing manufacturing excellence.
2. Extensive training and human resource development to fully integrate workers into all aspects of the manufacturing process. Similarly, they promote technical literacy among managers.
3. Relentless pursuit of continual improvement in both process and product. This is considered fundamental to building a sustainable competitive advantage.
4. Dedication to developing a competitive advantage based on superior-quality products. They also seek to advance the other basic competitive dimensions—cost, flexibility, dependability, and innovation—to sustain their competitive position.
5. Emphasis on long-term considerations over short-term profitability.

These five characteristics provide the foundation for manufacturing excellence and should be influential in designing a performance measurement system that effectively links the firm's strategic objectives to its daily operations. The performance criteria adopted by the firm should guide the firm in making decisions consistent with the attainment of these five characteristics. The most important function of the performance measurement system is thus to promote the improvement of the firm's internal and external environment, enabling the firm to achieve long-term competitive success [14].

Traditional Performance Criteria in a World-Class Setting

While traditional performance criteria provide the firm with relevant cost accounting and financial information, they lack the ability to fully guide the firm in its efforts to achieve manufacturing excellence. The three most prevalent approaches taken by today's manufacturing firms to improve competitiveness are: (1) the implementation of JIT manufacturing principles emphasizing simplicity, visibility, and the synchronization of flows; (2) the automation of the production process; and (3) the establishment of global manufacturing networks. Each of these approaches reduces the applicability of traditional performance criteria to world-class manufacturing environments.

Although the objective of JIT is the same as that of all manufacturing systems—to obtain low-cost, high-quality, on-time production—its emphasis on continual improvement is beyond the scope of traditional performance measurement systems. Both the required changes in manufacturing practice and the development of the human-resource base that is essential to the successful implementation of JIT are hindered by traditional volume- or activation-based efficiency criteria (such as labor and machine utilization measures). In contrast, performance criteria that focus on inventory levels, throughput lead time, defect rates by category, equipment downtime, and employee training not only enhance the firm's ability to successfully implement JIT but also provide the information necessary for continual improvement of the firm's competitive position.

Similar difficulties arise with automation-based approaches to manufacturing excellence. Wheelwright [23] contends that many companies use new technology simply to reduce costs when they should also use it for product and process enhancement. To merely substitute capital for labor to reduce costs is a waste of a potentially strategic resource. Current manufacturing practices guided only by traditional performance criteria can lead to misapplication of automation. The use of more specifically targeted performance criteria can help a firm understand the competitive potential of new manufacturing technologies.

An overemphasis on traditional cost-based performance criteria can cause substantial problems that limit the firm's flexibility and reduce its ability to offer high levels of customer service. Relying exclusively on cost measures can lead a firm to inappropriately deploy its productive resources, ultimately leading to increased system costs and inferior product quality. A performance measurement system suited for manufacturing environments should include criteria that assure product quality and emphasize network coordination.

The greatest problem associated with traditional performance criteria is their failure to provide sufficient guidance in the formation of tactical decisions. These performance measures are typically based on cost accounting and financial information. While this information is obviously important and is frequently used by top management to gauge a firm's overall position in the market, financial and cost accounting information by itself does not convey the critical information necessary to understand why a firm made or failed to make a profit. For example, a firm's performance may appear impressive based on ROI information when, in fact, its competitive position is about to deteriorate because a key competitor is introducing a high-quality, innovative product possessing significantly lower design-to-market lead time. In this scenario, managers armed with only traditional performance criteria do not possess information essential for making the operating decisions necessary to respond to this competitive challenge.

Cost-accounting criteria supply information on pricing, inventory valuation, and cost. Since direct labor historically represented the largest portion of product cost (although this is frequently far from the truth today), the goal of most traditional performance measurement systems remains to limit the amount of direct labor cost going into each product to improve labor productivity. The accounting methods used to allocate overhead costs to products are usually based on direct labor hours, leading to a further emphasis on direct labor cost reduction. Today, with labor costs accounting for only 5-15% of product costs, opportunities to improve productivity by reducing labor costs are limited. An over-reliance on measurement systems that promote these actions can actually reduce productivity, contributing to a decline in competitiveness. As an example, batching production to achieve economies of scale creates large inventory levels and an accompanying increase in indirect labor (in the form of expediting, warehousing, and quality control personnel). This, in turn, can lead to a decrease in employee morale as employment security decreases and pressure on labor output increases. Performance in quality, inventory turnover, delivery, lead times, and innovation often suffers as the drive to reduce costs prevails. Skinner [22] notes that when cost constraints drive corporate strategy, flexibility and the ability to develop new products gets lost.

Today, overhead and materials typically represent a much higher contribution to value in the conversion process than does direct labor. The trends toward JIT, automated production, and global manufacturing promise to reduce the emphasis on direct labor cost reduction. As more products are designed and shop-floor layouts are developed to accommodate cross-functional workers, direct labor accounting will become difficult, increasing the potential for errors in product costing. Firms can conceivably be manufacturing products that appear to be profitable, while actually accumulating substantial losses.

Excessive dependency on financial performance criteria can lead to an overemphasis on cost reduction along with a shortsighted view of profits. (Decreases in costs can be shown, on an income statement, to generate relatively large increases in net profit.) This short-term cost-profit relationship can cause decisions that do not promote long-term competitive strength, particularly when management incentives are based on financial performance criteria [12]. Business downturns can induce management to decrease expenditures on research and development, design, materials, and maintenance in an attempt to bolster financial performance measurements. While these cost reductions can increase short-term profits, the decisions may have damaging long-term effects if cost reductions come at the expense of customer service, product quality, flexibility, and innovation objectives. If information tied to strategic objectives of the firm is obtained through use of more appropriate performance criteria, competitive weaknesses can be identified and corrective efforts begun.

Decisions to invest in new projects are frequently justified by cost savings. Unfortunately, new machinery that promises to increase product quality or to reduce lead times may not meet the firm's required investment criteria if valued solely on projected annual savings. By failure in making this type of investment, the firm's long-run competitive position can be jeopardized. Management should look beyond cost justification to include the impact that individual investments will have on overall competitiveness. An analysis using a performance measurement system that effectively links strategic objectives to operations can lead to improvements in the acquisition, flow, storage, processing, and distribution of materials, and eventually result in prolonged increases in market share and profitability.

The Development of an Effective Performance Measurement System

An effective performance measurement system should consist of not only the traditional financial and cost-accounting criteria used by upper management but also tactical-performance criteria that are used to assess the firm's current level of competitiveness and direct its efforts in attaining a desired competitive position. These tactical performance measures will vary according to the needs of the different management levels within the organization as well as its various functional areas. Each functional area should develop and utilize a set of performance criteria consistent with its particular operating characteristics and strategic objectives. At each management level within a functional area the performance criteria can be aggregated to form an overall indication of that area's performance. **Figure 1** describes the steps necessary for developing and maintaining an effective performance measurement system.

An effective performance measurement system should lead to the integration of operations, marketing, finance, engineering, and accounting so that they act as one coordinated value-adding system. Further, performance criteria should promote the co-existence and integration of the firm's human and technological systems. Finally, the system must have a long-term orientation such that continual improvement in both product and process leads to a sustainable competitive advantage.

One approach to developing customized performance criteria that could be used by almost any firm involves the use of nominal group techniques [10]. In this technique,

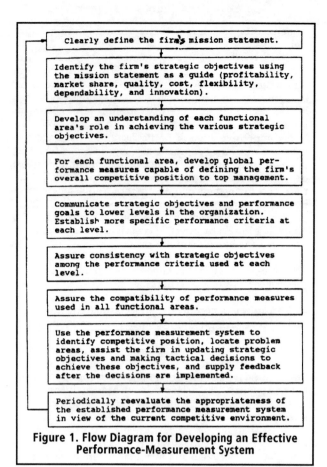

Figure 1. Flow Diagram for Developing an Effective Performance-Measurement System

The flow diagram contains the following boxes in sequence:

- Clearly define the firm's mission statement.
- Identify the firm's strategic objectives using the mission statement as a guide (profitability, market share, quality, cost, flexibility, dependability, and innovation).
- Develop an understanding of each functional area's role in achieving the various strategic objectives.
- For each functional area, develop global performance measures capable of defining the firm's overall competitive position to top management.
- Communicate strategic objectives and performance goals to lower levels in the organization. Establish more specific performance criteria at each level.
- Assure consistency with strategic objectives among the performance criteria used at each level.
- Assure the compatibility of performance measures used in all functional areas.
- Use the performance measurement system to identify competitive position, locate problem areas, assist the firm in updating strategic objectives and making tactical decisions to achieve these objectives, and supply feedback after the decisions are implemented.
- Periodically reevaluate the appropriateness of the established performance measurement system in view of the current competitive environment.

Quality
1. % defect reduction (Incoming shipments and workcenter output)
2. % scrap value reduction
3. % product returns or warranty claims reduction
4. % unscheduled downtime reduction
5. % supplier reduction
6. % of Inspection operations eliminated
7. % reduction in time between defect detection and correction

Cost
1. % inventory turnover increase
2. % average setup time improvement per product line
3. Total product cost as a function of lead time
4. % reduction of employee turnover
5. % reduction in total number of data transactions per product (logistical, balancing, quality, change)
6. % improvement in labor/desired labor

Flexibility
1. % increase in average number of direct labor skills
2. % increase in average number of setups per day (or percent average lot size reduction)
3. % decrease in number of bottleneck workcenters
4. % increase in vendor inputs obtainable in X-days or less
5. % increase in multipurpose equipment
6. % increase in portion of product made for which a specified level of slack time exists

Dependability
1. % reduction In lead time per product line
2. % reduction in average service turnaround per warranty claim
3. % increase in portion of delivery promises met
4. % reduction in purchasing lead time
5. % improvement in output/desired output

Innovation
1. % increase in annual investment dollars in new product and process research and design
2. % reduction in material travel time between workcenters
3. % Increase In annual number o(new product introductions
4. % increase in common parts per product

*[1, 3, 8, 11, 12, 15, 16, 18]

Table 1. Performance Criteria that Link Firm Strategy to Operating Decisions

ideas are generated from physically separated firm participants, who subsequently discuss their individual ideas in a group setting. A variety of appropriate performance measures can potentially be generated, from which the "best" can ultimately be selected on the basis of their relevance, understandability, and measurability. No more than five or six criteria should be tracked by any individual at a given level.

Table 1 shows a partial listing of performance measures (and improvement directions) that might be generated and adopted for use at different areas within the manufacturing function. These criteria are consistent with the characteristics of world-class manufacturing discussed above and are designed to help the firm achieve a high degree of competence along the competitive dimensions of quality, cost, flexibility, dependability, and innovation. When these criteria are combined with the more traditional performance measures, the firm will be better equipped to appraise its current competitive situation and move toward becoming a world-class manufacturer.

The objective of the performance measurement system should be to help a firm develop and maintain a competitive advantage based on adding value to the firm's products and enhancing customer satisfaction. The role of performance criteria is twofold: (1) to provide the firm with a method to assess its current competitive position with respect to its competitors and the demands of the market and to identify avenues for improvement; and (2) to monitor the firm's progress in moving toward its strategic objectives. Performance measures should be adopted for each of the firm's many value-adding activities required to produce and support its products, including activities such as material acquisition, product design, production, and distribution. Once the firm's competitive position is determined, strategic objectives may have to be re-evaluated and modified to be more consistent with the competitive environment. Tactical plans can then be developed to move the firm to its desired competitive position. Thus, an effective performance measurement system can guide a firm's efforts to achieve its strategic objectives and move down the path to continual improvement.

Conclusion

Over the years, the design of performance measurement systems has focused primarily on financial and cost-accounting information and led to the emphasis of efficiency criteria dealing primarily with direct labor. In recent years, the U.S. marketplace has been invaded by flexible, innovative manufacturers of high-quality, low-cost goods. If domestic firms intend to compete, the role and scope of performance criteria must change and managers must become more adept at using these criteria to link operating decisions to the strategic objectives of the firm. An increasing number of companies are responding to the competitive challenge and are acknowledging the need for more effective performance measurement systems.

When developed by the use of the guidelines suggested above and applied appropriately, an effective performance measurement system provides vital information that can be used to conduct a competitive audit of the firm, identify problem areas, and act as an indicator for tactical decision development. Additionally, when tactical decisions are formed and implemented, effective performance criteria will provide feedback on the success of these decisions, supplying the impetus for continued improvement.

Future research should seek to document the implementation of these performance measurement systems by (1) establishing the necessary steps in the implementation process, (2) understanding the obstacles that prevent successful implementation, and (3) identifying performance criteria that are appropriate for different operating and competitive environments.

Acknowledgments

The authors wish to thank Karen Gritzmacher, Beth Baugh, and the reviewers for their constructive comments.

References

1. Ashton, J. and Cook, F., "Time to Reform Job Shop Manufacturing," *Harvard Business Review,* Vol. 67, No. 9 (1989), pp. 106-111.
2. Cooper, R. and Kaplan, R., "Measure Costs Right: Make the Right Decisions," *Harvard Business Review,* Vol. 66, No. 5 (1988), pp. 96-103.
3. Cox, T., "Toward the Measurement of Manufacturing Flexibility," *Production and Inventory Management Journal,* Vol. 30, No. 1 (1989), pp. 68-72.
4. Crawford, K., Blackstone, J., Jr., and Cox, J., "A Study of JIT Implementation and Operating Problems," *International Journal of Production Research,* Vol. 26, No. 9 (1988), pp. 1561-1568.
5. Fawcett, S.E., "The Japanese Challenge: A note on the Emergence of Japanese Competitiveness," *OM Review,* Vol. 7, Nos. 1 and 2 (1989-90), pp. 46-53.
6. Globerson, S., "Issues in Developing a Performance Criteria System for an Organization," *International Journal of Production Research,* Vol. 23, No. 4 (1985), pp. 639-646.
7. Goldratt, E. and Fox, R., *The Race,* North River Press, NY (1986).
8. Haas, E., "Breakthrough Manufacturing," *Harvard Business Review,* Vol. 65, No. 2 (1987), pp. 75-81.
9. Hayes, R., Wheelwright, S., and Clark, K., *Dynamic Manufacturing: Creating the Learning Organization,* The Free Press, NY (1988).
10. Hendrick, T. and Ruch, W., "Determining Performance Appraisal Criteria for Buyers," *Journal of Purchasing and Materials Management,* Summer 1988, pp. 18-26.
11. Johnson, H. and Kaplan, R., *Relevance Lost,* Harvard Business School Press, Boston, MA (1987).
12. Kaplan, R., "Measuring Manufacturing Performance: A New Challenge for Managerial Accounting Research," *The Accounting Review,* Vol. 58, No. 4 (1983), pp. 686-705.
13. Kim, I., Park, H., and Besser, L., "Are You Ready for JIT?" *CMA Magazine,* Vol. 62, No. 6 (1988), pp. 44-48.
14. Krajewski, L., King, B., Ritzman, L., and Wong, D., "Kanban, MRP, and Shaping the Manufacturing Environment," *Management Science,* Vol. 33, No. 1 (1987), pp. 39-52.
15. Krajewski, L., and Ritzman, L., *Operations Management Strategy and Analysis,* 2nd Ed., Addison-Wesley, Reading, MA (1990).
16. Lea, R. and Parker, B., "The JIT Spiral of Continuous Improvement," *Industrial Management and Data Systems,* No. 4 (1989), pp. 10-13.
17. Miller, J. and Vollman, T., "The Hidden Factory," *Harvard Business Review,* Vol. 63, No. 5 (1985), pp. 142-150.
18. Rao, A. and Sheraga, D., "Moving from Manufacturing Resource Planning to Just-in-Time Manufacturing," *Production and Inventory Management Journal,* Vol. 29, No. 1 (1988), pp. 44-49.
19. Richardson, P. and Gordon, Jr., "Measuring Total Manufacturing Performance," *Sloan Management Review,* Vol. 21, No. 2 (1980), pp. 47-58.
20. Rosenblatt, M. and Carlson, R., "Designing a Production Line to Maximize Profit," *IIE Transactions,* Vol. 17, No. 2 (1985), pp. 117-121.
21. Skinner, W., "Manufacturing- Missing Link in Corporate *Strategy* "Harvard Business Review,* Vol. 47, No. 3 (1969), pp. 5-14.
22. ___."The Productivity Paradox," *Harvard Business Review,* Vol. 64. No. 4 (1986), pp. 55-59.
23. Wheelwright, S., "Restoring the Competitive Edge in U.S. Manufacturing," *California Management Review,* Vol. 27, No. 3 (1985), pp. 27-42.

About the Authors

Joel D. Wisner, Ph.D., is an assistant professor of operations management at the University of Nevada, Las Vegas. Dr. Wisner received his Ph.D. in business administration from Arizona State University. He is a member of APICS, the Decision Sciences Institute, the Production and Operations Management Society, and the Society of Logistics Engineers. His research interests include shop-floor control, manufacturing performance, and logistics systems implementation.

Stanley E. Fawcett, Ph.D., is an assistant professor of logistics and international management at Michigan State University. He received a Ph.D. in business administration from Arizona State University and an MBA and an MA in international studies from Brigham Young University. Dr. Fawcett has previously published articles in the areas of logistics and operations management.

Reprinted from the 1996 APICS International Conference Proceedings.

Tools from the Implementation Workbench: A Project Manager's Survival Kit

Brian T. Zimmer, CFPIM, and Gary Smith, CFPIM

Change rarely comes easy. There frequently are obstacles of various shapes and sizes throughout the implementation process, and in order to insure success, a Project Manager must have the right tools and know how to use them. Just as craftsmen master the tools of their trade, so too must the Project Manager—not only if they are to succeed, but if they are to survive.

This workshop will focus on the "how to"—the skill set needed to be a successful Project Manager, viewing the project management process and reviewing some basic but invaluable tools available to facilitate success. Although the most obvious application of project management in APICS circles involves the implementation of MRP software, the concepts and skill set can be easily applied to any project.

The success of every implementation will largely depend on one common denominator—people. It is people that facilitate the change process, not software or equipment. Never underestimate the importance of training, educating and working with the most valuable resource any organization has—its people.

There is an approach—referred to here as "Closed Loop Project Management"—that, if followed, will enhance the success rate of any project implementation.

The closed loop concept is not new to the APICS body of knowledge. Pioneered decades ago in relationship to MRP, it first involves starting with an achievable plan then executing it successfully. In order to gage the degree of success, appropriate measures must be in place to help assess the execution to the plan. Once a measure goes outside of a tolerable range, it signals that corrective action must be taken to get back to a valid plan.

The planning, execution and control elements common to closed loop concept can also be applied to the process of project management.

Planning

The planning process is often too narrowly focused to the detail planning of the project, ignoring some key segments that indeed must occur prior to that step. As such, planning (for our purposes) is broken down into (1) Project Organization, (2) Project Justification and (3) Project Planning.

Project Organization

Most projects result from the development of an idea, defining a particular need and then beginning the process of analyzing the resources required, the project risks-rewards, and then the major steps and minor tasks needed to help make it a reality. Once the scope of an initiative is deemed to require a project management focus, the question "Who?"

must be answered. The "Who" takes several forms: Who will serve as the core team that will spearhead the project through implementation ? Who on the project team will be responsible for the coordination, facilitation and organization (A.K.A. Project Manager)? Who will serve as members of an (informal or formal) oversight group to provide senior management support and direction ?

The Project Team identifies the core resources that will be the champions of the implementation process. A project team exists to complete a temporary task (the project) in a brief time period using predefined resources. By its very nature, a project team exists to put itself out of existence. It differs significantly from the traditional function-based organization, from where most of the team members are typically selected from. The Project Team members should represent the main areas affected by the change being implemented. They should be capable and knowledgeable about both the current reality (what exists today) and the desired result after implementation. With an MRP implementation, for example, this requires those familiar with the current system and method of operation, as well as having the capability to learn and grasp the new system tools (whatever they are). What is the "right" number of people needed to serve on this team ?—it depends on the nature of the project, its scope, the size of the organization (the smaller the business, the scarcer the people resources), and the ultimate implementation timeframe. A good rule of thumb with most projects is anywhere from three to nine team members—the bigger the project, the more people suggested.

There are times where it may be necessary to include some external resources as members of the project team. This might be people external to the immediate area (but company employees), outside consultants or temporary employees. For example, a company implementing MRP but having no one internal with any previous MRP experience may need to bring in someone from the outside with MRP experience—serving as a consultant or temporary employee—to help fill that internal gap. It is important to note that the ultimate ownership cannot be shifted to the outside resource. It must reside within the organization if there is to be any sustained momentum after the project is complete and the outside resources complete their support of the project. This user based approach gives both responsibility and control to the area which will work day to day with the project improvement long after implementation is complete.

Some larger organizations may also have corporate resources assigned to local implementations, acting as internal consultants throughout the implementation steps then moving on to the next project support challenge. If that is the case, it is equally important that ownership be acquired and maintained by those from within the operating unit involved.

The optimal profile of a project team member:

- an employee of the business area to be benefited by the project implementation
- knowledgeable about the current way work is performed
- good communication skills
- the ability to visualize the future
- capable of developing the steps necessary to turn the vision into reality
- familiarity or the ability to become familiar with the desired improvement
- committed to implementing positive change resulting in successful results

The Project Manager (PM) is responsible for the overall implementation process, starting at the planning stage through successful implementation. Due to the nature of the position, the Project Manager, although typically pulled from the functional ranks of an organization, must rely on a completely different skill set than traditional managers.

Rather than managing an on-going function with recurring budgets, the PM has a temporary assignment with a limited budget. They work with a user based project team from a diverse organizational background with some possible department self-interests at stake. The PM works as the leader of a group which they do not supervise, and must overcome internal conflicts as well as a diversity of values and perspectives to get those involved in the project working together as a team. Since most involved with the project have functional job responsibilities and are working part-time on the project, there will be times when project related work will be subordinated to those tasks which support the day to day operation of the business. The PM must be able to persuade, convince and motivate others as needed. Project Managers must always know what is going on, able to provide either a detailed or overview of the project scope and status at a moments notice. They also must be able to clearly articulate that scope and status to anyone at any level of the organization at any time.

In organizations truly committed to the successful implementation of change, the Project Manager needs to be a full-time position , not encumbered (at least during the duration of the project) with production related or functional responsibilities. Typically when faced with resource conflicts between serving the customer by focusing on production requirements or working on project implementation, the priority for a part-time Project Manager tends to gravitate away from Project Management work and towards production. Although projects can be completed by a part-time PM, this can result in diminished returns—not achieving all the benefits—and an extended implementation time frame.

It always is a plus if the PM has managed projects previously, and has a base technical understanding of the change being implemented. Weaknesses can be overcome with an increased dependency on consultants and outside education programs.

Although mentioned last here, one of the first groups established is the Project Steering Committee. Typically comprised of senior management, the Steering Committee provides direction through the establishment of project goals and objectives. They also are involved in the selection of both the Project Team and Project Manager.

The Steering Committee, although not involved with the day to day issues of project management, provides key support to the project team throughout implementation.

This might involve outward signs of support—including conducting meetings with employee associates to kickoff the implementation and establish a positive climate for the introduction of change. But even more important are the not so visible activities such as mentoring and counseling the project team, participating in the project justification process, reviewing the project plan and status, approving and improving project funding requests, establishing (with the project team) critical success measures, and providing a two way communication line between the project team and senior management.

In many environments—depending on the size of the organization and the significance of the project scope—the top management team (or a portion thereof) often serves as the steering committee. This might include the equivalent of the chief operating officer, chief financial officer and or senior manufacturing director. Anywhere from three to five members seems to be the right number for an effective Steering Committee.

Project Justification

Projects require justification as a condition for approval by top management. Departments fight each year for a portion of the capital budget. It is in fact a competition, and only those who can deliver a convincing argument for their projects will get the nod (and the funding) to proceed.

The process of justification has two objectives. First, justification validates the need for the acquisition of new technology. Second, it becomes the measurement stick for the project's actual performance.

A number of steps should be followed when developing a project justification:

1. Costs—Go the extra step and anticipate all of the costs that may be incurred during the project. If procuring software, will the existing PC's and LAN network have sufficient hardware to operate the new system, or are improvements and upgrades required ? When installing a new piece of automated equipment, will special rigging equipment be needed to install it ? Will utilities such as gas or electric need to be rerouted or enhanced in the facility? Too often project managers have needed to go back to their steering committee with that unanticipated purchase requisition in hand for approval. These situations can seriously damage a project manager's career. Senior level management do not look kindly upon approving expenditures for a project that was specified and approved already. A good word of advice—take the extra time and anticipate all possible costs. One option is to allow for a percentage of project cost as a contingency fund to cover those unexpected surprises.

2. Benefits—Avoid the mistake of accepting manufacturer's claim at face value. Validate all claims and benefits. If the new machine has a rated capacity of a given output and tolerance level, visit a company who is using the equipment and verify the claims. Or perhaps conduct an inspection of the equipment with production parts while still at the manufacturer's facility as a precondition of acceptance.

Software is more difficult to quantify benefits since much of the implementation success is dependent on people skills and organizational discipline. If preconditions for acceptance exist, they should be clearly noted as part of the project justification.

3. Payback Analysis—If the project is to be approved, benefits must exceed project costs. The time needed for the benefits exceed total project costs is the project payback. If the new technology does not have an acceptable payback—based on the organization' criteria—don't buy

it. Some initiatives may significantly improve productivity in one area, but have a serious negative impact (such as increased inventory) in another area.

4. Prepare the Documentation—Two documents (at a minimum) must come out of the justification phase. First, a one page summarization of the project's costs, benefits and payback analysis. Subjective or unmeasurable benefits should be excluded here unless they are significant to the company and/or the project is difficult to justify on the "hard" costs. This is the document forwarded to the Steering Committee of funding body for approval.

The second document is the detail behind the summary, delineating all project costs and benefits. It represents the calculation of the "bottom line," and is usually not included with the justification because top management usually have neither the time nor interest to wade through details when developing budgets or capital investment plans. If the project (based on the summary) fits into the company's strategic objectives and receives preliminary approval, they will then ask for the detail behind the bottom line projections. Too many great opportunities have been passed over or denied because they were not packaged properly.

Project Planning

This is the most common view of project management, and is one of the first critical steps begun by the Project Manager and the Project Team. Unlike the previous steps though, project planning is not a one time event. It must be a continuous activity that visited and revisited throughout the entire remaining implementation timeframe.

Project planning includes:
1. Identifying the critical sequence of steps that must be performed.
2. Assigning responsibility—who on the Project Team has ownership of the task and will be accountable for its completion
3. Establishing the time frame for the task—when should it start and when should it be completed.

Each task item is assigned a reference number which reflects when in relationship to the other tasks it should be performed. This is similar to the number assigned to an operation on a routing and can be used to easily sort and arrange the tasks in sequential order based on the start and due dates. From a strategic perspective, the Project Manager and Project Team must allocate resources and prioritize action items which focus on what is most critical to the success of the project. Some action items may need to be performed sequential or concurrent to others.

Several types of valuable software tools can be used for planning and reporting of project status. The project plan is well suited for a spreadsheet or database application. This facilitates the sorting off key criteria easily—based on start date, due date, responsibility or sequence number. There should also be other fields included (for use during implementation) for item status (complete, in-process, or not started) and a place for brief summary comments. This will enhance reporting status back to the user groups, project team and steering committee.

If multiple reports need to be formatted and reported regularly, this may indicate that a database application is more appropriate. Software available today makes this extremely achievable for the user even with limited experience and exposure to the software tools.

There also exist a number of PC based integrated project management software programs, which do much more than manage the action item task planning. The advantages of these packages include

1. Ease-of-use (user friendly) software with complete documentation and step-by-step instruction;
2. Build a project task list quickly and easily using existing formats;
3. Linking of multiple steps the ability to easily quantify time or other resources required, where tasks lists with increased capability
4. Variety of multiple formats, including Gantt and Pert charting;
5. Integration with the planning and tracking of expense and investment dollars that can be associated with each task;

The decision must be made as to is which system tools are appropriate for the project and the organization. The K.I.S.S. method of keeping it simple must be weighed against the more complex, but comprehensive support tools. But a number of capable software tools are available to enhance tracking and performance reporting.

Execution

Planning a project implementation is much like planning a wedding. A tremendous amount of energy, time, and money is spent in preparation. If the planning portion of the event comes off without a hitch, everyone is happy. Project management execution is very similar. If you follow the steps as previously outlined, execution does not become a major issue and can be an enjoyable experience. Unfortunately, too many project managers try to take a short cut and skip one or more of the steps during implementation. The execution process is significantly lengthened as more time is spent trying to get back on track instead of coordinating the overall direction of your team's efforts. The result is chaos and possibly eventual project failure.

One of the most critical issues facing any implementation team—especially with major projects such as MRP implementation—is where to begin and determining which of the three implementation approaches to use. There are three different approaches to use when implementing technology in an organization: the Big Bang, Step by Step, and Parallel Paths.

The Big Bang Approach—This is the sharp cutover of old technology to new. Turn off the old machine then turn on the new as of a predefined cutover date. This approach can be traumatic to an organization particularly if the technology you are implementing is complex or far reaching in the organization. This approach is appropriate in disciplined environments, environments where the project is simple, or where existing conditions are so poor that immediate benefits must be realized even if it means taking risks.

The Step Approach—Some projects are so large or complex that it makes sense to implement them in steps. This is popular in organizations who aren't in survival mode and can take the time necessary to complete the project by biting off several pieces at a time. This approach allows the project team to be highly focused on each section of implementation. It is also popular because downsizing has put serious strains on the availability of the people needed to see projects through. The downside to this approach is it may delay or stretch out the time to benefit of the new technology. Make sure that if you select the Step Approach that it isn't on an endless staircase.

Parallel Approach—This one is very similar to the Step Approach except that both technologies run in tandem until the new technology is fully functional. At that point, the old technology is turned off and removed. The major setback to this approach is that you may need a significant amount of additional resources to maintain two technologies until you are ready to turn off the old one. Few companies today have the extra resources to execute this kind of strategy on major projects. It is very appropriate on small scale projects and high risk ventures.

Approach—Pros and Cons

Big Bang: Quickest time to benefit. Least amount of human resources. Can be traumatic. Risks can be significant.

Step: Ideal for large, complex projects. Allows high degree of focus. Lengthens time to benefit. Cutover strategy can be complex.

Parallel: Ideal for small or high risk ventures. Safest. Requires large amount of support.

Static and Dynamic Data

Significant time can be taken off the project length by differentiating between dynamic elements of implementation and static ones. Static execution elements are ones that can be implemented early in the project and are not subject to change. Dynamic elements are project elements that are highly volatile and cannot be implemented until very late in the implementation process. Electrical wiring changes for a new machine would be an example of a static element. The production schedule for the new machine would be consider highly dynamic. Get as many static elements identified and implemented early in the process, then work your way through the dynamic ones. Your strategy should recognize and identify these elements.

Control

As George Plossl frequently has said, "You can't control what you do not measure." That holds true with project management. Here are some of the key measures a Project Manager needs to establish early and track through implementation.

Costs

Actual project investment and expense costs need to be compared to the plan, as taken from the original project justification. For projects involving significant costs, projections of cash flow may be appropriate to help make certain that any financing requirements be identified as early as possible. The format for all of these measures need not be particularly complex, simply identifying plan versus actual results, augmented with suitable description to identify any significant deviations from the plan, what was the cause, and how the Project Manager and Project Team intend to get back to a valid plan.

Benefits

Also in the justification, certain benefits were identified as part of the payback calculation. The promised results—whether they involve inventory, cycle time, quality, productivity, delivery performance or whatever—were identified as part of the justification and need to be measured on an ongoing basis to assess performance to date. Also as part of the justification, the measurements should be spelled out in detail in that document, identifying the specific calculations and regular measurement points. By establishing the critical success factors up front, this help

eliminates the subjectivity argument regarding the overall success of the project at a later time. These measurements ultimately become the Project Manager's "report card" of performance.

Project Plan

The Project Plan identifies key tasks to be completed in a predetermined time frame for the start and due date for each item. It also indicates who is responsible for the successful and timely completion of the task. That is all done as part of the planning process, and by adding actual start and completion dates, a status field and room for comments, the Project Plan now provides a detailed snapshot of where a project is at any time.

Depending on reporting requirements, either a summary or detailed Gantt Chart might be desired. If using integrated software, the charts and graphs might be easily linked to the project plan. But if not, there are a number of stand alone scheduling packages that can also be easily adapted to the reporting needs of the project.

The Project Plan must be maintained on an ongoing basis, and is typically reviewed at each Project Team meeting in at least some fashion, and sent to the Steering Committee on demand or a regular basis. By a "regular basis", this frequency can change throughout the implementation. During the early months of a long project, once a month will probably be sufficient. But as the finish line for project implementation approaches, a weekly formal update may be warranted.

Go/No-Go Criteria

As the final conversion date approaches, the project team should identify any prerequisites or conditions that must be properly in place before final conversion can occur. With an MRP implementation, it could be the completion of specific conversion or modification of programs or costing issues. New equipment installation might be dependent on a successful runout of test parts. What ever the implementation, it is important to identify any "stop signs" that will delay implementation.

This too takes some of the subjectivity out of the go versus no go decision. If any of the conditions exist that were determined to be "no go" in nature, then implementation is delayed until the issue is resolved, the programming complete, or the problem corrected.

On a regular basis, project status needs to be communicated—to the Steering Committee, the Project Team, and everyone else in the organization impacted by the change. As part of that communication to the Steering Committee, a structured narrative summary of the project complements the measurement summary. Periodic written updates and presentations to area or divisional associates to be affected by the change are also important. In short, you can't overcommunicate project status information.

Summary

Project Management is as much art as it is science. It centers around change and risk, not just planning, execution, and control. Most importantly, the core of any project's success is people. The steps outlined here will reduce the risks and minimize the disruptions that are a result of the changes that you and your project are imposing on the company. Done properly, a well planned and executed project can be a gratifying and enjoyable experience.

About the Authors

Gary R. Smith, CFPIM, is a Business Analyst for GE Transportation Systems located in Erie, PA. He received his B.S. and M.B.A. degrees from Gannon University.

With nearly twenty years of experience in a variety of manufacturing environments, Mr. Smith has been in numerous system and process improvement projects as both a Project Team member and Project Manager. He has also been an Adjunct Professor in the Materials Management Program at Mercyhurst College since 1981 and taught numerous courses for the Erie Chapter - APICS and Gannon University. Gary is certified by APICS at the fellow level.

A member and past President of the Erie Chapter of APICS, he also served five years on the APICS Board of Directors in various capacities. He has spoken at five previous APICS Conferences, and has made numerous presentations throughout the United States. He is a member of the 1996 APICS International Conference Committee.

Brian T. Zimmer, CFPIM, is Materials Manager for McInnes Steel, Corry, PA. In this capacity, he is responsible for the company's manufacturing system design and implementation, Purchasing, Production Control, and Information Systems.

Brian was previously Materials Manager for C&J Industries, Meadville, PA, where he participated in the implementation of a state of the art, closed loop MRP II system. In this position, Brian also spearheaded the start-up of several JIT programs with *Fortune* 500 customers. A fifteen-year manufacturing veteran, Brian has held a number of positions in materials including planning, scheduling and systems development.

Brian has recently served on Region III staff for the society as the Director of Strategic Planning after serving two years as Director of Communications and Public Relations. He is also an APICS Qualified Instructor in the areas of Inventory Management, Just in Time, Master Planning and Systems and Technology. He also presented at the 1993 and 1995 APICS International Conferences. APICS committee involvement includes the 1996 International Conference Committee and the 1992 Society Nominating Committee.